SCIENCE to SIXTEEN

Stephen Pople

Head of Physics,
Withywood Comprehensive School, Bristol

Michael Williams

Head of Science,
Withywood Comprehensive School, Bristol

Oxford University Press

Oxford University Press
Walton Street,
Oxford OX2 6DP

London Glasgow New York Toronto
Delhi Bombay Calcutta Madras Karachi
Kuala Lumpur Singapore Hong Kong Tokyo
Nairobi Dar es Salaam Cape Town Salisbury
Melbourne Wellington
and associate companies in
Beirut Berlin Ibadan Mexico City

ISBN 019 914057 X

Phototypesetting and illustrations by Parkway Group,
London and Abingdon.

Printed in Great Britain
at the University Press, Oxford
by Eric Buckley
Printer to the University

First published 1980
Reprinted with minor corrections 1980
Reprinted 1981

The front cover photograph is a 'heat picture' of
a man drinking a cup of tea.
The rear cover photographs are for use in the
chapter on light. See pages 175 and 180.

Contents

Introduction

This book is about science. Science is about asking questions. How big is the Universe? What is inside an atom? What happens to electricity after you've used it? Why do babies grow up similar to their parents, but not quite the same?

To work as a scientist, you need to ask questions. You then need to find answers! This is often done using experiments. You can also look up the answers in a reference book—if you are prepared to trust someone else's work. This reference book contains the answers to many questions that scientists have asked. This is how to use it:

Use the contents page   If you are looking for information on a large topic—the human skeleton, for example—look it up in the contents list. You will find it in *Chapter 9: Human Life* listed as section 9.1. You can then turn straight to this section for the information you want. But if you can't find it on the contents page, then:

Use the index   Suppose there is something small that you want to check up on—teeth, for example. Look up 'teeth' in the index. The index gives a page number—page 147. Turn to page 147, and somewhere on it you should find what you want.

Use the questions   Asking questions and answering them is a good way of learning. To help you learn, there are questions on every section. These should help you to check that you have read and understood that section properly. At the end of each chapter, you can test yourself using the exam level questions.

Science is important   The information that scientists have gained is important. You can use this information to help understand your world, and you can use it to help understand yourself. Enjoy asking questions. Enjoy finding answers. It's part of what life is about.

Stephen Pople.
Michael Williams.

Chapter 1

The Earth
and its Elements

What's the biggest thing you can think of?
What's the smallest?

1.1 Galaxies, stars and planets

The Sun is only one star in a huge galaxy of over one hundred billion stars. But even this vast collection of stars is not all there is in the Universe—beyond it lie many billions of other star systems.

Galaxies and stars

Each star system in the Universe is known as a *galaxy*. Our own Sun is a member of a collection of stars called *the Galaxy*.

The Galaxy shown in the photo is similar to our own Galaxy. Its size is enormous. On the photograph, a region the size of a pinhead might contain more than a million stars yet a journey between just two of them might take thousands of years at the speed of today's rockets. To cope with the vast size of the Galaxy, scientists measure the distances between stars in *light years*.

A light year is the distance a beam of light would travel through space in one year.

Light travels very fast—nearly 300 000 kilometres every *second*—so by Earth standards a light year is a very long distance indeed. Even the star nearest the Sun is over 4 light years away and appears only as a point of light. The Galaxy itself is about 100 000 light years across and the Sun lies about half way out from its centre.

The Sun

As stars go, the Sun is neither very big nor very hot, yet it has a diameter of nearly 1½ million kilometres and a surface temperature of 6000 degrees centigrade. At its centre, the temperature rises to 15 *million* degrees centigrade.

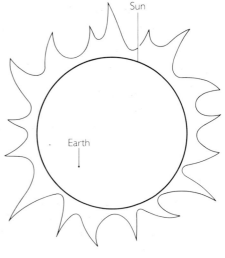

The Sun contains more hydrogen gas than anything else. A non-stop nuclear explosion deep in the Sun releases large amounts of heat as the hydrogen is slowly changed into helium gas. It is this heat which keeps the Sun shining.

The Solar System

The Sun is at the centre of a system of planets and smaller bodies which together are called the *Solar System*. The scale diagram below shows the relative distance of each planet from the Sun.

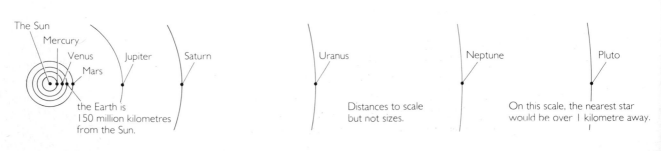

The Sun
Mercury
Venus
Mars
Jupiter
Saturn
the Earth is 150 million kilometres from the Sun.
Uranus
Distances to scale but not sizes.
Neptune
Pluto
On this scale, the nearest star would be over 1 kilometre away.

The planets move around the Sun in more or less circular paths called *orbits*—the further a planet is from the Sun the longer it takes to complete an orbit. Many of the planets have moons in orbit around them.

Scientists think that the planets were formed from a vast cloud of gas and dust which once encircled the Sun. All are very much smaller and cooler than the Sun. None give off their own light though they do reflect some of the sunlight which strikes them—it is difficult to tell at a glance whether a point of light in the night sky is a star or a planet.

Mercury is not much larger than our own Moon. It has a crater-pitted surface and conditions are hot and hostile.

Venus has a thick atmosphere rich in carbon dioxide gas. The surface of the planet is very hot.

The Earth is the only planet in the Solar System known to have the conditions needed to support life.

Mars is often called the Red Planet because of its rust coloured surface. It has a thin atmosphere mostly of carbon dioxide gas and polar caps of frozen carbon dioxide and water.

The asteroids are many thousands of minor planets which orbit the Sun. The largest, Ceres, is less than 700 kilometres across.

Jupiter is more massive than all the other planets put together. It is made up very largely of hydrogen.

Saturn is encircled by bright rings. These are made up of billions of particles of rock and dust, each like a tiny moon. These particles may be the remains from a moon that broke up.

Uranus, Neptune and Pluto are the coldest of the planets because of their great distance from the Sun.

Many other bits of rock, dust, ice and even gas orbit the Sun. *Meteors* are tiny specks of rock which flare up if they hit the Earth's atmosphere. Larger rocks strike planets now and again —these are called *meteorites*. *Comets* are collections of ice, gas and dust which reflect light from the Sun.

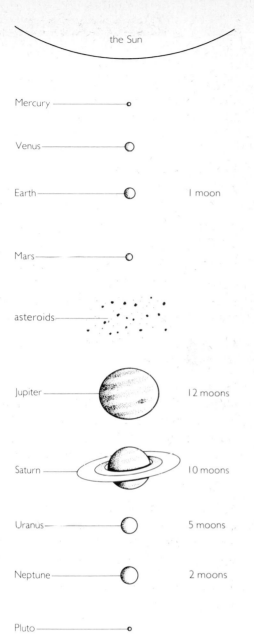

[sizes to scale but not distances]

Questions
1. What is (a) a galaxy (b) the Galaxy (c) a *light year*?
2. How far away is the star nearest the Sun?
3. What is the temperature on the surface of the Sun?
4. What is the most common substance in the Sun?
5. How far is the Earth from the Sun?
6. Which is the largest planet in the Solar System?
7. Which planet is sometimes called the Red Planet?
8. Which planet has 10 known moons in orbit around it?
9. Which planet in the Solar System is furthest from the Sun?
10. Which planet takes longest to complete one orbit of the Sun?
11. What is the difference between meteors and meteorites?

1.2 The Earth

The Earth was formed 4500 million years ago from part of the cloud of dust and gas around the sun. As the dust and gas started to cling together a ball of hot rock formed. It's not so hot today—there's water on the surface and air around it, but there's plenty happening under the surface.

Zones of the Earth
The deepest holes that men have drilled are no more than pinpricks on the surface of the Earth. The Earth is about 12 600 km across. By studying the waves sent out by earthquakes, scientists now believe that there are 3 zones inside the Earth.

1. Core The central *core* is very dense, extremely hot rock and is under great pressure. It is partly liquid and consists of the same kind of material as meteorites.

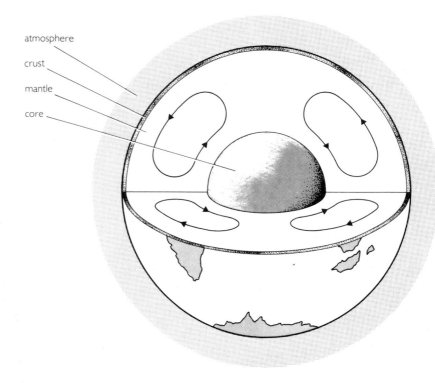

2. Mantle Surrounding the core is a thick layer called the *mantle*. The rocks in this layer are also heavy but less dense than the core. The pressure is lower nearer the outside and the rocks are cooler, although still hot enough for some to be liquid. Convection currents (explained in Section 5.8) cause slow movements of the rocks within the mantle. In places, rock from the mantle has pushed up through the outer layer and is exposed on the surface.

3. Crust The thin outer layer is made of rock less dense and much cooler than the mantle beneath it. Under the oceans it is only 6 km thick and is no more than 70 km thick under the highest mountain peaks.

The crust is something like the shell of a cracked egg; it is made of a number of large sections called *plates*. These plates are moved very very slowly by the currents in the mantle below. Where the plates rub against each other, pressure builds up. From time to time cracks appear on the surface *(faults)* and violent shaking movements occur *(earthquakes)*. Mountains formed in past ages when plates were pushed together and the rocks at the edges were forced upwards.

The results of an earthquake.

Types of rock in the crust

There are 3 different kinds of rock in the crust.

1. Igneous rock   The deepest layer of the crust, next to the mantle, is rock called *basalt*. This is the rock under the oceans. On top of the basalt layer are huge rafts of *granite* which make up the continents. These igneous rocks make up 90% of the crust but they do not show on the surface very much except where there have been volcanoes. *Volcanoes* occur when hot liquid rock, formed in pockets where plates meet, forces its way through cracks to the surface and bursts out as dust, gas and burning liquid *(lava)*.

Section through a lump of granite.

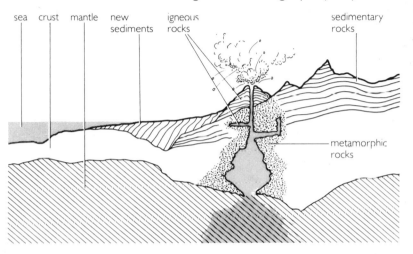

Mount Vesuvius erupting.

2. Sedimentary rock   Wind, rain and frost break down the rocks on the Earth's surface. The small bits are washed or blown away and deposited in layers, usually where rivers meet the sea. As the layers build up, the lower ones become compressed and hardened into sedimentary rocks. Mountain-building movements cause the hardened layers *(strata)* to tilt and fold. This process has been repeated again and again for over 3000 million years. Most of the earth's surface is covered with a thin layer of sedimentary rock. *Limestone* and *sandstone* are common examples.

3. Metamorphic rock   Sedimentary and igneous rocks can be changed by heat and pressure into different, often harder, forms. Heat from a volcano sometimes causes surrounding limestone rocks to change into *marble*. Compressed mud can be changed by pressure into *slate*.

Questions

1. How long ago did the Earth form?
2. What is the depth of the centre of the Earth from the surface?
3. How thick is the crust under (a) oceans, (b) high mountains?
4. What are the large sections of the crust called?
5. What causes earthquakes? How were mountains formed?
6. What kind of rock comes from volcanoes?
7. How do sedimentary rocks form? Why are they often folded?
8. Name 2 igneous, 2 sedimentary and 2 metamorphic rocks.

Folded rocks exposed in a cliff.

1.3 Minerals, elements and atoms

Substances which can be dug out of the Earth's crust and which are valuable to Man are called minerals. But what are minerals made of?

Minerals

The term mineral is rather vague. It usually means substances which are found in a fairly pure state. Diamonds, quartz and alum crystals are examples.

An uncut diamond.

Alum crystals of different shapes.

Pure minerals are formed from rocks by the actions of heat, pressure or water. Some are extremely valuable (gold and diamonds), and others are important because of the substances which can be made from them. Rock salt, for instance, provides us with chlorine gas and household bleach.

Not all minerals are pure solids however. Coal, crude oil and natural gas are some of the impure materials in the Earth which are important minerals.

Quartz crystals.

Elements

Many minerals can also be broken down into even simpler substances. The simplest of all are *elements*. They cannot be broken down further.

About 90 elements—joined together in lots of different ways—make up all the materials of the Earth. Oxygen is the most abundant element. It is present in air, water and nearly all rocks, making up about half the total weight. The next most common element is silicon.

The diagram shows the amounts of the 9 most common elements in the Earth's crust.

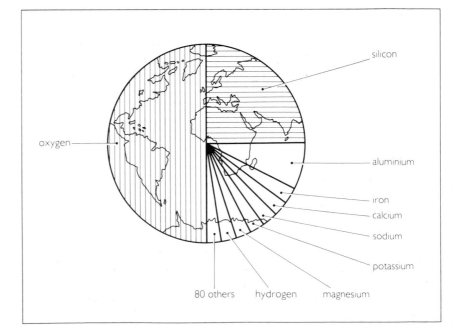

The two kinds of elements

Elements may be grouped into two kinds: metals and non-metals.

Metals   These are hard, shiny solids which only melt on strong heating.
They can be bent, drawn out into wires or beaten into shapes. They are good conductors of heat and electricity.

Non-metals   These are either gases or solids which melt easily. The solids are usually powdery or brittle. They do not bend. They are poor conductors of heat and electricity.

Some elements do not show all the properties typical of their kind. Carbon, for example, is a non-metal but in the form of diamond it is the hardest substance known.

Atoms

An iron nail appears to be solid but it can be cut into smaller pieces. The smallest pieces which can exist by themselves are called *atoms*. All elements are composed of atoms. The atoms of an element are all alike but they are different from the atoms of any other element.

Atoms are so incredibly tiny that it is difficult to picture just how small they are. A penny, for instance, contains about 34 thousand, million, million million atoms!

Atoms of elements are often shown as *symbols*. The symbol is either the first letter of the name (sometimes the Latin name) or the first letter followed by a small letter. Thus, the atom of carbon is C, calcium is Ca, copper is Cu (from cuprum). Other symbols are shown below.

Iron in the pylon and aluminium in the cables—both typical metals.

Metals			
aluminium	Al	magnesium	Mg
calcium	Ca	potassium	K
copper	Cu	silver	Ag
gold	Au	sodium	Na
iron	Fe	tin	Sn
lead	Pb	zinc	Zn

Non-metals			
bromine	Br	iodine	I
carbon	C	nitrogen	N
chlorine	Cl	oxygen	O
fluorine	F	phosphorus	P
helium	He	silicon	Si
hydrogen	H	sulphur	S

Questions

1. What kind of substances are called minerals?
2. How are minerals formed? Name 4 minerals.
3. What are elements? How many are there in the Earth?
4. What are the 2 most abundant elements?
5. Give 3 properties each of metals and non-metals.
6. What are the smallest possible pieces of elements called?
7. About how many atoms are there in one penny?
8. Give the symbols for sodium, calcium, iron, oxygen, carbon and copper.

1.4 Inside atoms

The idea of atoms being the smallest possible pieces of an element has been around for thousands of years. It is now known that the 90 or so different atoms are themselves made up of even smaller parts.

Sub-atomic particles

Of the many tiny particles which make up atoms, only three, *protons, electrons* and *neutrons,* are needed to explain how atoms differ from each other.

The proton p, and the electron e   Protons are packed together as a central core or nucleus with electrons orbiting round, somewhat like planets round the sun. Electron paths are constantly changing but they are usually drawn as circles. Protons are nearly 2000 times heavier than electrons.

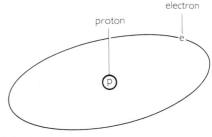

A hydrogen atom.

The proton and the electron have a mysterious property called *charge.* Charge exerts a force of attraction between the particles and holds the atom together. Protons are said to have positive (+) charge and electrons to have negative (−) charge. Atoms always have equal numbers of protons and electrons so that the charges are balanced. The simplest atom, hydrogen, has one proton and one electron. The next atom, helium, has two of each, whilst the heaviest naturally-occurring atom, uranium, has 92 of each particle.

The neutron n   This is about as heavy as the proton but is not charged. Most atoms have neutrons packed together with the protons in their nuclei. The helium atom, for example, has 2 neutrons in addition to 2 protons in its nucleus.

Atomic Number and Mass Number   The Atomic number of an element, (sometimes known as the *Proton Number*), tells you the number of protons in each atom of the element. For example, helium has an Atomic Number of two. Other elements have different Atomic Numbers.

Sir James Chadwick, who discovered the neutron in 1932.

The Mass Number of an element tells you the total number of protons and neutrons in an atom. Helium, with two protons and two neutrons, has a Mass Number of four.

The helium atom is sometimes shown as $^{4}_{2}\mathrm{He}$ — 4 ----- Mass number, 2 ----- Atomic number

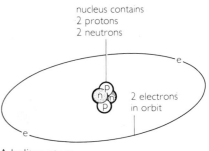

nucleus contains 2 protons 2 neutrons

2 electrons in orbit

A helium atom.

Isotopes

All atoms of a particular element have the same Atomic Number. They have the same number of protons in the nucleus and electrons in orbit. The number of neutrons is not fixed, however, and different forms of the same element can exist. Every lithium atom, for instance, has 3 protons, but some also have 3 neutrons (Mass Number = 6), whilst others have 4 neutrons (Mass Number = 7). These two forms of the element are called *isotopes*. A great many elements are mixtures of isotopes.

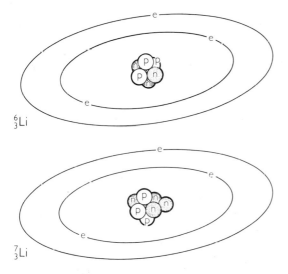

$^{6}_{3}Li$

$^{7}_{3}Li$

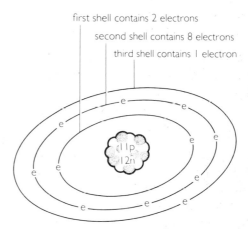

first shell contains 2 electrons

second shell contains 8 electrons

third shell contains 1 electron

A sodium atom.

Electron shells

The electrons in an atom orbit the nucleus in clearly defined regions called *energy levels* or *shells*. The first shell is close to the nucleus and has room for only 2 electrons. The second shell can contain up to 8 electrons. There can be as many as 7 occupied shells of electrons. Lithium has 3 electrons: 2 in the first shell and 1 in the second. Sodium has 11 electrons: 2 in the first shell, 8 in the second shell and 1 in the third. The shells nearest to the nucleus fill up first.

The way an element behaves largely depends upon the electrons in the outermost shell. These outer electrons are the ones most commonly involved when atoms join up with each other. There are some atoms which do not join up with others: these atoms usually have their outer shells filled with 8 electrons.

Niels Bohr was the Danish scientist who first worked out the idea of electron shells.

Questions

1. Name the particles present in the nucleus of an atom.
2. What is it that holds an atom together?
3. What is the Atomic Number of an atom?
4. Which element has an Atomic Number of 92?
5. What is Mass Number and what does it show?
6. What are isotopes? Give an example.
7. What are electron shells? How many electrons will the 2nd shell hold?
8. Which electrons are involved when atoms join together?

1.5 Atoms joining together

The world is not made up of separate atoms floating about—atoms stick together. Sometimes just a few join up: sometimes thousands are linked together in some way. When two or more atoms join together as a single unit, the new particle is called a molecule.

Molecules of elements

Many elements are made up of molecules which contain two or more identical atoms linked together. Air consists mainly of the elements nitrogen and oxygen: both gases have molecules made up of two atoms strongly bound together. The yellow, powdery element, sulphur consists of molecules having eight atoms each.

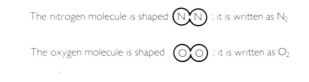

The nitrogen molecule is shaped (N N) : it is written as N_2

The oxygen molecule is shaped (O O) : it is written as O_2

The sulphur molecule is shaped (S S S S S S S S) : it is written as S_8

Molecules of compounds

Molecules made from two or more different atoms linked together make up *compounds*. Water, perhaps the most common compound of all, has simple molecules in which two atoms of hydrogen are joined to one atom of oxygen. The molecule is represented by the formula H_2O.

The *formula* of a compound shows exactly the numbers of all atoms present in the molecule. Note that the formula for water is H_2O and not H_2O_1. If only one atom of any kind is present the symbol alone is shown wthout the figure $_1$. The formulae of some common compounds are shown in the following table.

A water molecule model.

Compound	Molecule	Formula
carbon dioxide		CO_2
ammonia		NH_3
methane		CH_4
sulphuric acid		H_2SO_4
hydrogen chloride		HCl

Equations

When substances combine together to form different materials, a *reaction* or *chemical change* has taken place. The burning of a match is a good example of a chemical reaction. *Equations* are a shorthand way of describing chemical reactions, using symbols and formulae to show how atoms and molecules rearrange themselves.

When coke (a form of carbon) burns in air (containing oxygen) to form carbon dioxide the equation would be written:

carbon + oxygen $\rightarrow$ carbon dioxide
$$C + O_2 \rightarrow CO_2$$

The equation shows that one atom of carbon combines with one molecule of oxygen to give the molecule of carbon dioxide.

The equation for the burning of natural gas (methane) is:

methane + oxygen $\rightarrow$ carbon dioxide + water
$$CH_4 + 2O_2 \rightarrow CO_2 + 2H_2O$$

The equation shows that one molecule of methane combines with 2 molecules of oxygen to give one molecule of carbon dioxide and 2 molecules of water.

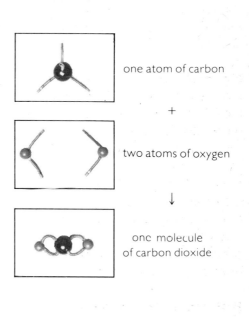

one atom of carbon

+

two atoms of oxygen

$\downarrow$

one molecule of carbon dioxide

Covalent bonding

The way in which atoms join to form molecules is related to the number of electrons in their outermost shells.

A full shell of 8 electrons is a stable state. Atoms will share pairs of electrons between them if, by doing so, they can achieve full outer shells. Thus 2 chlorine atoms, both having 7 electrons in their outer shells, will share 2 electrons, one from each atom, to make up shells of 8.

The shared pair of electrons acts as a 'glue' sticking the 2 atoms together. It is called the *covalent bond* and is sometimes drawn as a line between atoms:

Cl—Cl

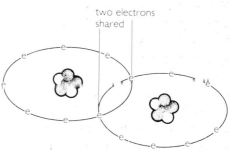

Atoms of chlorine showing outer shells of electrons only.

Questions
1. What is a molecule? Give 2 examples of molecules of elements.
2. What are compounds composed of? What does the formula of a compound show? Give the formula for sulphuric acid.
3. What is meant by a 'chemical reaction'?
4. What do equations represent?
5. Write the equation for the burning of natural gas.
6. What part of an atom is involved in bond formation?
7. Show how 2 chlorine atoms combine to form a chlorine molecule.
8. What is the covalent bond?

1.6 Electron-swapping compounds

Chloroform and common salt are both compounds containing chlorine atoms. Why are they so very different?

Ionic compounds

When sodium is heated in chlorine, the elements combine to form the compound sodium chloride. It is the electrons in the outer shells of the atoms that are involved in the bonding. In this case they do not form the 'electron glue' that sticks covalent compounds together as explained in the previous section. Instead an electron is transferred from the sodium atom to the chlorine atom so that each atom has a full shell of 8 electrons on the outside.

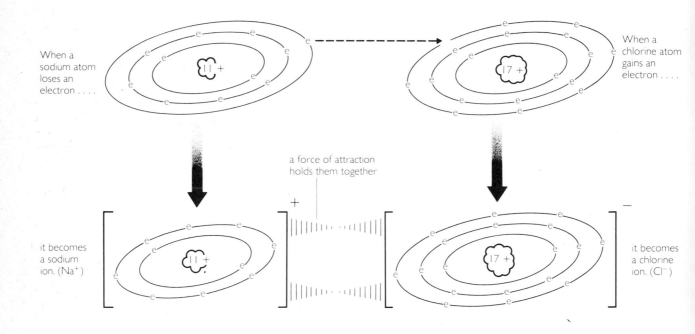

When a sodium atom loses an electron . . . .

When a chlorine atom gains an electron . . . .

a force of attraction holds them together

it becomes a sodium ion. (Na⁺)

it becomes a chlorine ion. (Cl⁻)

Ions Sodium chloride does not consist of molecules but of ions. *Ions* are atoms which have either lost or gained electrons. The sodium ion Na^+ is positively charged because it has lost a negative electron. When the chlorine atom accepts an extra negative electron it becomes the negative ion Cl^-. The compound is held together by force of attraction between the oppositely charged ions. This is called *ionic bonding*.

Other atoms may gain or lose 2 electrons and some 3 electrons. Complex ions are formed when groups of atoms lose or gain extra electrons.

Positive ions (cations)	
calcium	Ca^{2+}
copper	Cu^{2+}
iron	Fe^{3+}
ammonium	$(NH_4)^+$

Negative ions (anions)	
oxide	O^{2-}
sulphate	$(SO_4)^{2-}$
carbonate	$(CO_3)^{2-}$
nitrate	$(NO_3)^-$

Structure and formulae of ionic compounds

Ionic compounds have rigid structures something like the framework of a large building. Positive and negative ions are placed alternately. The structure is held together very tightly because all the positive ions attract all the negative ions close to them. The ions fit together as closely as possible.

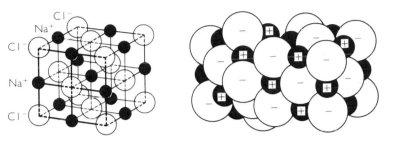

Formula   The formula of an ionic compound shows the ratio of the ions present. It is the smallest number of each ion which will provide a balance of positive and negative charges.

The formula represents the smallest part of the compound which can take part in a chemical change. It may be used in equations in the same way as the formula of a covalent molecule.

Compound	Ions	Formula
sodium chloride	$(Na)^+\ ^-(Cl)$	$NaCl$
copper sulphate	$(Cu)^{++}\ ^{--}(SO_4)$	$CuSO_4$
calcium nitrate	$Ca^{++}\ ^-(NO_3)\ ^-(NO_3)$	$Ca(NO_3)_2$

General properties of compounds

Chloroform and common salt have quite different properties because of the way they are bonded. The differences between them are typical of the differences between covalent compounds and ionic compounds.

Property	Covalent compounds	Ionic compounds
Melting point	Low—often gases or liquids	High—solids
Smell	Yes	No
Dissolve in water	No	Yes
Conduct electricity	No	Yes—when melted or dissolved

Questions
1. What is formed when sodium is heated in chlorine? What happens to the electrons in the outer shells of the atoms?
2. Give the 2 ions present in sodium chloride.
3. What is ionic bonding? Give the formula of the sulphate ion.
4. Describe the structure of an ionic compound.
5. What is the formula of an ionic compound? What does it show?
6. Write the formula for (a) copper sulphate, (b) sodium carbonate.
7. State 2 general differences between covalent and ionic compounds.

Questions on Chapter 1

1 a Name the 2 planets which orbit between the Earth and the Sun.
b Name the planet with rings round it.
c What orbits between Mars and Jupiter?
d Complete the sentences:
Stars produce their own . . . . as a result of . . . . of the gas . . . . A group of stars is known as a . . . . The distance between stars is measured in . . . . The star nearest the Earth is . . . . which is . . . . distant.
e Scientists always consider the surface of Mars to be more interesting than the Moon. Suggest 2 reasons why astronauts have been to the Moon but not to Mars.   SWEB

2 a What name do we give to rock which was once hot and molten?
b Give one example of this kind of rock.
c What name do we give to rock which has changed its form as a result of heat or pressure?
d Give one example of this type of rock.   SWEB

3 a Which atomic particle has the least mass?
b Which atomic particle has a positive charge?
c Name the lightest element.   WYLREB

4 The nucleus of an atom of oxygen contains some of the following particles:
a neutrons, b protons, c ions,
d electrons.
Write down the correct answer.   WREB

5 The diagrams below show a simple way of representing atomic particles. Copy and label each diagram correctly: 'uncharged atom', 'negative ion', 'positive ion', 'electron'.   SREB

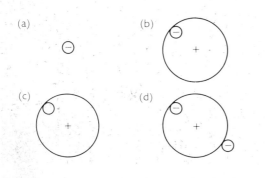

6 a Give the chemical symbols for i carbon,
ii calcium, iii chlorine, iv copper.
b Sometimes the symbol O may be used, and sometimes the symbol O_2. When used in this way:
i what does the symbol O stand for,
ii what does the symbol O_2 stand for?   NWREB

7 Give the chemical names of the following.
a $MgSO_4$, b NaCl, c $CaCO_3$,
d Na_2CO_3, e NaOH.   NWREB

8 The rectangles shown contain symbols arranged to represent molecules of
a hydrogen and b oxygen.

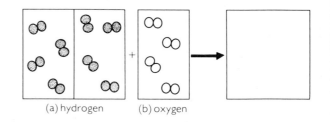

(a) hydrogen   (b) oxygen

Using the same symbols and a box similar to that given, draw in the correct number of molecules representing the new substance formed.   EAEB

9 An atom of the element lithium has 3 electrons, 3 protons, and 4 neutrons.
a Make a simple labelled sketch of this atom.
b What charge is carried by i the neutrons,
ii the protons, iii the electrons?   EAEB

10 Write out the following table and put a tick in the correct column for each substance.

Substance	Element	Compound	Mixture
sodium chloride			
air			
water			
lead			
soil			
copper sulphate			
diamond			

Chapter 2

Water and Air

You are two-thirds this. What is it?

It puts the fizz in pop, it puts out fires,
and is vital to life on Earth. What is it?

2.1 Water

Life on this planet began in the water that covers much of its surface. Water and air together provide the conditions which support life as we know it. This section and the following three are concerned with that most essential substance—water.

Water in living things

Plants make their food and their own bodies from water and air. More than nine-tenths of a lettuce, for instance, is simply water. There is much more water than any other substance in the human body. It is present both combined in the materials that make up the cells and in the juices which carry out the body functions.

The water cycle

The sea is the source of all water in the world. The sun heats the sea and some of the water becomes vapour. The vapour collects as clouds and when these are blown over high ground they release the water as rain. Rain seeps through the ground and runs as rivers back to the sea. Plants absorb water from the ground and return a lot of it to the air. Rain water is collected in reservoirs, supplied to houses and industries and returned after treatment to the sea. So water circulates over and over again.

80% water

67% water

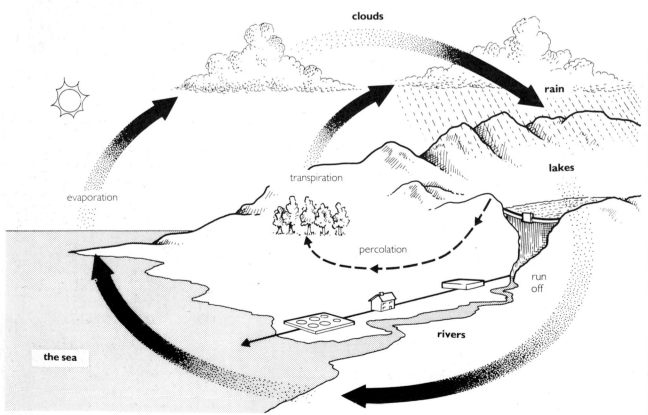

clouds

rain

lakes

transpiration

evaporation

percolation

run off

rivers

the sea

20

Water as a dissolving agent

One of the most important properties of water is its ability to dissolve things. If you shake a sugar cube with water, the sugar vanishes. It is still there of course—you can taste it—but it has *dissolved:* it has mixed in with the water. The millions of sugar molecules which made up the cube are now evenly spread among the billions of water molecules. The mixture of sugar and water is called a *solution.* Substances which dissolve in water are said to be *soluble.* All sorts of things are soluble in water to some extent.

The sea   This is a gigantic solution of nearly all the substances found on the Earth. Rain water dissolves compounds from the rocks and soil and carries them into the sea. Common salt (sodium chloride) is the most abundant dissolved solid and makes up 2.7% of the sea. The percentage varies because the sea evaporates at different rates at different times and places.

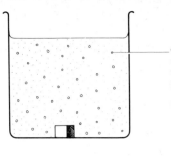

evenly spread sugar particles – too small to be seen

Dehydration

Potatoes are nearly eight tenths water. When they are carefully warmed they lose their water and a solid is left. This is *dehydrated* potato. It will keep for a very long time because the bacteria and moulds which cause food to go bad cannot work without water. Powdered dried potato can be made into mashed potato by simply adding water. Other foods commonly dehydrated are: milk (for babies), peas and fruit; whilst hay is dried grass.

Tests for water

Pure water freezes at 0 °C and boils at 100 °C.
Blue copper sulphate crystals turn white when they are dehydrated by heat. The dehydrated copper sulphate turns blue again when water is added.

Dried potato.

Questions

1. How much water is there in (a) a lettuce, and (b) the human body?
2. Explain what happens in the water cycle.
3. What happens to sugar when it dissolves in water?
4. Explain what is meant by the term 'soluble'.
5. What is the main dissolved substance in sea water? How did it get there?
6. What is meant by 'dehydration'? Name 3 dehydrated foods.
7. Give the boiling point and freezing point of water and one other test for water.

Another form of dried food.

2.2 Solutions

Blood, saliva and urine are just three of the many solutions produced by the body. All the processes of living depend upon the ability of water to carry substances round the body as various kinds of solutions.

Aqueous solutions

A uniform mixture of the molecules of two different substances is a *solution*. The substance forming the bulk of the solution is called the *solvent*, and the dissolved substance is the *solute*. Solvents are usually liquids. The most common solvent is water and its solutions are given the name *aqueous*.

Solubility Usually there is a limit to how much solute will dissolve in a fixed amount of solvent. When no more solute will dissolve, the solution is *saturated*. The *solubility* of a substance in water is the mass in grammes which will dissolve in 100g of water to produce a saturated solution. Hot water often dissolves more of solids than cold water: the temperature has to be stated when solubility figures are quoted.

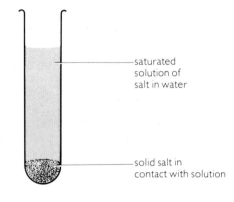

saturated solution of salt in water

solid salt in contact with solution

Solutions of gases Most gases will dissolve in water although their solubilities are much lower than those of solids. Oxygen, for instance, dissolves very little, but there is enough of it in water for fish to breathe using their gills.

Solubilities—grams of solute in 100 g of water at 20 °C			
Solids		Gases	
sodium chloride (salt)	36.0	nitrogen	0.002
sodium carbonate (soda)	21.5	oxygen	0.004
ammonium sulphate	71.0	carbon dioxide	0.169
calcium sulphate	0.2	hydrogen sulphide	0.385

Suspensions and colloids

The particles of a solute in a solution are about the same size as the molecules of the solvent. Particles many times larger than the solvent molecules will not dissolve to form solutions: they are either *suspensions* or *colloids*.

Suspensions These consist of particles large enough to be seen, mixed with water. The particles are not dissolved and will settle to the bottom if the suspension is allowed to stand. Powdered calcium carbonate shaken with water forms a milky liquid. This can be separated quickly by filtering. The large particles of the suspended solid will not pass through the fine holes in filter paper.

Colloids A little concentrated iron (III) chloride solution poured into a beaker of hot water produces a brown, cloudy liquid. This will not clear on standing nor by filtering. It is a colloid. Its particles are bigger than those of a solution but smaller than those of a suspension. A beam of light from a strong torch will show up the particles.

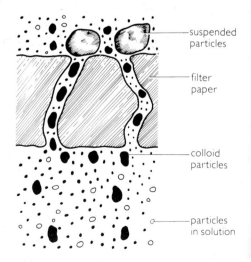

suspended particles

filter paper

colloid particles

particles in solution

Colloidal solutions

Many natural substances are colloidal. Blood contains colloidal particles as well as substances in solution. Common colloids are glue, butter, potter's clay, ink, smoke and fog.

Pastes These are concentrated suspensions of colloidal solids in liquid solvents. Paints, putty, dough and toothpaste are examples.

Jellies These are colloidal solutions even though they are semi-solid. They melt easily when warmed.

Emulsions Cooking oil, shaken with water and a few drops of detergent, produces a milky liquid consisting of tiny oil drops suspended in water. This is an emulsion and it does not separate. Common emulsions are milk, salad cream and ointments.

Some common colloids.

Other kinds of solution

Water is by no means the only liquid solvent. Many liquids have good solvent properties for particular solutes. Oil paint dissolves in white spirit, grease dissolves in petrol and nail varnish is dissolved by acetone.

All the examples of solutions considered so far have been of solid, liquid or gas solutes in liquid solvents. However, the solvent can also be a solid or a gas. Solder does not seem to be a solution, but it is actually solid tin dissolved in solid lead. Other examples of unusual solutions are shown in the photographs.

Brass is a solution of zinc metal in copper.

Smoke is a colloidal solution of solid in air.

Questions
1. Explain the terms 'solution', 'solvent' and 'solute'.
2. What is the commonest solvent? Name 3 other solvents.
3. When is a solution said to be saturated?
4. Explain what is meant by 'solubility'. How does temperature affect it? Give the solubilites of salt and oxygen.
5. How is a colloidal solution recognised? What size are its particles?
6. Give examples of 4 different kinds of colloidal solutions.
7. Name a good solvent for grease.
8. Give 2 examples of solutions with non-liquid solvents.

Air is a solution of oxygen in nitrogen.

2.3 Separating mixtures

Good cooks sieve flour to remove large lumps; keen gardeners sift stones from the soil of seed beds; in limestone quarries the crushed rock is graded into piles of the same-sized chippings. In the home and in industry, mixtures (including solutions) often need to be separated into their component parts.

Filtering

A *filter* is a very fine sieve made from interlocking fibres or from solid particles packed closely together. Gauze pads will filter dust and liquid sprays from air. Large, suspended solids can be removed from water by fine filter paper or by a pad made of fine powder. The smaller particles of a dissolved solid will, however, pass through a filter paper.

Separating salt from sand Rock salt can be purified by dissolving it in water and filtering off the insoluble sand and mud. The salt solution which passes through the fine pores of the filter paper can be evaporated to give purified white salt.

Distilling

Distilling separates and recovers the solvent from a solution. Distilled water, needed for car batteries, is obtained by boiling water and condensing the vapour. All the dissolved impurities are left behind and the distillate is absolutely pure water. Sea water can be made fit for drinking by distillation.

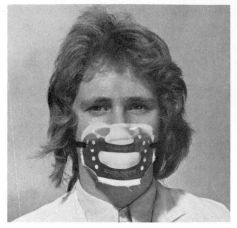

A gauze mask will filter dust from air.

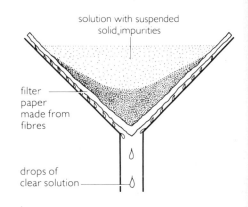

solution with suspended solid impurities

filter paper made from fibres

drops of clear solution

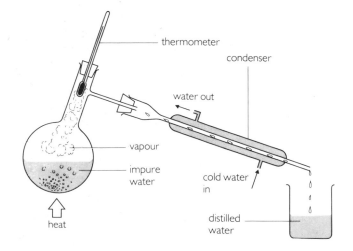

thermometer
condenser
water out
vapour
impure water
cold water in
distilled water
heat

Fractional distillation This separates mixtures of liquids. Whisky is distilled by boiling a fermented mixture of barley, water, yeast and some ethanol. The water and ethanol become gases. Much of the water condenses in the long necks of the boiling vessels and runs back. Some of the water and all of the ethanol vapour pass into the condensers to form a spirit much richer in ethanol.

Crystallising

If a little sodium chloride is stirred with water in a beaker, the salt will dissolve easily to produce a *dilute* solution. It tastes only slightly of salt. Left standing in a warm place for several days, the water gradually *evaporates*—it passes into the air as water vapour. The remaining salt solution becomes more and more *concentrated*. Eventually it becomes saturated and any further evaporation causes solid salt to be deposited on the bottom of the beaker. This is *crystallisation*. The slower the rate of evaporation, the larger are the crystals that form.

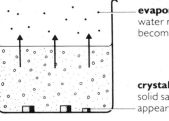

evaporation: water molecules becoming gas

crystallisation: solid salt appearing

Chromatography

Mixtures of solids can be separated by carrying away the lighter particles with water, oil or air. Water is used to wash sand and dirt away from gold dust and from tin ore. A similar idea is used in *chromatography* to separate mixtures of dissolved substances. Dyes in a spot of black ink on a filter paper can be separated by dripping water slowly on to the blot. As the water spreads out it carries the dyes with it. The dyes are slowed down by the filter paper by different amounts and separate into bands of colour. The dyes in different coloured felt tip pens can be compared by marking a series of dots on blotting paper which is then dipped in a bowl of water. Water soaks up into the paper drawing the dyes up to different heights. The same dyes in different inks will rise to the same heights. Non-coloured substances can also be identified by this method which is used a great deal in medical work.

Panning for gold. If there is any, the gold stays whilst other less dense substances get washed away.

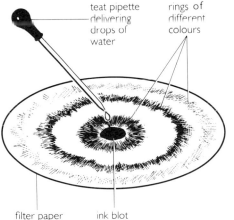

teat pipette delivering drops of water

rings of different colours

filter paper   ink blot

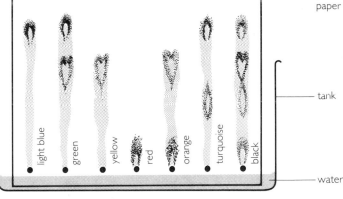

blotting paper

tank

water

light blue   green   yellow   red   orange   turquoise   black

Questions

1. What is a filter? Give examples of 2 different kinds.
2. Explain how rock salt can be purified.
3. Explain how distilled water is made.
4. What is 'fractional distillation'? Give an example.
5. Explain the terms 'evaporation' and 'crystallisation'.
6. What is meant by 'chromatography'? How can you show that black ink contains a number of different dyes?
7. In what kind of work is chromatography used?

2.4 Water supplies

Because our bodies are two-thirds water, we need to take in about two litres a day to remain healthy. We use many times this amount in washing, cooking and flushing the lavatory. Include the water used by industry and each of us uses about 300 litres a day.

Collecting water

There is a huge amount of water in the oceans—but it is not pure. Fresh water can be obtained easily, although expensively, by the large scale distillation of the sea. Britain is lucky to be supplied with more than enough water, distilled for nothing by the sun. All we have to do is to tap the various sources that collect rain and make sure that the water is fit for drinking.

Mountain reservoirs   Much of our water is collected by building dams across streams in upland areas. The water is piped direct to cities or used to control the flow of rivers.

Collecting water at Claerwen dam, in Wales.

Rivers   Some towns get their water from the nearest point on a big river. This water needs careful treatment because it is usually muddy and sometimes contains harmful wastes.

Wells   Natural underground reservoirs often fill with water seeping through the ground. Well water was once very common, and still provides about a quarter of England's water supply.

Purifying water

To make water safe for drinking it goes through four processes.
1. It is passed through coarse and fine *strainers* which remove floating objects, suspended solids and organisms such as algae.

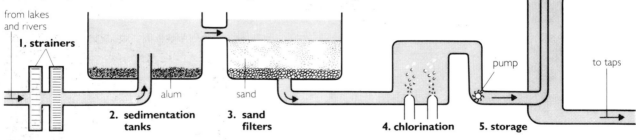

from lakes and rivers

1. strainers

alum

2. sedimentation tanks

sand

3. sand filters

4. chlorination

5. storage

pump

to taps

2. If the water is muddy, a *settling agent* (usually alum) is added. The colloidal particles clog together to form a spongy mass (floc) which settles out in sedimentation tanks.
3. The water is filtered through sand beds. This produces clear, clean water.
4. The clear water still contains bacteria and other micro-organisms. These are destroyed by adding carefully measured amounts of *sterilising agents* which are harmless to man in low concentrations. Ozone gas is the best, but very costly: chlorine gas is more commonly used.

Treating used water

Once water has been used it becomes *sewage*—water mixed with organic wastes (human excrement and unused food), grease, soap and dirt. It flows away through drains into main sewers and on to *sewage* works.

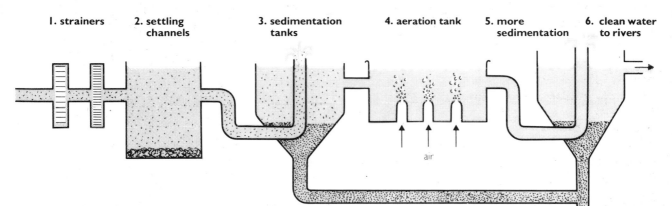

1. strainers 2. settling channels 3. sedimentation tanks 4. aeration tank 5. more sedimentation 6. clean water to rivers

1. Strainers remove rags, tins and pieces of wood.
2. Grit and sand settle out in channels.
3. The crude sewage flows very slowly through *sedimentation* tanks where about one-third of the organic matter settles at the bottom as sludge.
4. The cleaner water then passes to either *trickling filters* or *aeration tanks* containing sludge agitated with air. Here carefully chosen bacteria live off the sewage breaking down all the remaining polluting matter.
5. More sedimentation tanks collect all the remaining sludge. The clean water is discharged into rivers or the sea.
6. The sludge is collected and warmed in large, sealed tanks. More bacteria *digest* the harmful part of it and produce methane gas and a semi-solid waste. The gas is used at the works to produce electricity: the waste is dumped at sea or dried and used as fertiliser.

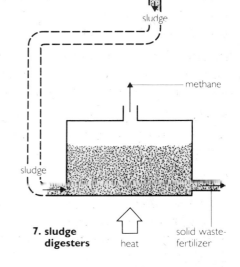

7. sludge digesters   heat

Questions
1. How much water does the body need each day?
2. Give 3 sources of drinking water. Why does it need treating?
3. Briefly describe the 4 processes in the treatment of water.
4. What is commonly used to sterilise drinking water?
5. What is sewage? What happens in sedimentation tanks?
6. What happens in aeration tanks?
7. What gas is produced in the sludge digesters? What is it used for?

A sewage plant. The sedimentation tanks are clearly visible. The pits on the left are for sludge storage before final treatment.

2.5 Air

We cannot see air but there is a lot of it about—5000 million million tonnes in all. Apart from keeping us alive—a useful function—the gases in the atmosphere have many other uses.

Gases in the atmosphere

Air is a mixture of gases, mainly nitrogen and oxygen, with small amounts of many others. Water vapour is always present but no percentage is given because the amount varies so much.

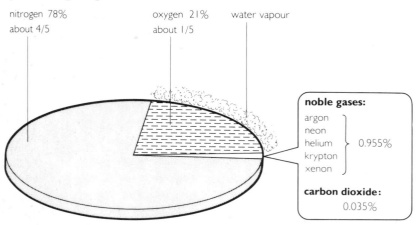

nitrogen 78%
about 4/5

oxygen 21%
about 1/5

water vapour

noble gases:
argon
neon
helium   0.955%
krypton
xenon

carbon dioxide:
0.035%

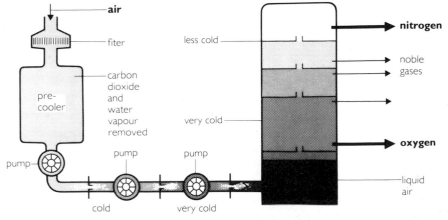

Air distillation.

Oxygen

Oxygen is the reactive part of the air. Oxygen enables living things to breathe—it is the gas that combines with materials when they burn. Pure oxygen can be separated from the other gases in air and used to assist breathing in hospitals, aircraft and submarines. Huge quantities are also used in the making, cutting and welding of steel.

Separating oxygen from the air Air is pumped through a filter to remove dust and then carbon dioxide and water are removed. It is then compressed, and then allowed to expand through a narrow jet. This makes it very cold. This cooling process is repeated until the air gets so cold that it changes to liquid.

The extremely cold liquid air contains liquid oxygen, liquid nitrogen and the noble gases in liquid form. This mixture is allowed to warm up slowly and the nitrogen boils away first leaving the others. As the temperature rises the noble gases boil away one by one leaving the oxygen as liquid. The product finally piped away may be high quality gas or liquid or medium purity oxygen gas.

air

fiter

carbon
dioxide
and
water
vapour
removed

pre-
cooler

pump

pump

pump

cold

very cold

less cold

very cold

nitrogen

noble
gases

oxygen

liquid
air

Making oxygen in the laboratory

Some compounds containing a lot of oxygen will release it when they are decomposed (broken down into simpler substances). A solution of *hydrogen peroxide* gives off oxygen easily and safely. Manganese dioxide is used to make the hydrogen peroxide decompose more quickly. The manganese dioxide is not used up: it acts as a *catalyst*. The reaction is:

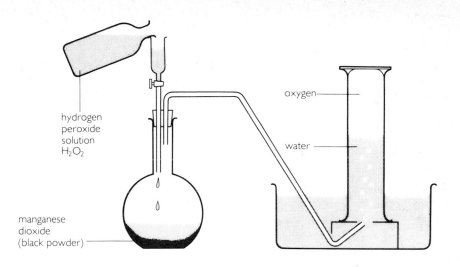

hydrogen peroxide solution H_2O_2

oxygen

water

manganese dioxide (black powder)

hydrogen peroxide → water + oxygen

$$2H_2O_2 \rightarrow 2H_2O + O_2$$

Nitrogen and the noble gases

Originally the nitrogen produced by liquefying air was wasted because it does not react much. However, this unreactiveness can be a positive advantage. Nitrogen is pumped into oil storage tanks when they are empty, to prevent the possibility of fire.

Liquid nitrogen is very cold. It is used for quickfreezing and transporting food. It can also be used for "shrink fitting". In this process, one very cold metal part is slipped inside another. As it warms up, it gets bigger and fits tightly in place.

Nitrogen can be combined with hydrogen to make the gas *ammonia,* which in turn is used to make nitric acid.

The noble gases   These have no natural reactions at all. Precisely for this reason they find uses in electric light bulbs, in strip lights and in electric arc welding. Helium, being very light, is used for filling balloons.

Producing frozen peas.

Questions

1. List the gases in dry air and give their percentages.
2. What other gas is always present? Why is no percentage given for it?
3. The diagram shows what happens when iron filings are left in a tube with damp air for some days. How far has the water risen in the tube? What proportion is this? What does it show?
4. How is oxygen obtained from the air? Give 3 uses of pure oxygen.
5. How is oxygen made in the laboratory?
6. Give 2 uses of liquid nitrogen and 2 uses of the gas.
7. Give the names of the noble gases and some of their uses.

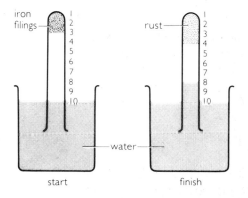

iron filings

rust

water

start   finish

2.6 Burning

When a match is lit, the flames give out heat and light energy and the match burns away. Only a thin piece of charcoal is left. Or is anything else formed that we cannot see?

Burning

Burning is the rapid combining of a substance with oxygen, making flames and heat. Air usually provides the oxygen. The main products of burning are *oxides*—the compounds formed when oxygen joins with the elements in the burning substance. These oxides are often invisible gases.

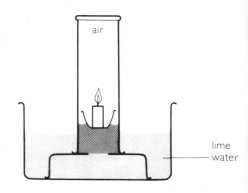

The diagram shows a burning candle in a basin floating on lime water. When covered by a large jar, the candle continues to burn for a short while and then goes out. The lime water rises up the jar—and also turns milky. This shows that only part of the air is used in burning (the one fifth which is oxygen)—and that carbon dioxide is formed.

Increase in weight on burning   This can be shown by weighing a bundle of magnesium ribbon in a crucible and then heating it. The lid must be raised from time to time to let air in. Gradually the magnesium changes to the grey ash, magnesium oxide. On reweighing, the magnesium oxide is found to weigh more than the magnesium.

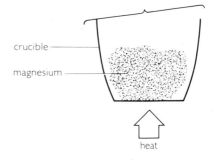

Corrosion

Many metals *corrode* in air: they react slowly with oxygen to form oxides and the surface becomes eaten away. The presence of water greatly assists corrosion. Iron becomes coated with rust in a few days if exposed to both air and water. Dry air or air-free water alone will not cause iron to rust. To prevent iron articles rusting they must be coated with oil, grease, paint or another metal. Galvanised iron is iron coated with zinc.

Fuels

Fuels are substances which burn easily and release a lot of heat energy. Most fuels are compounds of carbon and hydrogen which give carbon dioxide and water as the main products of combustion. Natural gas is an excellent fuel.

methane + oxygen   → carbon dioxide + water + heat
$$CH_4 + 2O_2 \rightarrow CO_2 + 2H_2O$$

Respiration of the body   This is a kind of 'slow burning' or combustion which does not involve flames. The fuel is mainly glucose made from the sugars in food. In the body cells these react with oxygen dissolved in the blood to give carbon dioxide and water. Most of the energy released heats the body.

Using one fuel to make another one suitable for use.

Burning of elements in oxygen

Yellow sulphur powder held in a combustion spoon burns with a feeble blue flame when heated. Lowered into a jar of pure oxygen, it burns much more brightly and gives off a gas with a sharp, choking smell. This gas is sulphur dioxide and it will turn a piece of damp litmus paper red.

Many other elements also burn vigorously in oxygen to form *oxides*. Oxides may be put into three groups according to their effect on litmus paper. One group turn litmus red: these are always oxides of non-metals. Another group turn litmus blue: they are oxides of metals. The third group do not affect litmus at all. Water, the oxide of hydrogen, belongs to this group.

Section 3.1 explains in more detail how the "litmus red" oxides when dissolved in water make *acids*. "Litmus blue" oxides, called *bases*, are the "chemical opposites" of acids.

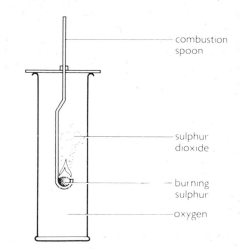

combustion spoon

sulphur dioxide

burning sulphur

oxygen

Element	How it burns	Oxide formed	Effect on litmus
Non-metals SULPHUR CARBON PHOSPHORUS	blue flame glows red yellow flame	sulphur dioxide—gas carbon dioxide—gas phosphorous(V) oxide–white smoke	RED RED RED
HYDROGEN	blue flame	hydrogen oxide—water	PURPLE
Metals MAGNESIUM CALCIUM SODIUM IRON	bright flash red flash yellow flash glow red	magnesium oxide—grey ash calcium oxide—white solid sodium oxide—yellow solid iron oxide—black solid	BLUE BLUE BLUE PURPLE

Testing for oxygen

Things which burn in air will burn much more fiercely in pure oxygen. A smouldering wood splint will burst into flames when put in the gas. This reaction is used as the test for oxygen.

Using pure oxygen gas, this diver can produce a flame hot enough to cut metal underwater.

Questions

1. What is meant by burning?
2. How can it be shown that a candle uses up oxygen when it burns and produces carbon dioxide?
3. Why does magnesium weigh more after burning than before?
4. Name 2 compounds formed when a fuel burns.
5. Write the equation for the burning of natural gas.
6. Give an example of combustion without flames. Name the fuel.
7. What happens when metals corrode? How is iron protected?
8. Name 2 metal oxides and 2 non-metal oxides and state how they affect litmus.
9. What is the test for oxygen?

2.7 Carbon dioxide

There is only a very small proportion of carbon dioxide gas in the air—3 parts in 10 000—and yet all plant and animal life depends on it. Why is it so vital? Will there always be enough of it? How else is it used?

The vital gas

The many different compounds which make up living things are all based on chains of carbon atoms. These are all made from the carbon dioxide in the air. Plants make their food and body cells by absorbing carbon dioxide (through their leaves) and water (through their roots) and changing them into glucose. Oxygen is given off at the same time. Sunlight and the green substance chlorophyll are needed to help the process which is called *photosynthesis*.

$$\text{carbon dioxide} + \text{water} \xrightarrow[\text{sunlight}]{\text{chlorophyll}} \text{glucose} + \text{oxygen}$$

$$6CO_2 \quad + 6H_2O \longrightarrow C_6H_{12}O_6 + \quad 6O_2$$

Some of the glucose is changed into more complex substances, often combined with nitrogen and other elements. Animals eat plants, using the carbon compounds to grow their own bodies.

All living things breathe, turning some of the compounds back into carbon dioxide. All fuels produce carbon dioxide when they burn. The amount of carbon dioxide in the air remains roughly the same because breathing and burning replace the carbon dioxide removed by photosynthesis.

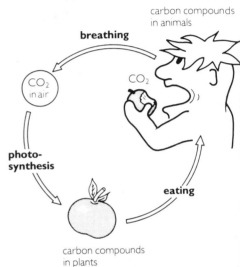

Making carbon dioxide

In the laboratory You can make carbon dioxide by adding moderately dilute hydrochloric acid to chips of marble (a form of calcium carbonate) using the apparatus shown.

$$\begin{array}{ccccccc}
\text{calcium} & & \text{hydrochloric} & & \text{calcium} & & \text{carbon} \\
\text{carbonate} & + & \text{acid} & \rightarrow & \text{chloride} & + \text{water} + & \text{dioxide} \\
CaCO_3 & + & 2HCl & \rightarrow & CaCl_2 & + H_2O + & CO_2
\end{array}$$

To obtain dry gas it is passed through a tube containing lumps of calcium chloride. It then pushes the air out of a gas jar.

All carbonates will give off carbon dioxide when treated with acid. Most naturally occurring carbonate rocks will also give off the gas when strongly heated, as explained in section 3.6.

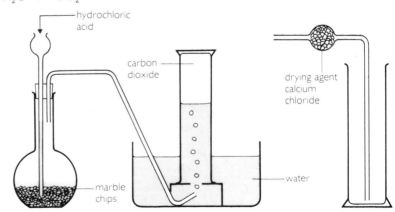

Industrially Large quantities of carbon dioxide are obtained during the manufacture of hydrogen from natural gas, Carbon dioxide is also made during the production of ethanol (alcohol) when sugar solution is fermented by yeast.

Properties and uses of carbon dioxide

Carbon dioxide has six main properties.

It has no colour or smell. This makes it difficult to detect.

It does not let things burn in it. It also changes to a liquid when pressurised. Cylinders of liquid carbon dioxide are used for inflating life rafts, for serving drinks and as fire extinguishers. Being a heavy gas, it forms a blanket over the flames. It is more effective and much less messy and damaging than the liquid produced by the soda-acid type of extinguisher.

Carbon dioxide can solidify when cooled. The solid is called *dry-ice* and is used for refrigeration. It is especially good during the transport of ice-cream and frozen foods because it keeps them very cold ($-79\,°C$) and changes directly back into gas leaving no mess.

It dissolves in water to give carbonic acid. This has a pleasant, tingling taste and is used to make soda water and fizzy drinks. The same acid, present in rain water, slowly eats away rocks. It can be made to react with a solution of common salt and ammonia to give *bicarbonate of soda* (sodium hydrogencarbonate). This white powder is used in baking, in health salts and in making washing soda.

Lime water turns milky when carbon dioxide is bubbled through it. This is used as the test for the gas.

Carbon dioxide changes into carbon monoxide when heated with carbon. This highly poisonous gas is often present in car exhaust fumes. Carbon monoxide burns in air: it is used as a fuel and in separating iron from the iron ore dug out of the ground.

Carbon dioxide gas may be stored under pressure in cylinders.

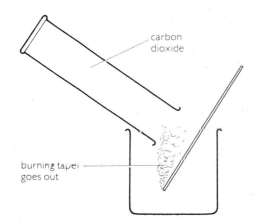

Carbon monoxide is produced by car engines even when they are running properly.

Questions
1. What is the proportion of carbon dioxide in the air?
2. How do plants make their food? What is the name of the process?
3. Why is the carbon dioxide in the air not used up?
4. What is marble and what does it give off when hydrochloric acid is added? Write the equation for the reaction.
5. Give 2 ways of making carbon dioxide industrially.
6. What two properties of carbon dioxide are shown in the diagram?
7. What is 'dry-ice'? Why is it good for keeping things cold?
8. What acid is in fizzy drinks? What is bicarbonate of soda made from?
9. Give the test for carbon dioxide.

carbon dioxide

burning taper goes out

Questions on Chapter 2

1 a How would you show that ordinary air contains **i** oxygen, **ii** water vapour?
b Name **i** two processes that remove oxygen from the air, and **ii** one process that liberates oxygen into the air.
c The diagram represents a simplified water cycle.

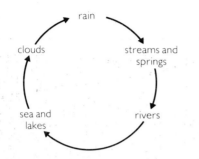

i At which point in the cycle is water most pure?
ii Why is water from underground sources preferred to rain water for drinking purposes?

EAEB

2 a Name 3 solvents (other than water) which are used in the home or in industry and give one example of the use of each.
b Draw and fully label a diagram of apparatus which could be used to obtain drinking water from sea water.
c What name do we give to the process drawn in **b**?
d Why is very little drinking water obtained in this way?

3 Explain, using simple diagrams where necessary, how the sewerage entering sewerage plants is treated to make it safe to discharge into rivers.

4 Using diagrams, briefly explain how you would carry out these separations:
a Clear water from muddy water.
b Salt from salt water.
c Red and yellow dyes from an orange mixture of these dyes.
d Alcohol from a mixture of alcohol and water.

5 a Briefly describe the industrial extraction of oxygen from the air.
b Give one industrial and one non-industrial use of oxygen.
c What is the approximate percentage of oxygen found in the atmosphere?
d How does the air we breathe out differ from the air we breathe in?
e What is the process called in plants whereby oxygen is given off into the atmosphere?

SREB

6 The diagram below represents the approximate composition of dry air by volume. Give the letter which corresponds to **i** oxygen, **ii** nitrogen, **iii** inert (noble) gases, **iv** carbon dioxide.

WJEB

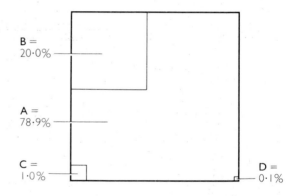

7 Write out the following table and put ticks in the appropriate spaces to show whether the processes listed would increase, decrease, or have no effect on the amount of carbon dioxide in the atmosphere.

Process	Amount of carbon dioxide		
	Increase	Decrease	No Effect
Burning carbon			
Photosynthesis			
Transpiration			
Burning magnesium			
Respiration			
Raining			
Burning fuel oil			
Perspiring			

EAEB

Chapter 3

Acids, Bases and Salts

Mix the first with the second, and you get the third, which could go on chips. What are they?

The photograph is of 'solid drips'. Hard water?

3.1 Acids and bases

The sour taste of unripe fruit, stiffness in tired muscles and the stings of nettles and bees are all due to the presence of natural acids. These acids, and other more powerful ones can be made artificially. The chemical opposites of acids are called bases.

Acids

Acids can exist as syrupy liquids or solids, but they are most useful as solutions in water. Many oxides of non-metals react with water to give acids, for example:

carbon dioxide + water → carbonic acid

$$CO_2 + H_2O \rightarrow H_2CO_3$$

Acids can be recognised by their reactions with magnesium metal or washing soda (sodium carbonate). Both materials dissolve in acids with a vigorous fizzing.

Acids are corrosive, attacking many materials including flesh! Concentrated acids are very dangerous and should never be handled. Even dilute acids must be treated with care. Keep them well away from the eyes, mouth and any broken skin.

All acids contain hydrogen. Some, or all of this hydrogen is given up when an acid reacts. *Strong acids* release hydrogen very easily whilst *weak acids* release hydrogen with difficulty.

Bases

These are the chemical 'opposites' of acids. Mixed with acids they react strongly, and the acids lose their 'hydrogen'. Many oxides of metals are bases. Many bases are insoluble solids; the few which do dissolve in water are called *alkalis*.

Bases are also commonly found in the home and their alkaline solutions are just as corrosive as acids. You should take care not to get alkalis on your skin or clothes. Wash off any splashes with plenty of water.

Frequently-used bases include ammonia solutions in bath and sink cleaners; potassium hydroxide (caustic potash) in oven cleaners; calcium hydroxide (lime) for adding to acid soils; and sodium hydrogencarbonate (bicarbonate of soda) in cooking and medicines.

Some common bases. Sodium carbonate is sometimes used when washing clothes; magnesium hydroxide is used to relieve stomach upsets; sodium hydroxide is used to make soap and potassium hydroxide is used in oven cleaners.

Vinegar contains acetic acid.

Some more acids in use. Sulphuric, citric, tannic, and tartaric acids are present. Can you sort out which is present in which?

Neutralisation

Acids will react with bases to form water and compounds with the general name of *salts*. The reaction is called *neutralisation*.

Acid + base → salt + water

Neutralisation is common in everyday life: tooth decay is caused by acids from food and sugar residue; toothpaste is slightly alkaline and counteracts the acid. When the hydrochloric acid in the stomach gets out of balance, sharp pains result. These may be relieved by doses of mild alkali such as bicarbonate of soda or milk of magnesia. Bicarbonate of soda eases acidic bee stings, whereas vinegar (acetic acid) will neutralise the alkaline sting of wasps.

Indicators

Many natural materials have different colours depending on whether they are in acidic or alkaline solutions. These dyes are called *indicators*. You can make one in the laboratory by warming red cabbage leaves with a mixture of water and industrial methylated spirits. Other indicators can be made from beetroots and coloured petals. The most common indicator, litmus, is extracted from lichen. Its colours are:

Red—acid;   Purple—neutral;   Blue—alkaline.

pH paper   This is a sensitive indicator. The paper contains a mixture of dyes which give a range of colours when the paper is dipped into different acids and alkalis. The paper turns red in a strong acid and blue in a strong alkali. Each colour is given a number on the scale 1 to 14. Thus hydrochloric acid has a pH = 1 and is strongly acidic, whilst acetic acid which has pH = 4 is weakly acidic. Water is neutral and has pH = 7. Sodium hydroxide is a strong alkali and its solution is about pH = 14. Sodium hydrogencarbonate is very weakly alkaline at pH = 8.

This substance is useful for easing acidic bee stings. What substances shown on the left hand page would be useful for alkaline wasp stings?

Using universal indicator to test for acidity or alkalinity. The colour of the indicator is matched against a printed colour chart.

Questions

1. Name the acid formed when carbon dioxide reacts with water.
2. Name 4 acids found in foods or drinks.
3. Give 2 reactions by which acids may be recognised.
4. What element is present in all acids? What is the difference between strong acids and weak acids? How should all acids be treated?
5. What is a base? What is a soluble base called?
6. Give the names and uses of 2 alkalis found in the home.
7. What are formed when an acid is neutralised by a base?
8. Give 2 examples of neutralisation.
9. What is an indicator? Give the colours of litmus.
10. What kind of solution has a pH of 4 or 5?

3.2 Salts

The salt that we use on our food is sodium chloride. We eat it because it makes food taste better and because our bodies need it. There are hundreds of similar compounds, all called salts. Many are necessary in our diet and others have important industrial uses.

Making salts

All acids contain hydrogen. A salt is formed when hydrogen in an acid is replaced by a metal. Some of the substances which will neutralise acids in this way are shown below.

Acid	Neutraliser	Salt formed	Common name	Other products
sulphuric	magnesium	magnesium sulphate	Epsom salts	hydrogen
sulphuric	sodium hydroxide	sodium sulphate	Glauber's salts	water
hydrochloric	sodium carbonate	sodium chloride	common salt	water + carbon dioxide
nitric	ammonia	ammonium nitrate	nitram	—

Making copper sulphate   Copper sulphate can be made in the laboratory by warming dilute sulphuric acid and stirring in small amounts of black copper oxide. The copper oxide dissolves, neutralising the acid and changing it into blue copper sulphate solution. The blue colour darkens until all the acid is used up and no more copper oxide will dissolve. The mixture is then filtered and the clear blue solution is collected in an evaporating basin. Left to stand for several days, the water gradually evaporates off leaving blue crystals of copper sulphate in the dish.

$$\text{copper oxide} + \text{sulphuric acid} \rightarrow \text{copper sulphate} + \text{water}$$

$$CuO + H_2SO_4 \rightarrow CuSO_4 + H_2O$$

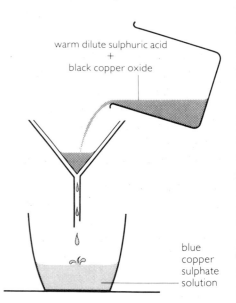

warm dilute sulphuric acid
+
black copper oxide

blue copper sulphate solution

Natural salts

Rain water dissolves a little carbon dioxide from the air and becomes a very dilute, weak acid. It gradually dissolves rock as soluble salts. Small amounts of these salts are essential to plant growth. Plants absorb them through their roots from the water that is trapped in the soil. Most of the salts are washed away in streams and rivers and collect in the sea. The large deposits of natural salts found in many parts of the world, were formed when seas dried up millions of years ago.

Quite often natural salts are found as beautifully coloured and shaped crystals. The photograph shows a strange formation of calcium carbonate crystals. On the opposite page, gypsum crystals are shown, magnified 1000 times.

Properties of salts

Most salts consist of ions (see section 1.6). Positive (+) ions are provided by the metals, and negative (−) ions come from the acids. For instance, sodium chloride consists of the ions Na^+ and Cl^-. Their ionic nature causes all salts to behave in similar ways.

They are solids with distinct crystal shapes.
Most of them dissolve in water.
When melted or dissolved in water, they conduct electricity. Because of this they are called electrolytes.

Crystals

Crystals of a salt have a definite shape, which varies with the salt. For example, common salt crystals are simple cubes, and alum crystals are double pyramids. Salts often seem to be powders. If you look at them under a microscope, however, the crystals show up. The picture shows powdered gypsum magnified 1000 times.

Growing crystals Crystals form when a saturated solution of a salt evaporates. The more slowly the water evaporates the larger will be the crystals formed. A crystal of alum can be made larger by hanging it on a thread in a beaker of saturated alum solution. The beaker must be loosely covered to slow down evaporation and it should be kept at an even temperature. Crystals 2 to 3 cm long will form after several weeks.

Water of crystallisation Many salt crystals contain water: they are called *hydrated* crystals. They give off steam when heated and change to powder. Blue crystals of copper sulphate are hydrated. When heated, they give off their water and turn to a white powder. This is *anhydrous* (dehydrated) copper sulphate. If a few drops of water are added to anhydrous copper sulphate, it goes back to the blue form. This is used as a test for water.

hydrated copper $\rightleftharpoons$ anhydrous copper $+$ water
sulphate (blue)   sulphate (white)   (steam)

$$CuSO_4.5H_2O \rightleftharpoons CuSO_4 + 5H_2O$$

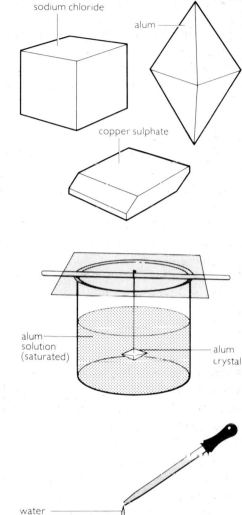

sodium chloride

alum

copper sulphate

alum solution (saturated)

alum crystal

water added

anhydrous copper sulphate turns blue

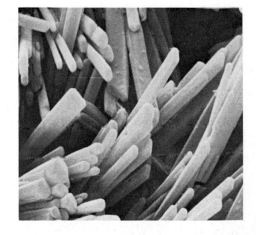

Questions

1. Name 3 kinds of substances which replace hydrogen in acids.
2. Name the acids from which (a) Epsom salts and (b) washing soda come.
3. Give the chemical names for the 2 salts in Question 2.
4. Describe how copper sulphate can be made in the laboratory.
5. How are the salts essential to plant growth formed?
6. Why are salts classed as electrolytes?
7. How can large alum crystals be grown? What shape are they?
8. What is hydrated crystal? What happens when it is heated?
9. Describe a test for water.

3.3 Common salt

Sodium chloride or common salt is an essential part of our diet. We need it for our digestive and nervous systems and for our blood. Being so vital, it was one of the first things ever traded. It has even been used as money! Today it is the starting material for many important chemical processes.

How salt is obtained

The huge quantities of salt required by industry come from sea water which contains 2.7% by weight of salt. In Australia and other hot countries, sea water is trapped in large, shallow pools where the sun evaporates the water. The deposits of salt left behind are scooped up by mechanical diggers.

Solid salt is found underground in Cheshire and many other places. The large crystals, coloured brown by impurities, are called *rock salt*. Beds of rock salt were formed when seas of bygone ages dried up. Rock salt is mined like coal and is used in its natural state for de-icing roads and as a fertiliser.

Salt is also obtained by drilling pipes into the salt beds, dissolving the salt in water and pumping the solution *(brine)* to the surface. The salt crystals which remain when the water evaporates are quite pure. Fine crystals for table salt and baking, are made by re-dissolving the salt and evaporating the solution quickly. Other grades of crystals are used for dyeing, leather-making and curing bacon.

Making salt in the laboratory

Sodium chloride crystals can be made by first using a pipette to measure out some sodium hydroxide solution. This is run into a conical flask and a drop of indicator is added. Dilute hydrochloric acid is then added, a little at a time, from a burette. When the solution becomes neutral the amount of acid used is noted. The process is repeated, using the measured amount of acid but leaving out the indicator. Small crystals of salt can be obtained from this solution by boiling off the water.

sodium hydroxide + hydrochloric acid → sodium chloride + water

$$NaOH + HCl \rightarrow NaCl + H_2O$$

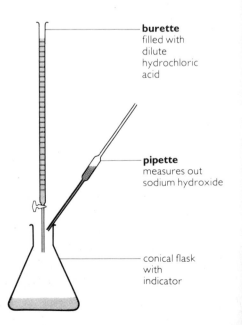

burette
filled with dilute hydrochloric acid

pipette
measures out sodium hydroxide

conical flask with indicator

Uses of salt

Rock salt   Large quantities of crushed rock salt are used each winter to keep roads clear of snow and ice. A solution of salt in water freezes at a much lower temperature than pure water. Wet roads which have been salted will not freeze up unless the temperature falls to 20 °C below freezing point—much colder than most frosty nights in Britain.

Rock salt is also used as a fertiliser for sugar-beet and wurzels.

Alkali industry   Salt is a cheap and abundant raw material and a great many substances are made from it. Some of these are shown in the diagram:

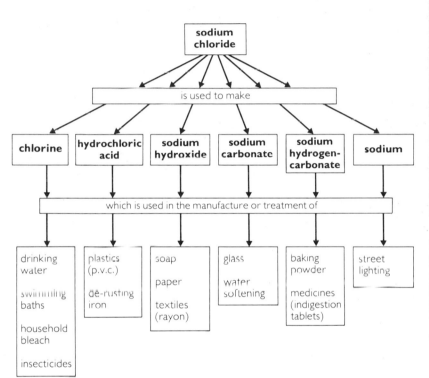

Sodium is used to make street lamps.

Chlorine is used in swimming pools.

Questions

1. For what parts of the body is salt essential?
2. What percentage of salt is there in sea water?
3. How is salt obtained from sea water?
4. Give 2 methods of obtaining salt from underground deposits.
5. Give 2 uses of rock salt and 3 uses of crystallised salt.
6. Describe how crystals of sodium chloride can be made by neutralising sodium hydroxide with hydrochloric acid.
7. List 5 chemicals made directly from salt and give a use of each.
8. List 5 other substances, found in the home, which come from salt.

3.4 Hydrogen

Less than 1% of the Earth's mass is hydrogen. However, hydrogen is a vital part of water and of all living things.

Making hydrogen from acids

All acids contain hydrogen. When metals such as magnesium, zinc, aluminium or iron are put into acids, there is a fizzing as the hydrogen is given off as gas. The metal dissolves to take the place of the hydrogen in solution.

Zinc and dilute sulphuric acid are often used to make hydrogen in the laboratory.

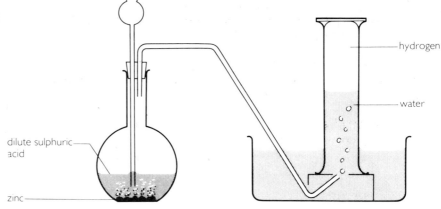

zinc + sulphuric acid → hydrogen + zinc sulphate

$$Zn + H_2SO_4 \rightarrow H_2 + ZnSO_4$$

Properties of hydrogen

Hydrogen has no colour, no smell, and is neutral to litmus. It is much lighter than air—in fact it is the least dense of all gases. If you bubble hydrogen through soap solution, the bubbles rise quickly. They will also burn vigorously if you touch them with a lighted taper.

Hydrogen burns very easily and can form dangerously explosive mixtures with pure oxygen. A mixture of hydrogen and air in a tube will explode with a shrill 'pop' when held near a flame. This reaction is used as the test for hydrogen.

The reaction between hydrogen and oxygen produces water. This can be shown by burning a jet of pure, dry hydrogen and playing the flame onto a cool flask. Drops of water may be collected.

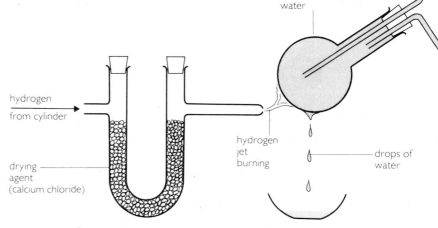

hydrogen + oxygen → water

$$2H_2 + O_2 \rightarrow 2H_2O$$

Water is often formed when substances containing hydrogen react with oxygen or oxygen-containing compounds. The very name 'hydrogen' means 'water producer'.

Hydrogen from water

Water can be made to give up hydrogen in various ways.

Coke Steam passed over red-hot coke produces hydrogen and carbon monoxide gas. This mixture, known as water gas, is used as a fuel and as a source of hydrogen for making ammonia.

$$\text{coke} + \text{water} \rightarrow \overbrace{\text{carbon monoxide} + \text{hydrogen}}^{\text{water gas}}$$
$$C + H_2O \rightarrow CO + H_2$$

Very reactive metals Sodium, potassium and calcium are very reactive metals. They combine with water as though it was acid and give off hydrogen gas.

Electricity If an electric current is passed through water containing some acid or salt, the water splits up into oxygen gas and hydrogen gas. This is an industrial method of making hydrogen.

Uses of hydrogen

Hydrogen gas is used for filling balloons, in blow torches for welding and as a fuel for space ships. Large quantities of hydrogen, obtained from natural gas and oil, are converted into a number of other important compounds. Some of these are shown.

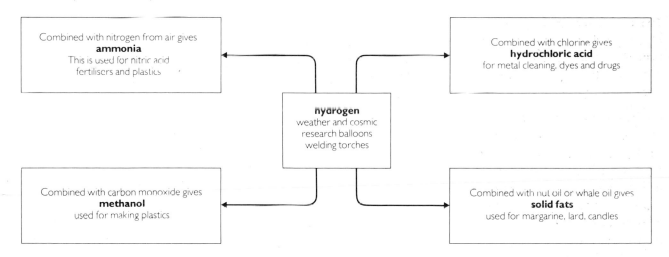

Combined with nitrogen from air gives
ammonia
This is used for nitric acid fertilisers and plastics

Combined with chlorine gives
hydrochloric acid
for metal cleaning, dyes and drugs

hydrogen
weather and cosmic research balloons welding torches

Combined with carbon monoxide gives
methanol
used for making plastics

Combined with nut oil or whale oil gives
solid fats
used for margarine, lard, candles

Questions

1. Name 3 metals which displace hydrogen from dilute acid.
2. Write the equation for zinc dissolving in dilute sulphuric acid.
3. Why is hydrogen used for filling weather balloons?
4. Describe the test for hydrogen.
5. How could you show that water contains hydrogen and oxygen?
6. What is water gas and how is it made?
7. Give 2 ways of making hydrogen in large quantities.
8. Give 4 compounds manufactured from hydrogen.
9. What is ammonia used for?
10. What does hydrogen react with to form margarine?

A hydrogen filled balloon.

3.5 Sulphuric acid

The most commonly used acid both in the laboratory and in industry is sulphuric acid. Four million tonnes of it are made each year in Britain! It is made from natural sulphur or sulphur compounds.

Sulphur

Sulphur is a yellow solid found in many parts of the world where there have been volcanoes. It is one of the few minerals which melt easily and catch fire. This is why it was an ingredient of the first explosive, gunpowder, which is still used in fireworks. Today the main uses of sulphur are the hardening of rubber and the manufacture of sulphuric acid.

Sulphur is extracted from underground deposits by melting it with hot water under pressure and forcing it to the surface with compressed air. It is either allowed to cool and set hard, or is transported in heated containers whilst still liquid.

The Contact process

This is a 3 stage process which converts liquid sulphur into concentrated sulphuric acid.

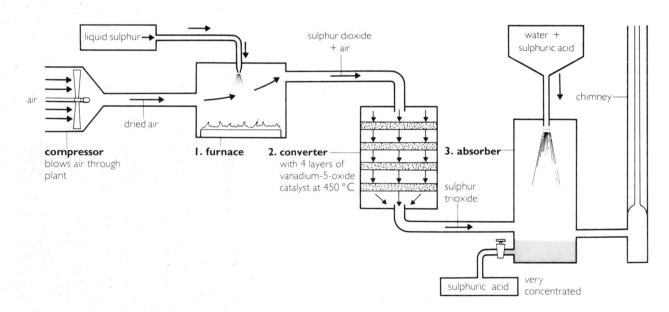

Stage 1: the furnace Liquid sulphur is burned in a stream of cleaned and dried air, blown through the plant by a huge fan. Sulphur dioxide gas is produced and this passes on to the second stage.

sulphur + oxygen → sulphur dioxide
       (in air)

$$S + O_2 \rightarrow SO_2$$

Stage 2: the converter   Here the sulphur dioxide is combined with more air to form sulphur trioxide. Layers of catalyst pellets, vanadium-5-oxide, heated to 450 °C help the reaction.

sulphur dioxide + oxygen → sulphur trioxide
$$2SO_2 \quad + \quad O_2 \quad \rightarrow \quad 2SO_3$$

Stage 3: the absorber   Here the sulphur trioxide is combined with water to make sulphuric acid.

sulphur trioxide + water → sulphuric acid
$$SO_3 \quad + \quad H_2O \rightarrow \quad H_2SO_4$$

The sulphur trioxide dissolves best in water which already has sulphuric acid in it. The very concentrated acid produced can be diluted as needed.

Uses of sulphuric acid

Sulphuric acid is both a strong acid and a powerful dehydrating agent. Because of these properties it has many uses.

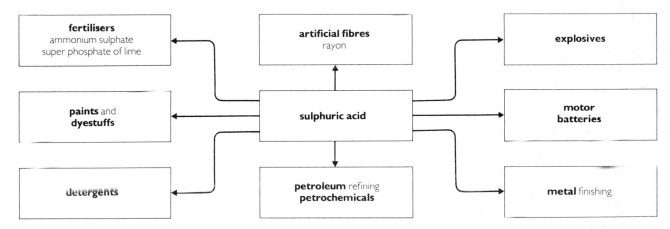

fertilisers ammonium sulphate super phosphate of lime	**artificial fibres** rayon	**explosives**
paints and **dyestuffs**	**sulphuric acid**	**motor batteries**
detergents	**petroleum** refining **petrochemicals**	**metal** finishing

Caution

When mixed with water, concentrated sulphuric acid gives out enough heat to make the mixture boil and spit. This makes it very dangerous. It causes severe burns on skin because of the heat given out as it absorbs water from the flesh. *It should never be handled.*

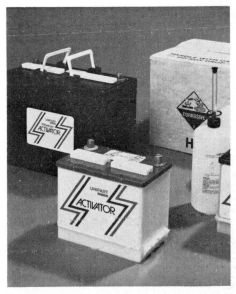

Sulphuric acid is used in car batteries.

Questions

1. How much sulphuric acid is made in Britain each year?
2. Why is sulphur an ingredient of gunpowder?
3. How is sulphur obtained from underground deposits?
4. Give 2 uses of sulphur today.
5. Briefly describe what happens in the 3 stages of the Contact process for making sulphuric acid.
6. Give the 2 main properties of concentrated sulphuric acid.
7. List 6 uses of sulphuric acid.
8. Why is concentrated sulphuric acid very dangerous?

3.6 Limestone

Limestone is perhaps the commonest rock in the British Isles. In no way a precious stone, it is still an extremely valuable raw material. This section gives some of the reasons why this is so.

A limestone quarry.

Calcium carbonate rock

The term limestone covers all types of calcium carbonate rock. These rocks formed millions of years ago from the shells and bones of creatures which lived in deep, warm seas. You can often see the imprints of shells in limestone rocks: these are called *fossils*. The shell beds were compressed, lifted and folded by later earth movements. They now appear in different forms: carboniferous and oolitic limestones, chalk, marble and calcite.

Quarrying Carboniferous limestone is quarried by removing the soil and blasting the exposed rock with explosives. The large rocks are crushed and graded. Smaller chippings are used for making concrete, iron and glass, and as roadstone and railway ballast. Larger pieces are made into quicklime by heating them strongly in a lime kiln:

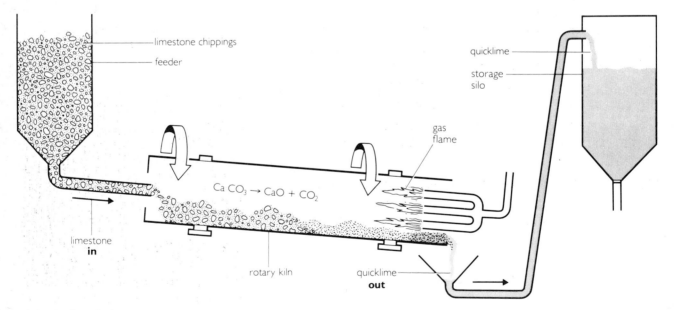

Calcium oxide—quicklime

Heated to 1100 °C, calcium carbonate loses carbon dioxide and changes to the white solid calcium oxide (also called quicklime).

calcium carbonate → calcium oxide + carbon dioxide

$$CaCO_3 \rightarrow CaO + CO_2$$

Large quantities of pure quicklime are needed for making steel and other metals. Sodium hydroxide and calcium carbide (from which acetylene gas is made) are also produced from quicklime.

Calcium hydroxide—slaked lime

Calcium oxide reacts vigorously with water, giving off heat and crumbling to a powder called calcium hydroxide or slaked lime.

calcium oxide + water → calcium hydroxide

$$CaO + H_2O \rightarrow Ca(OH)_2$$

Slaked lime, like quicklime, is strongly alkaline. It is used by farmers to neutralise acid soils, to lighten clay soils and to kill pests. Lime is used to absorb acid gases in the chemical industry and for softening water. Combined with chlorine it forms a *bleaching powder* which is used in the cotton industry.

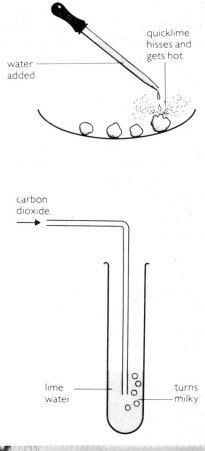

water added — quicklime hisses and gets hot

Lime water

Calcium hydroxide only dissolves slightly in water giving the mild alkali, lime water. This solution absorbs carbon dioxide forming a milky precipitate of pure calcium carbonate.

lime water + carbon dioxide → calcium carbonate + water

$$Ca(OH)_2 + CO_2 \rightarrow CaCO_3 + H_2O$$

This reaction is the test for carbon dioxide. The 'precipitated chalk' formed is used in paper-making, in toothpaste and in pills.

carbon dioxide → lime water — turns milky

The building industry

The building industry depends entirely upon limestone and limestone products. The stone, particularly the oolitic type, has been used for centuries for buildings of all kinds, from cottages to cathedrals. Roads are made from chippings coated with tar.

Cement This is a grey powder made by burning limestone, clay and sand in a rotary kiln and grinding the clinker formed with gypsum. Mixed with sand, limestone chippings and water, it sets hard to form concrete, the foremost building material of this century.

Mortar Brick and stone walls are held together by mortar—a varying mixture of slaked lime, sand, water and cement. Lime mortar sets hard by absorbing carbon dioxide from the air.

The Guggenheim Museum in New York was designed by the famous architect Frank Lloyd Wright. The whole structure is of concrete and steel.

Questions

1. What is the chemical name for limestone? How is it formed?
2. Name 3 kinds of limestone. What are fossils?
3. Describe how small chippings of limestone are produced.
4. What is quicklime and how is it made? Write the equation.
5. What happens when water is added to quicklime? What is formed? Write the equation for this too.
6. Give 3 uses each of quicklime and slaked lime.
7. Why does carbon dioxide turn lime water milky?
8. How is cement made? What is mortar?

47

3.7 Hard water

Is ice hard water? No, the term is used to describe water which has calcium or magnesium compounds dissolved in it. This sometimes makes it hard to use.

Soft water
Rain-water is pure because it has nothing dissolved in it except a tiny amount of carbon dioxide. In some parts of the country, tap water is almost pure because the rocks in the area do not dissolve when rain falls on them. This *soft water* lathers easily with soap and leaves no deposit when boiled away. It does not cause radiators or steam irons to block up. Distilled water is the softest of all.

Recognising hard water
Hard water is not pure: it contains calcium salts dissolved out of rocks. These salts give a pleasant taste to the water and are left as a white film if a beaker of hard water is boiled dry. They combine with soap to form a grey scum. Hard water is easily recognised by the large amount of soap it takes to make a lather and by the scum that it leaves. This is what happens:

Distilled water is used to top-up car batteries.

calcium salts + sodium stearate → calcium stearate + sodium salts
  (hardness)   (soap)   (scum)

Temporary hardness
There are two kinds of hardness, temporary and permanent. *Temporary hardness* can be reduced by heating. It is caused by the substance calcium hydrogencarbonate which dissolves out of limestone rocks when rain-water trickles over them.

Rain-water absorbs a little carbon dioxide from the air as it falls. This slightly acid solution attacks the calcium carbonate of limestone, and changes a little of it into soluble calcium hydrogencarbonate. This dissolves easily and the rocks are slowly eaten away leaving pot-holes and caves: the water contains small amounts of limestone in soluble form.

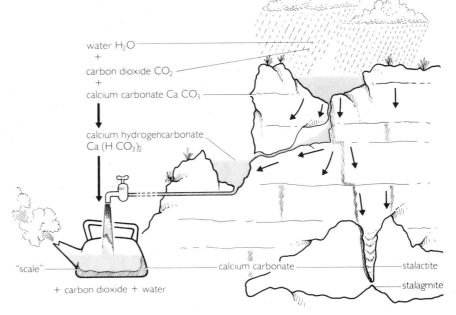

water H_2O
+
carbon dioxide CO_2
+
calcium carbonate $Ca\,CO_3$

calcium hydrogencarbonate $Ca(H\,CO_3)_2$

"scale"

+ carbon dioxide + water

calcium carbonate — stalactite — stalagmite

water + carbon dioxide + limestone ⇌ temporary hardness
$$H_2O + CO_2 + CaCO_3 \rightleftharpoons Ca(HCO_3)_2$$

Scaling   The reaction between water, carbon dioxide and limestone to produce temporary hardness is *reversible*. When water with temporary hardness in it is heated or allowed to evaporate, the dissolved salt changes back to limestone and is deposited as a solid. This deposit is the 'scale' in kettles. It also builds up as stalactites and stalagmites in limestone caves.

Permanent hardness

Other calcium salts which occur in rocks are calcium sulphate (gypsum) and calcium chloride. Small quantities of these salts dissolve in water to produce *permanent hardness*. Heating this kind of water does not affect the dissolved salts and the hardness remains the same. Magnesium salts also cause permanent hardness.

Removal of hardness

Hard water is often a nuisance because it can use up to five times as much soap for washing as soft water and produces a scum which is difficult to rinse out. Temporary hardness also causes blockages in hot water pipes—wasting heat and making regular de-scaling necessary. For these reasons hard water is often softened by adding substances which remove the calcium salts.

Slaked lime (calcium hydroxide)   This cheap material is made from limestone as explained in the last section. It can only remove temporary hardness, converting the soluble calcium hydrogencarbonate back into insoluble calcium carbonate. Slaked lime is added to water storage reservoirs in some limestone areas.

Washing soda (sodium carbonate)   This is often used by housewives to soften water. It removes all kinds of hardness, changing the calcium salts into insoluble calcium carbonate.

Ion exchange   Certain natural substances such as greensand will remove calcium ions from hard water when the water is passed through them. The sand is regenerated from time to time by passing a strong solution of sodium chloride through it. Nowadays man-made resins from crude oil are used instead of sand.

Using hard water

Hard water has some advantages over soft water. The calcium salts help children to develop strong teeth and bones. It is also good for brewing beer!

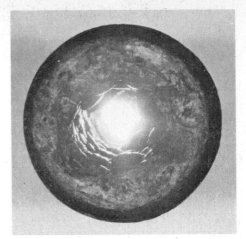

Cross-section through an old water pipe. Use of softened water in heating systems prevents this problem.

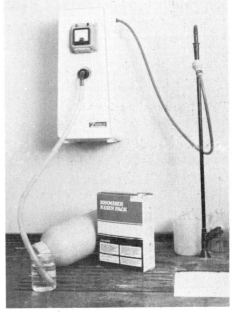

A water softener of the type used in many schools.

Questions

1. What is hard water? Is rainwater hard or soft?
2. Give 2 ways of recognising hard water.
3. What are the 2 kinds of hardness? How do they differ?
4. Describe how temporary hardness is formed.
5. What is the 'scale' that forms in kettles? How does it get there?
6. Name 2 substances which cause permanent hardness.
7. Name 2 advantages and 2 disadvantages of hardness in water.
8. Briefly describe 2 ways of removing hardness.

Questions on Chapter 3

1 Put these stages in the preparation of copper sulphate crystals into the right order:

   a Unused copper oxide powder filtered out.
   b Liquid heated to remove some water.
   c The mixture is warmed.
   d Black copper oxide powder is added to dilute sulphuric acid.
   e Slow cooling of the remaining liquid gives crystals of copper sulphate.
   f Resulting clear solution is blue in colour.
   g Excess copper oxide added to use up all the acid.

2 Name the substances formed when the following chemicals react together:

   a Hydrochloric acid and sodium carbonate;
   b Sulphuric acid and sodium hydroxide.   EAEB

3 Write out the following table putting a tick in the correct column.

All acids:	True	False
a turn litmus red;		
b burn clothing;		
c contain hydrogen;		
d have a sour taste;		
e react with bases to form salts;		
f contain oxygen.		

ALSEB

4 The following crystalline substances are commonly found in the home: *washing soda, sugar, common salt* and *Epsom salts*. Which ones give up water on heating? EAEB

5 Which of the following substances is used

   a as a fertilizer   **b** to soften water
   c to make soap   **d** on food?
   sodium chloride, sodium carbonate, ammonium sulphate, sodium hydroxide, acetic acid.   WMEB

6 The following diagram, which is incomplete, shows the relationship between some compounds of calcium. Copy the diagram into your book and then answer the questions below.

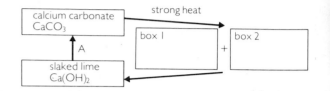

a In boxes 1 and 2 fill in the names and formulae of the compounds which are formed.
b One of the compounds you have named in **a** can be converted to slaked lime. How can this be done?
c What is the correct chemical name for slaked lime?
d What do we call the solution which is formed when a small quantity of slaked lime is dissolved in water?
e Slaked lime in solution can be converted to calcium carbonate as shown by arrow **A**. How can this be done?
f Give one common name for calcium carbonate as it occurs in its natural state.
g Give one important commercial use for calcium carbonate.   ALSEB

7 Explain the main stages in the Contact Process for making sulphuric acid from sulphur.   YREB

8 **a** Write a word equation to show the action of heat on calcium carbonate.
b Describe in detail the action of rain water on rocks containing calcium carbonate. In your answer include any reactions which occur and name any compounds formed.
c List the materials used in the manufacture of cement.
d Describe the manufacture of cement.   EAEB

Chapter 4

Natural Resources

Think of a pure, valuable metal? And an impure, strong one?

This photograph has something to do with copper. Can you work out what?

4.1 Extraction of metals

Metals were the first elements to be used and purified by Man. They are just as important today.

Smelting

Small amounts of some metals can be found lying about in the ground. Gold, silver and copper are the metals most often found uncombined. Meteorites, falling to earth, have left lumps of iron in some places. Primitive men used these metals for simple tools. Most metals are found combined with other elements as ores. These other elements, usually oxygen or sulphur, can be removed by *smelting*—heating with charcoal. Lead oxide can be smelted to a silvery bead of lead by heating it on a charcoal block. Blowing a bunsen flame on to the ore with a blowpipe helps the carbon to remove the oxygen from the ore. Removal of oxygen from a substance in this way is called *reduction*.

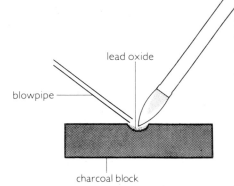

lead oxide + carbon →lead + carbon monoxide
$$PbO \quad + \quad C \quad \rightarrow \quad Pb \quad + \quad CO$$

Tin, lead and copper are all easily extracted from their ores by charcoal smelting. The higher temperature needed to reduce iron ore is produced in the blast furnace.

The blast furnace

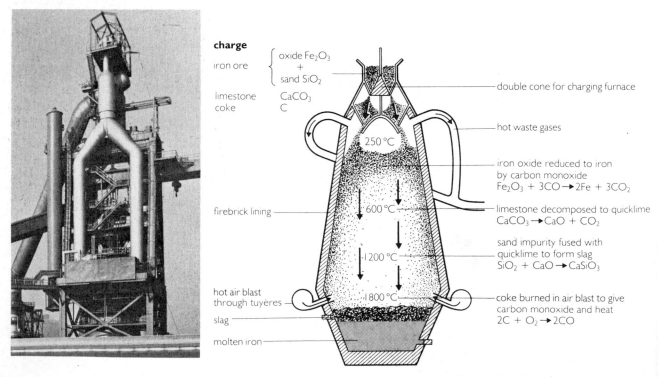

charge

iron ore	oxide Fe_2O_3 + sand SiO_2
limestone	$CaCO_3$
coke	C

double cone for charging furnace

hot waste gases

iron oxide reduced to iron by carbon monoxide
$Fe_2O_3 + 3CO \rightarrow 2Fe + 3CO_2$

limestone decomposed to quicklime
$CaCO_3 \rightarrow CaO + CO_2$

sand impurity fused with quicklime to form slag
$SiO_2 + CaO \rightarrow CaSiO_3$

coke burned in air blast to give carbon monoxide and heat
$2C + O_2 \rightarrow 2CO$

250 °C
600 °C
1200 °C
1800 °C

firebrick lining

hot air blast through tuyères

slag

molten iron

Activity league

Metals are alike in many ways. They are shiny, hard and strong; they conduct heat and electricity. However, they all differ in their ability to form compounds. The *activity table* has the most reactive metals at the top and the unreactive metals at the bottom.

Metal	How found—ore		How obtained
sodium calcium aluminium	rock salt limestone bauxite	$NaCl$ $CaCO_3$ Al_2O_3	Very reactive. Their compounds can only be reduced by large currents of electricity
zinc iron	calamine haematite	$ZnCO_3$ Fe_2O_3	Moderately reactive. They are extracted by heating strongly with carbon
tin lead copper	cassiterite galena chalcopyrite	SnO_2 PbS $CuFeS_2$	Feebly reactive. They are easily extracted by heating with carbon
silver	argentite	Ag_2S	Unreactive ores reduced by heat alone
gold	pure metal		

Metals at the top of the table form compounds so strongly that it is difficult to extract them. These ores can only be decomposed by powerful currents of electricity.

Electrolysis of bauxite

Aluminium is one of the metals which is extracted by electrolysis. The cell illustrated is one of about 200 used in an aluminium production plant.

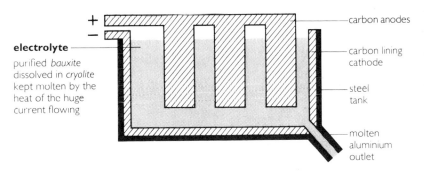

electrolyte

purified *bauxite* dissolved in *cryolite* kept molten by the heat of the huge current flowing

Aluminium ore being reduced to the metal by electrolysis.

Questions

1. Name 3 metals which occur uncombined in some places.
2. What is meant by (a) an ore, (b) smelting?
3. Name 3 ores which are easily smelted.
4. What does haematite consist of? Explain how it is reduced to iron in the Blast Furnace and how slag is formed.
5. Give 3 ways in which metals are similar.
6. Name a very reactive metal and one of its ores.
7. Describe how aluminium is extracted from bauxite.

4.2 Uses of metals

Gold is used as an international currency—other pure metals are extremely valuable too. But mixtures of metals are often more useful than pure metals for making things.

Pure metals

Pure gold is used as an international currency. Being unreactive and easy to shape, it has always been prized for ornaments and jewellery. Other pure metals used today are: lead for pipes and roofing; zinc for batteries; aluminium for saucepans, foil wrapping and milk bottle tops; copper for electrical wiring, pipes and hot water cylinders.

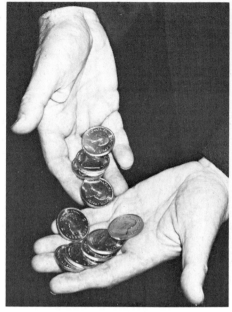

Two pure metals in use—lead and gold.

Pure metals are generally too soft for engineering purposes. The hardness, strength and resistance to corrosion of a metal are increased by mixing it with another metal to form an *alloy*.

Copper alloys

Copper is one ingredient in three important alloys:

Coin metal   Pure metal coins quickly wear out because the metal is too soft. 'Silver' coins used to be alloys of silver with copper but are now nickel and copper alloys.

Bronze   This alloy of copper and tin was first made about 5000 years ago by smelting mixed ores of copper and tin. It is harder and stronger than pure copper, and is easily melted and cast. It was the first metal to be widely used for weapons and tools. It is still used for statues, coins and cutlery and also for gun metal (with zinc), springs (with phosphorus), pumps and propellers (with aluminium) and for wheel and engine bearings (with lead).

Brass is made by dissolving solid zinc in molten copper and solidifying the alloy in sand moulds. Like all alloys its composition can vary—a typical brass will be 70% copper and 30% zinc. Brass is strong, does not corrode and can be die cast (pressed into shape when cold). Shell cases, electrical fittings, car radiators, and some nuts, bolts and screws are made of brass.

Bronze is used to make church bells.

Iron alloys

Iron is a very important substance, but is often used as an alloy rather than pure:

Pig iron is produced in a blast furnace. It contains about 4% carbon and smaller amounts of other elements. The high carbon content makes this alloy very hard—it is useful for castings such as cylinder blocks and cookers. Unfortunately it cannot be welded and snaps under strain.

Steel has a much lower carbon content (between 0.1% and 1.5%), and is much stronger than pig iron. It is made by burning away most of the carbon impurity from molten pig iron using a jet of pure oxygen. *Mild steel* (up to 0.5% carbon) is by far the most important metal. It can be rolled out into sheets, made into girders, stamped into shapes and welded together. *Hard steel* (0.5 to 1.5% carbon) is used for tools because cutting edges remain sharp.

Two alloys in use—different types of steel for penknives and bridge cables.

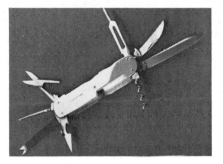

Special steels contain other metals in addition to the carbon. Chromium in *stainless steel* adds strength, prevents rusting and gives an attractive finish. Ballbearings and drills are made from stainless steel besides the familiar cutlery, sinks and teapots. *Manganese steel* is extremely hard and tough and is used for rock-crushing, drilling and for railway points.

Lead alloys
Lead forms alloys with low melting points. Mixed with tin, it forms *solder* for electrical connections and joints in pipes. Lead/antimony/tin alloys are used for printing *type-metal* and as *white metal* for wheel bearings.

Questions
1. State uses of 4 different pure metals.
2. What are alloys? Why are they preferred to pure metals?
3. What is a 50p piece made of?
4. State the metals present in bronze and 5 uses of bronze.
5. How is brass made? What is die casting?
6. How is pig iron converted into steel?
7. Give 3 uses each of mild steel and hard steel.
8. What elements does stainless steel contain?
9. Name 3 lead alloys and their uses.

In this machine, a bar of typemetal is gradually being melted and poured into moulds which will form it into the letters required.

4.3 Fossil fuels

Anything that burns is a fuel. Coal, oil (petroleum) and natural gas are called fossil fuels because they have been buried deep underground for millions of years. They are the remains of plants and animals and consist mainly of compounds of carbon and hydrogen (hydrocarbons).

Burning of fossil fuels

When fuels burn, their hydrocarbons combine with oxygen in the air forming carbon dioxide and water. Flames are produced and heat is given out. This heat is used to warm houses, for industrial furnaces, to drive motors and to make electricity.

hydrocarbons + oxygen → carbon dioxide + water + heat

A certain amount of the poisonous gas, carbon monoxide, is produced when the air supply to a burning fuel is limited. It is the deadly gas present in car engine exhaust fumes.

Coal

Most of the coal in Britain came from the swampy forests that grew 250 million years ago. Trees and giant ferns grew quickly and died forming thick layers of rotting trunks and leaves called *peat*. The swamps sank slowly and the peat layers were covered with mud and sand. Seas then flooded the land, gradually covering the peat and mud with the shells of dead sea creatures.

A fossil fern in a lump of coal.

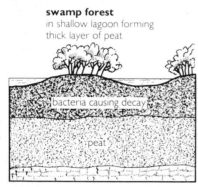

swamp forest
in shallow lagoon forming thick layer of peat

area submerged
deep under the sea

swamp forest
growing again

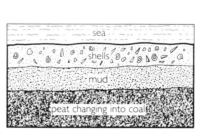

After thousands of years, the seas retreated and swamp forests again grew in the tropical conditions. The cycle was repeated many times, over millions of years, and the layers were pushed down deeper and deeper. Because of the heat and pressure, the peat lost much of the hydrogen and oxygen in the original woody tissue and hardened into coal seams.

Types of coal There are three main types of coal which differ in age and in the alteration of the original peat.

Lignite (70% carbon) is brown, soft and woody.
Bituminous (85% carbon) is older, black and breaks easily.
Anthracite (93% carbon) is oldest, shiny black and very hard.

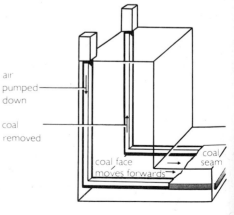

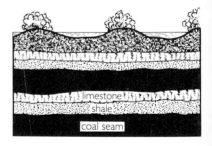

Oil (petroleum)

Crude oil is a sticky, smelly liquid, dark brown or greenish in colour. It comes from the decayed remains of sea creatures and plants which were trapped millions of years ago in the mud and sand of the sea bed. The decay process used up most of the oxygen present in the rotting bodies leaving hydrogen and carbon compounds. As the mud was buried and hardened by later deposits, the hydrocarbons were squeezed out. They moved upwards through soft, porous rock and reached the surface in some places. In other places, such as the North Sea, the hydrocarbons lie trapped under layers of solid rock shaped like domes (anticlines). In these oilfields, as they are called, the hydrocarbons are contained in soft rock like water in a sponge.

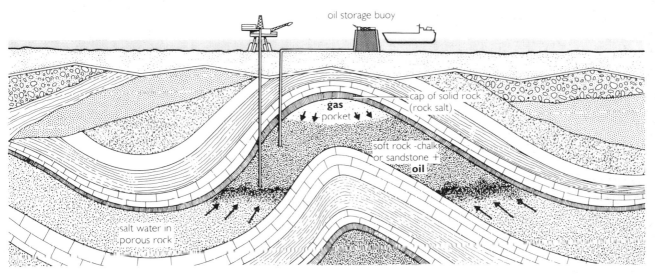

oil storage buoy

gas pocket

cap of solid rock (rock salt)

soft rock - chalk or sandstone + oil

salt water in porous rock

Natural gas

Methane and a small proportion of other simple hydrocarbons separate from the oil as natural gas. There is usually a pocket of natural gas under the dome in an oilfield. The pressure of this gas forces the oil to the surface if shafts are drilled into the oilfield. In some fields only the gas has been trapped. This natural gas is piped ashore and supplied direct to consumers through a network of underground pipes. Natural gas is now used as a source of hydrogen which is used in turn to make ammonia and nitric acid.

Questions

1. Name the fossil fuels and their main constituents.
2. What do fuels form when they burn?
3. When was Britain's coal formed?
4. Explain the formation of coal seams.
5. Name 3 types of coal. How do they differ?
6. What is crude oil and how was it formed?
7. What are the usual features of an oilfield?
8. Name the main hydrocarbon of natural gas and one substance made from it.

Laying a pipe for North Sea Gas supply.

4.4 Coal and oil products

Look around you at any time and you will see many things made from coal and oil—clothes, furniture, house fittings, car parts and all sorts of containers.

Distillation of coal

When coal is strongly heated with no air present, it does not burn but breaks down (distils) into 4 main products:

coal gas—once used for heating;
ammonia—made into fertilisers;
tar—drugs, dyes and plastics;
coke—still used for furnaces and for extracting metals.

Although natural gas and oil have replaced coal gas and tar at the present time, this process may be of major importance again when the world's oil supplies run out.

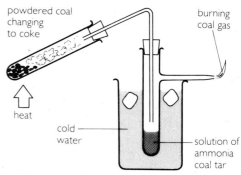

Distillation of oil

The compounds of carbon and hydrogen that make up crude oil are separated by distillation into *fractions* (groups of hydrocarbons with molecules of similar size).

In the laboratory fume cupboard   5 fractions can be obtained using the simple apparatus shown. On gentle heating a watery liquid distils over. As the heating is increased the fractions become darker and more oily. Finally a yellow/brown grease collects.

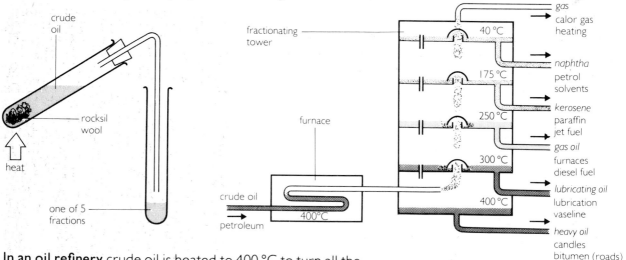

In an oil refinery crude oil is heated to 400 °C to turn all the components into gases. These pass into a fractionating tower where they turn back into liquids at different levels. The heavy oils condense at the bottom of the tower and the light fractions condense at the top. Each of the fractions is further refined by having impurities removed and by being distilled again to give a range of products.

Cracking of oil

Crude oil contains only a small proportion of the more useful lighter fractions such as petrol. Some of the heavier oil fractions are turned into petrol and jet fuel by the process of *cracking*. The large oil molecules are broken down into smaller petrol molecules by heating with steam or with a catalyst. As an example:

heavy oil $\xrightarrow{\text{heat}}$ petrol type compound + gas (propene)

$$C_{11}H_{24} \longrightarrow C_8H_{18} + C_3H_6$$

The propene gas produced during cracking is made into plastics. The gases ethene and butene are also produced by cracking. They too are used as raw materials in the plastics industry.

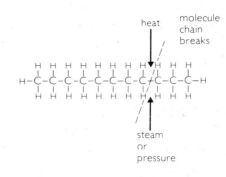

Plastics

Plastics are tough, man-made materials which are easily moulded by heat and pressure. Celluloid was one of the first plastics, invented over 100 years ago, and is still used for table tennis balls. Many plastics used to be made from coal tar, but now the cracking of oil provides most of the starting materials. All plastics are made by joining together small molecules called *monomers* to make very big ones—made of hundreds of carbon atoms linked into chains. The giant molecules are called *polymers* and the linking process is *polymerisation*.

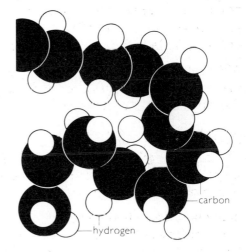

Polythene is made by causing lots of molecules of ethene gas to join together. This can be done by heating them under pressure with aluminium and titanium compounds acting as catalysts.

Other plastics based on materials produced from ethene include: PVC (drain pipes, clothing); PVA (glue, emulsion paint); polystyrene (heat insulation).

Nylon and terylene are polymers made from more complex products of oil refining. Their long chains are arranged side by side, giving them properties like those of cotton fibres.

Questions

1. Name the 4 products of the distillation of coal.
2. Describe how crude oil is separated into fractions industrially.
3. List 6 final products of an oil refinery.
4. Why is coal gas no longer used?
5. What is cracking? Name the gases formed as by-products.
6. What is polymerisation? Explain how polythene is made.
7. Name 2 other plastics based on ethene and give a use for each.
8. Why do the properties of nylon make it suitable for clothing?

The plastic 'Alkathene' in use for road markers.

4.5 Detergents

Water, by itself, is not a good washing agent. It does not get grease off a plate or stains off a handkerchief without a great deal of rubbing. We rely on detergents to help.

Detergent action

Detergents are substances which help water to squeeze between the fibres of cloth and which also react with dirt. Detergent molecules have water-attracting heads and long, grease attracting tails. The first problem the detergent has to overcome is *surface tension* which holds the water into small droplets, as explained in more detail in section 5.3. The water-attracting heads break this down, helping the water to penetrate the cloth.

Second, the grease-attracting tails of the detergent molecules attach themselves to the grease. They form layers which pull the grease away from the cloth, holding it as a suspension in the water. Because of this, the grease can be rinsed away, and harsh rubbing of the cloth becomes unnecessary.

Solid particles of dirt are also removed by detergents. The process is similar to grease removal but double layers of detergent molecules form around the dirt particles. These double layers pull the dirt away from the cloth.

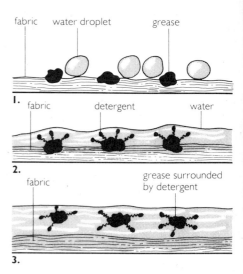

Soap

Soap, the first detergent, was originally made from animal fats combined with alkali obtained from wood ashes. Soap can be made

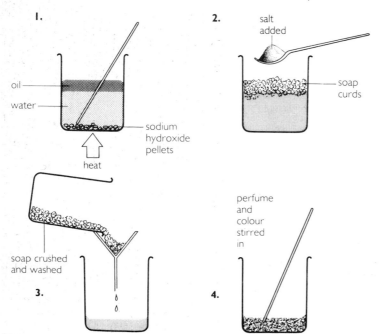

This machine presses soap into moulds in the industrial manufacture of soap.

in the laboratory by stirring cooking oil or fat with sodium hydroxide solution and boiling it for an hour.

The large scale manufacture of soap is based on the same principle. Peanuts are one source of the oils boiled with sodium hydroxide to make the sodium salts which are soap. Glycerine is formed at the same time, and this is separated and used to make medicines and explosives.

Soapless detergents

Soap is expensive because the vegetable oils from which it is made are very costly. Soap does not deal very well with heavy grease and it combines with the calcium salts in hard water forming a messy scum. Scientists experimented for many years to produce detergents which did not suffer from the disadvantages of soap. Since 1950, a variety of soapless detergents have been developed, mostly based on substances obtained from crude oil.

Long chain hydrocarbons from oil provide the tails of the detergent molecules. The heads come either from sulphuric acid or from other oil products. Sodium salts are often added: sodium phosphate to loosen the dirt and sodium perborate as bleach. *Biological* washing powders have enzymes added instead of bleach to digest stains.

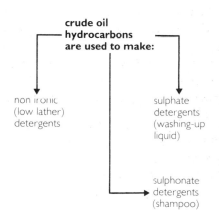

crude oil hydrocarbons are used to make:

non ironic (low lather) detergents

sulphate detergents (washing-up liquid)

sulphonate detergents (shampoo)

Soft detergents

Soapless detergents are such good lathering agents that rivers receiving used water containing detergents can become covered with thick layers of foam which cause pollution. Foam can also cause trouble in sewage works. 'Soft' or *biodegradable* detergents have been developed to avoid this problem. Their molecules break down when attacked by the usual bacteria that cause decay.

The problem of "foaming rivers" has largely been solved since the introduction of biodegradable detergents.

Questions

1. State two ways in which detergents help water to wash things.
2. Describe the structure of a detergent molecule.
3. Describe how detergent molecules remove grease.
4. Describe how soap can be made in the laboratory.
5. Give 3 disadvantages of soap as a detergent.
6. What are biological washing powders?
7. What are biodegradable detergents?

Questions on Chapter 4

1 a Draw and fully label a large diagram of a blast furnace.
b i Name one ore of aluminium.
ii Describe the extraction of aluminium from the ore.
iii Give 2 uses of aluminium in buildings.

EAEB

2 Why is aluminium extracted by electrolysis and not in a blast furnace?

WMEB

3 Lead can be obtained by the reduction of lead oxide on a charcoal block.
a Explain the term reduction.
b What is the reducing agent in this reaction?
c What is being oxidised in the reaction?

WMEB

4 a What is an alloy?
b What is the difference in composition between steel and iron?
c Select the alloys from the following list: lead, iron, solder, tin, brass, zinc, copper, steel and silver.
d Give one use for lead.
e Describe one method by which you could extract lead from lead oxide in the laboratory. Give the equation for the reaction in words or symbols.

WYLREB

5 Which of the following metals is most likely to be found in its natural state? Tin, lead, iron, gold, calcium, sodium.

WYLREB

6 State 2 physical properties and 2 chemical properties of a named metal.

EAEB

7 a How would you do a very simple test to find out whether or not a material is a metal?
b State one physical property of gold and one chemical property of zinc.

8 What are *fossil fuels*? Where does the energy in fossil fuels originally come from?

9 a What is the chief element found in coal?
b If this element were burned in plenty of oxygen, what would be formed?
c What is the test for the substance produced in **b**?
d How would a solution of the substance formed in **b** react with litmus?

YREB

10 Describe how natural gas was formed and say in what conditions it may be found in quantity.

EMREB

11 Describe a laboratory experiment in which you could collect samples of at least 3 of the main products of the destructive distillation of coal. Draw a diagram of the apparatus and say in what ways each of the products obtained in your experiment are important to us.

EMREB

12 Name 3 fractions (products) of the distillation of petroleum (crude oil).

ALSEB

13 What are the properties and uses of 2 of the following polymers?
a nylon
b polythene
c P.V.C.

WREB

14 Describe **a** how you would prepare a sample of soap and **b** how you would test its pH value.

EMREB

15 Detergent dissolves in water to give a neutral solution. Explain how a household detergent acts on dirt particles on cotton fibres to remove the dirt during the washing process. (Labelled diagrams could be used).

SREB

Chapter 5

Moving Molecules

Hot ones in the balloon. Is it full of them?

They keep you warm because they keep vibrations in. What are they?

5.1   Hot molecules

Scientists have devised a theory to explain why solids, liquids and gases behave in the way they do. No-one can prove that the theory is true but all the evidence seems to support it. It's called the kinetic theory of matter.

Solids, liquids and gases

According to the *kinetic theory of matter,* solids, liquids and gases are made up of tiny particles called *molecules* which strongly attract each other when they are close together. These molecules are constantly on the move:

Solids   In a solid, strong forces of attraction pull the molecules close together. The molecules move by vibrating from side to side.

Liquids   In a liquid, the forces of attraction still pull the molecules into the smallest possible space but the molecules have enough freedom to be able to move about as they vibrate—the liquid can flow.

Gases   In a gas, the molecules are well spaced out and virtually free of any attractions. They move about at very high speed and quickly fill any space available to them. As they move they collide with each other and with the walls of any container they happen to be in.

Heating solids, liquids and gases

As a substance gets hotter its molecules move faster. If the molecules of a solid are heated they begin to overcome the attractions which hold them together and the solid may become a liquid.

If the molecules of a liquid are moving fast enough to completely break free of attractions, the liquid becomes a gas.

Water is one common substance you will recognize in all three forms—as a solid called ice, as a liquid, and as a gas known as steam.

If ice is heated sufficiently it melts to form liquid water.

If liquid water is heated sufficiently it boils to form steam.

A liquid tends to change into a gas long before it is hot enough to boil but the change happens most rapidly at the boiling point.

Changing state

Water can be made to change state quite easily, from solid to liquid to gas and back again. Not many other familiar substances do this. The concrete in buildings does not melt on a hot day, and the air does not liquefy on a cold one!

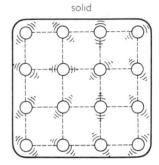

solid

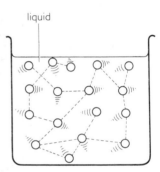

liquid

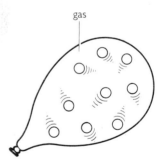

gas

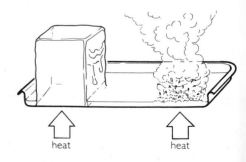

heat   heat

Temperature: the Celsius scale

The degree of hotness of a solid, liquid or gas is measured using a *scale of temperature*. The most commonly used scale of temperature is the *Celsius* or Centigrade scale; the numbers on this scale are called *'degrees Celsius'* and written °C. On this scale:

pure ice melts at 0 °C;
pure water boils at 100 °C.

The chart below gives some typical temperature values.

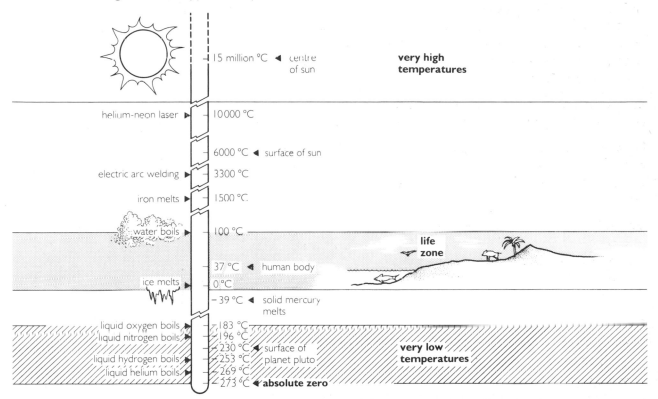

	15 million °C ◄ centre of sun	**very high temperatures**
helium-neon laser ►	10 000 °C	
	6000 °C ◄ surface of sun	
electric arc welding ►	3300 °C	
iron melts ►	1500 °C	
water boils	100 °C	**life zone**
	37 °C ◄ human body	
ice melts ►	0 °C	
	− 39 °C ◄ solid mercury melts	
liquid oxygen boils ►	−183 °C	
liquid nitrogen boils ►	−196 °C	
	−230 °C ◄ surface of planet pluto	**very low temperatures**
liquid hydrogen boils ►	−253 °C	
liquid helium boils ►	−269 °C	
	−273 °C ◄ **absolute zero**	

Absolute zero   According to the kinetic theory, molecules move more slowly as they get colder. At a certain temperature, −273°C all movement stops. This temperature is called *absolute zero* and it is the coldest temperature possible. (It is now known that molecules have *least* movement at absolute zero, rather than no movement at all.)

Questions
1. Describe the movements of the molecules in (a) a solid (b) a liquid (c) a gas. Are molecular attractions least in a solid, a liquid or a gas?
2. What happens to molecules as they become hotter and hotter?
3. What names are given to water in its solid, and gas forms?
4. At what temperature does ice melt on the Celsius scale?
5. At what temperature does water boil on the Celsius scale?
6. At what temperature does liquid oxygen boil?
7. What is absolute zero? What is special about this temperature?

'Cold molecules'. This equipment is used to investigate low temperatures.

5.2 Wandering molecules

The kinetic theory can be used to explain several strange effects that it would be difficult to account for otherwise. Here are a few examples.

Brownian motion

Smoke is made up of billions of tiny particles of ash. Viewed through a microscope, these particles can be seen to wander about in a jerky zig-zag way. The effect is called *Brownian motion* and it happens because the smoke particles are light enough to be moved when individual molecules in the air crash into them.

The diagram shows the apparatus used to show the Brownian motion of smoke particles.

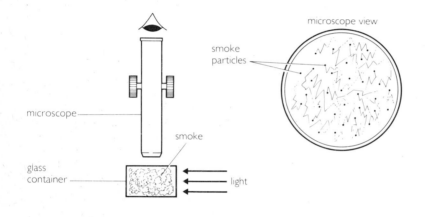

Some liquid dye has been carefully added to still water in the beaker.

Diffusion

If a small amount of coloured dye is dropped into a beaker of water, the colour soon spreads throughout the water. The molecules in the dye spread by a process called *diffusion*—they wander at random through the water as they are bumped and jostled by the molecules around them.

Diffusion will cause a small amount of leaking gas to spread throughout a room. It also causes smells to spread—smells are molecules which come from whatever it is that happens to be smelling.

After twelve hours the dye has diffused upwards through the water.

Osmosis

The experiment on the right shows a process called *osmosis* in action.

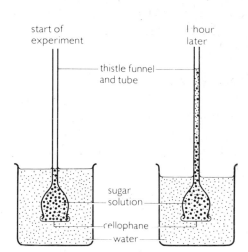

The tube contains concentrated sugar solution (a mixture of sugar molecules and water molecules) but the beaker contains water only. The sugar solution and the water are separated by a thin sheet of cellophane—called a *membrane*—which is stretched across the mouth of the funnel.

At first, the sugar solution and the water are at the same level—but the level of the liquid begins to rise as water passes through the membrane and into the sugar solution. The sugar solution becomes more dilute as the height of the liquid increases.

The process by which water passes through the membrane is called osmosis. The pressure which builds up above the membrane is called *osmotic pressure.*

How the kinetic theory explains osmosis   The cellophane has tiny holes in it which are so small that the sugar molecules are too large to wander through. But the water molecules are able to. They go through the membrane—though more go into the sugar solution than out of it because more are in contact with one side of the membrane than the other (see diagram).

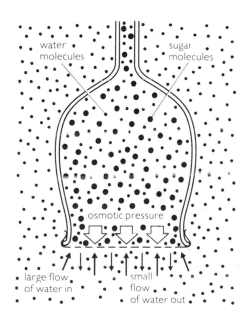

Semi-permeable membranes   Materials such as cellophane which allow some substances to pass through but not others are described as *semi-permeable.* Water will move by osmosis through any semi-permeable membrane that separates a weak solution from a strong one.

The cells in the roots of plants are able to absorb water from the soil by osmosis.

Osmosis in cells   Semi-permeable membranes form the outside of the tiny liquid-filled cells from which animals and plants are made. They are useful in a variety of ways, as suggested below:

Osmotic pressure inside plant cells keeps them firm rather as balloons are kept firm by the air pressure inside them. The firmness of the cells keeps plants strong and upright—without water, they wilt.

Dried fruit swells when soaked in water because cells in the fruit absorb water by osmosis.

Questions

1. Why do the smoke particles in the experiment on the opposite page appear to dance about?
   What name is given to these movements?
2. What is diffusion? Give three examples of diffusion.
3. What happens to the sugar solution in the experiment described above? Why?
4. A thin sheet of cellophane is semi-permeable. What does this mean?
5. Give two examples of osmosis in action in plants.

The effect of reduction in osmotic pressure.

5.3 Surface tension and its effects

A drop of water behaves as if its surface was covered with a stretchy skin. The effect is caused by attractions between molecules—it makes life easier for mosquitoes and pond skaters but harder for house builders!

Surface tension

The fact that there is tension in the surface of a liquid can be demonstrated using soapy water and the wire frame shown in the diagram. The frame is first dipped in soapy water so that a thin film of liquid stretches across it.

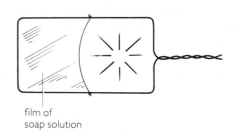

thread

If the film to the right of the thread is popped, the film remaining pulls the thread firmly to the left.

Surface tension pulls drips from a tap into round droplets and it makes mercury collect in round blobs. It enables you to float a needle on the surface of water without it sinking and it allows insects to stand on the surface of ponds.

film of
soap solution

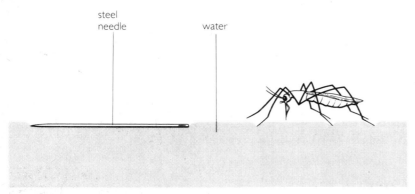

steel needle   water

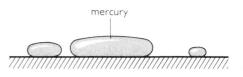

mercury

Cohesion   A liquid does not really have a stretchy skin. The tension in its surface is caused by the attractions which pull all the molecules together. Attraction between molecules of the same type is known as *cohesion*. These attractions will pull small amounts of a liquid into round droplets. They will also resist attempts by needles and the feet of insects to push molecules apart by breaking through the surface of water.

Adhesion   Molecules of a liquid may also be attracted to molecules of other materials—an attraction of this type is known as *adhesion*.

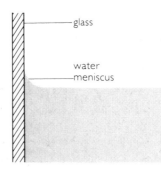

glass

water
meniscus

If you empty water out of a beaker, drops of water stay clinging to the glass. This is because the water molecules are more strongly attracted to the glass than they are to each other—the adhesion of water to glass is stronger than the cohesion of water.

The strong attraction of water molecules to glass makes the surface (the *meniscus*) of water curve upwards where it meets glass.

Capillary attraction

Glass attracts water molecules strongly enough to pull a thin column of water up through a narrow tube (a *capillary* tube) made of glass. The effect is called *capillary attraction*. The narrower the tube, the further the water rises, because the weight of water needing support is less.

Water, alcohol and many other liquids can be drawn up through narrow gaps by capillary attraction.

Materials like blotting paper and cotton wool which 'soak up' liquids contain thousands of tiny air spaces through which liquids can move by capillary attraction. Soil and porous rocks also contain air spaces and they absorb water in the same way.

In the walls and floors of houses, capillary attraction would cause rising damp through the bricks and concrete if steps were not taken to prevent it—there are air spaces in concrete and in brickwork.

In new houses a waterproof sheet of polythene is laid in the concrete base to stop the upward movement of water from the ground. For the same reason, a waterproof layer is set into the outer brick walls just above ground level. This waterproof layer is called a *damp course* and it is made from a mixture of felt and bitumen.

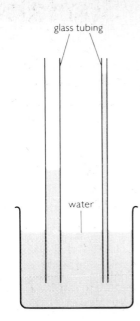

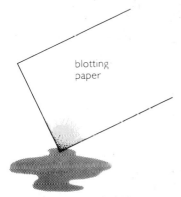

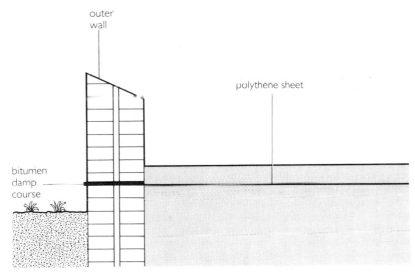

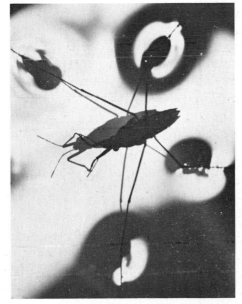

A pond skater demonstrates the effect of surface tension.

Questions
1. How could you show that there is tension in the surface of a liquid?
2. Give three examples of the effects of surface tension.
3. What is cohesion? How is it different from adhesion?
4. Why do drops of water cling to the sides of a glass beaker?
5. What happens if a narrow glass tube is dipped in water? What would be the effect of using an even narrower tube?
6. Give two practical examples of capillary attraction.
7. What is a damp course? What is its purpose?

5.4 Expanding solids

Solids expand when they are heated—by so little that you would not normally notice it. Yet an expanding solid can produce enough force to crack concrete or buckle steel. And it all happens because vibrating molecules need room to move.

How solids expand

When a solid is heated its molecules vibrate more vigorously than before. As the vibrations become larger the molecules are pushed further apart and the solid expands.

Solids do not expand very much when heated but the forces produced by their expansion can be extremely high. It is possible to stop a solid expanding but only by clamping it very firmly to something rigid.

Problems with expansion

Concrete and steel beams are often used in construction work but tey can cause considerable damage if they do not have enough room to expand when the weather gets hot.

Gaps are left at the ends of bridges to give room for expansion. One end of a bridge is often supported on rollers so that movement is possible as the bridge expands.

gap rollers

Railway lines are laid down in very long lengths. Any expansion in the rails is resisted by fastening them to heavy concrete sleepers embedded in chippings—this prevents buckling in hot weather. Some expansion does take place at the ends of each length of rail, but the lengths are linked by overlapping joints which allow movement.

100 m of steel

When 100 m of steel is heated 10 °C........   ....it expands 11 mm

Expansion in different materials

A 100 metre length of steel railway line heated through 10 °C expands only 11 millimetres.
The expansion would be lower still if the line were shorter or its temperature rise were less.

The table on the opposite page shows how much different materials would expand compared with the length of steel.

70

Expansion of 100 m length of material heated through 10 °C			
Brass	19 mm	Invar (metal)	1 mm
Iron	12 mm	Concrete	11 mm
Steel	11 mm	Glass	9 mm
Platinum alloy	9 mm	Pyrex glass	3 mm

The information in the table above is useful when selecting materials to do particular jobs:

Steel rods can be placed in concrete beams to strengthen them because the steel and the concrete will expand equally in hot weather. If the expansion of each was different, the steel rods might crack the concrete.

Platinum alloy wires sealed in glass are used to carry the electricity into a light bulb. When the bulb heats up the expansion of the platinum alloy will be the same as that of the glass, so there is no risk of the glass cracking.

Pyrex glass expands less than ordinary glass and so is much more use in the kitchen. If boiling water is poured into a glass dish, the inside of the dish begins to heat up and expand a few moments before the outside. As the inside of the dish pushes against the outside the glass may crack. A pyrex dish is less likely to crack because its glass does not expand so much.

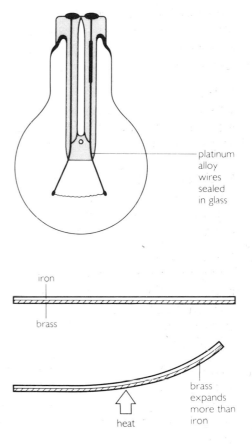

platinum alloy wires sealed in glass

The bimetal strip
Thin strips of brass and iron can be bonded together to form a *bimetal strip*.

If a bimetal strip is heated, the brass expands about 1½ times more than the iron. This makes the bimetal strip bend with the brass on the outside—the longer side—of the curve.

The bimetal strip has many uses, some of which are described in the next section.

Questions
1. Why do solids expand when heated?
2. How is expansion allowed for in a bridge? Where else might expansion be a problem?
3. In the table at the top of the page:- Which material expands least? Which material expands most?
4. Which material expands the same amount as concrete? Why is this useful?
5. What advantage does pyrex glass have over ordinary glass?
6. What happens to a bimetal strip when you heat it? Why?

5.5 Using expansion

Whilst expansion is often a nuisance, it can be very useful too.

Joining metals using expansion

Expansion can be used to produce a tight fit between two pieces of metal. In the diagram below, a steel tyre is being fitted to the rim of a train wheel.

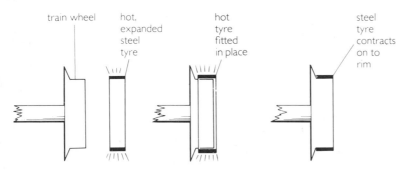

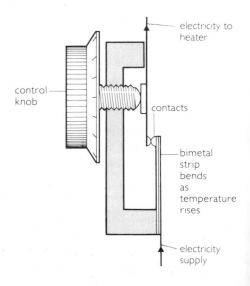

To begin with, the inside of the steel tyre is slightly smaller than the rim of the wheel. The tyre is then heated until it expands enough to fit loosely over the rim. When the steel tyre cools, it contracts (gets smaller) and tightly grips the rim of the wheel.

The bimetal thermometer

A bimetal strip can be used to make a simple thermometer. The bimetal strip is in the form of a long spiral and the centre of this spiral is attached to a pointer.

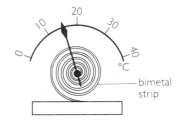

When the temperature rises, the bimetal strip coils itself into an even tighter spiral and the pointer is moved across the scale.

The bimetal thermometer is less accurate than many other thermometers but it is tough and easy to read.

The thermostat

Thermostats are devices which control temperature. Ovens, immersion heaters and refrigerators are all fitted with thermostats—so too are some electric room heaters.

The thermostat in the diagram is connected to an electric room heater. As the room warms up, the bimetal strip bends and the two electrical contacts are moved apart. This switches off the heater. As the room cools down, the bimetal strip cools and straightens. The heater is switched on again as the contacts touch. In this way, the thermostat switches the heater on and off to keep the room at a more or less steady temperature.

The temperature is selected by turning the control knob. If the control knob is screwed inwards, the bimetal strip has to bend further before the contacts separate—the room needs to be warmer before the heater is switched off.

Flashing indicators

The indicator bulbs on many cars flash on and off because of movements made by a tiny bimetal strip. The diagrams below show one simple system in which a bimetal strip makes a light bulb flash on and off.

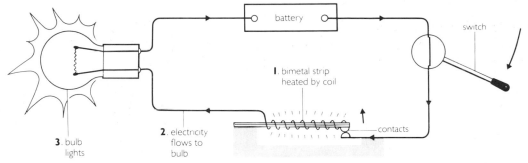

1. bimetal strip heated by coil

2. electricity flows to bulb

3. bulb lights

switch

contacts

When you turn the switch on, electricity flows from the battery to the bulb and the bulb lights up. On its way, this electricity also flows through a small heating coil wound round a bimetal strip. Heated by the coil, the bimetal strip starts to bend. As it bends, it moves one of the contacts away from the other.

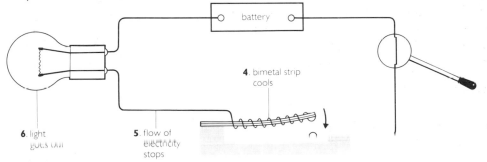

4. bimetal strip cools

5. flow of electricity stops

6. light goes out

With the contacts apart, no electricity can reach the bulb or the heating coil—the light goes out and the bimetal strip cools and straightens.

The contacts touch again as the bimetal strip becomes straight— electricity once more flows through bulb and coil, and the whole process repeats itself.

In this way, the light bulb continues to flash on and off until you turn the indicator switch off.

Questions
1. Why is a steel tyre heated before being fitted to a train wheel?
2. What is a thermostat used for? What pieces of equipment might a thermostat be fitted to?
   How does the thermostat in the diagram switch off electric current? If the control knob is screwed outwards, what effect will this have?
3. When you first turn on the switch in the diagrams above, the bulb lights up. Why does the light then go out? Why does the light come on again after this?

5.6 Expanding liquids

Just like solids, liquids expand as they get hotter. In fact, they expand very much more than solids, and their high rate of expansion makes them very useful in thermometers.

Liquid-in-glass thermometers

Mercury thermometers A typical mercury thermometer is shown in the diagram on the right.

When the temperature rises, the expansion of the mercury in the bulb pushes the mercury 'thread' further up through the narrow glass tube. The tube is the same width from top to bottom—it is made narrow so that a small expansion of the mercury produces a large upward movement of the thread.

To mark an accurate temperature scale on the thermometer, two points on the scale are first fixed:

The thermometer must read 0 °C when placed in pure melting ice.

The thermometer must read 100 °C when placed in the steam above pure boiling water (the water must be boiled under standard atmospheric conditions).

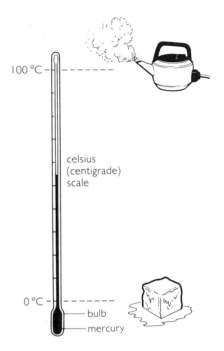

The clinical thermometer Doctors and nurses use a mercury thermometer with two special features:

The thermometer only covers a narrow range of temperatures close to the average body temperature of 37 °C but it can measure temperatures in this range very accurately.

The tube has a narrow bend (a constriction) in it to stop the mercury thread moving back down the tube after the thermometer is removed from the patient's mouth. The temperature can be read any time after this, but the mercury then has to be shaken back down the tube.

Alcohol thermometers Alcohol is sometimes used in thermometers rather than mercury. It expands about six times as much as mercury for the same temperature rise and is less poisonous should the thermometer break. An alcohol thermometer can also be used in arctic temperatures that might freeze mercury. Mercury freezes at −40 °C, alcohol at −115 °C.

Disadvantages of alcohol are that it needs to be coloured to be seen easily and that it tends to cling to the side of the tube when the thread is falling.

The maximum and minimum thermometer A maximum and minimum thermometer is shown in the diagram on the right. It is an alcohol thermometer with two small steel pointers to record the highest and lowest temperatures reached over a period of time.

When the temperature rises, the expanding alcohol pushes the mercury thread further along the glass tube, and the mercury thread carries the pointer to a higher position on the maximum scale. The pointer sticks in the tube at the highest point reached. Similarly, when the temperature falls, the mercury thread moves back along the tube and the other pointer is carried further along the minimum scale. Both pointers can be pulled back again with a small magnet.

The expansion of water

Water behaves in a most unusual way when heated from 0 °C. As its temperature is raised from 0 °C to 4 °C, water actually *contracts*. From 4 °C upwards, water expands like other liquids.

Water therefore takes up least space at 4 °C—it has its greatest *density* at this temperature. It will sink down through warmer or colder water around it.

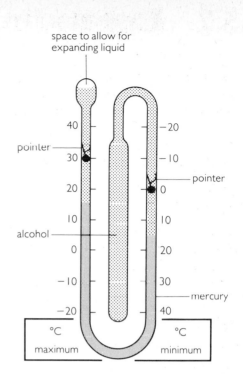

Water may still be at 4 °C at the bottom of a lake even though conditions on the surface are freezing. Fish and other forms of water life are able to survive a severe winter by staying in this deeper water.

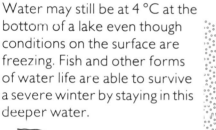

Questions

1. Which expand most when heated, liquids or solids?
2. Why is the tube in a liquid-filled thermometer narrow?
3. How is a clinical thermometer different from an ordinary mercury thermometer?
4. What are the advantages of using alcohol rather than mercury in a thermometer? What are the disadvantages?
5. What were the maximum and minimum temperatures recorded by the pointers on the thermometer shown on this page?
6. What happens to water when it is heated from 0 °C to 4 °C?
7. Why might fish survive winter at the bottom of a lake?

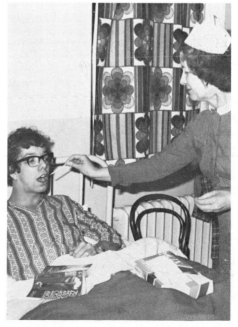

A clinical thermometer in use.

5.7 Conduction

It is very difficult to keep heat in one place—the vibrations of molecules always try to spread out as much as possible. Home insulation isn't keeping the cold out, but the vibrations in!

How materials conduct heat

When a material is heated, its molecules begin to move more quickly. Each molecule bumps against those around it and eventually all the molecules speed up. In this way, heat is conducted to all parts of the material.

In metals, some heat is conducted as above but most is conducted in another way.

Some of the electrons in the metal atoms are free to drift about between the atoms. When a metal is heated these *free electrons* speed up and carry their heat to all parts of the metal.

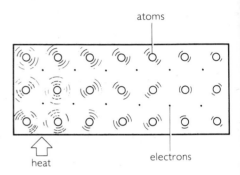

atoms

heat

electrons

Good conductors of heat

Most metals conduct heat well because they contain free electrons—these same electrons also make metals good conductors of electricity.

Of all the metals, silver and copper are the best conductors.

Good conductors often feel cold to touch. A metal bar feels cold when you pick it up because it rapidly conducts heat away from your hand.

good conductors
most metals especially: 　silver 　copper 　aluminium

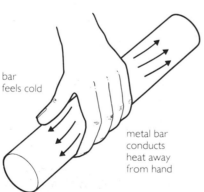

bar
feels cold

metal bar
conducts
heat away
from hand

Uses of good conductors   Good conductors have many uses: saucepans are often made of aluminium because it readily conducts heat from a gas ring or a hotplate. The bases of saucepans are sometimes made of copper for the same reason.

If wire gauze is placed over a bunsen flame, the gauze conducts heat away from the flame. This cools the hot burning gas so that no flame appears above the gauze. A glass beaker can be safely heated on the gauze because this protects it from the concentrated heat of the flame.

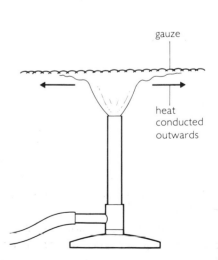

gauze

heat
conducted
outwards

Poor conductors of heat

Non-metals tend to be poor conductors of heat (and electricity) because none of their electrons are free to move about.

Materials such as cork, plastic and asbestos are poor conductors of heat, so are most liquids. Gases are even worse than liquids at conducting heat. Many materials act as poor conductors because they contain trapped air.

Materials which are poor conductors of heat are known as *insulators*.

Uses of insulators   Insulating materials are useful in the kitchen, to stop heat going where it isn't wanted. For example:

Table mats are often made of cork to protect table tops from hot dishes. Saucepan handles are often made from plastic so that as little heat as possible is conducted to your hand.

There are many examples of trapped air acting as an insulator:

Furry animals keep warm because their fur traps air. Even snow with air trapped in it can act as an insulating blanket. Woollen jumpers are warm because they trap air, so are the fillings used in sleeping bags. Fibreglass and polyurethane foam are good insulators because of the air trapped inside them.

poor conductors (insulators)
water, most liquids
cork
PVC and other plastics
glass
wood
asbestos
air and other gases
materials which trap air:
wool
fur
fibreglass
plastic foam

Insulating the house   The diagram shows a house in which a number of insulating materials have been used to cut down losses of heat.

Although glass is a poor conductor of heat, a single sheet of window-glass is thin enough for heat losses through it to be noticeable.

A *double-glazed* window consists of two sheets of glass with an insulating layer of air trapped between them.

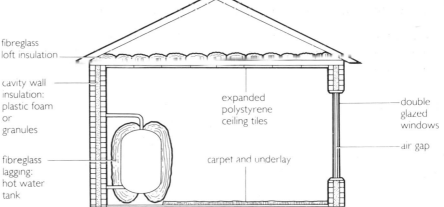

fibreglass loft insulation

cavity wall insulation: plastic foam or granules

fibreglass lagging: hot water tank

expanded polystyrene ceiling tiles

carpet and underlay

double glazed windows

air gap

Questions
1. How is heat conducted through a metal?
2. Name three good conductors of heat.
3. Which materials would you recommend for a table-mat, the base of a saucepan, the handle of a kettle?
4. Which are usually the poorest conductors of heat, liquids or gases?
5. What makes fur and fibreglass good insulators?
6. What is a double-glazed window? Why is it useful?

Natural insulation.

5.8 Convection

If liquids are such poor conductors of heat why does a kettleful of water warm through so quickly?
If gases are such poor conductors of heat why is the air above a bunsen flame so hot?
This section looks at the way in which heat can be carried by a rising stream of liquid or gas—the process called convection.

Convection in a liquid

The circulating stream of water in the diagram is called a *convection current*—the potassium permanganate crystals colour the water so that the current can be seen easily.

The current circulates as warm water rises above the heat of the flame and cooler water sinks to take its place. The water expands when heated and is pushed upwards by the cooler, denser water around it.

The domestic hot water system   Most household water systems make use of convection to circulate hot water through the pipes. The diagram shows the layout of a simple system—in many houses the storage tank is in an upstairs cupboard and the header tank is in the loft.

Water heated in the boiler rises by convection to the top of the storage tank. Cooler water in the bottom of the tank sinks back down to the boiler where it is heated. In this way, a supply of hot water collects in the storage tank from the top downwards.

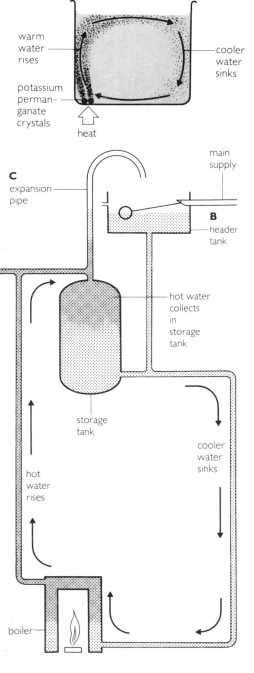

The *hot taps* (A) are supplied with water from the top of the storage tank.

The *header tank* (B) provides the pressure needed to push hot water out of the taps. It also replaces water in the system as it is used. When the water level in the header tank drops the plastic float also drops—this opens a valve to let in more water from the main water supply. As the tank fills, the float rises and the supply of water is shut off.

The *expansion pipe* (C) serves as an overflow should steam or air bubbles build up in the system.

78

Convection in air

When convection takes place in air:
hot air rises and *cooler air sinks.*

Warming a room by convection   Many room heaters, including 'radiators' are designed to circulate warm air by convection.

The diagram shows a convector heater in use. The heater is placed close to the floor and warm air rises above it. A convection current is set up as cooler air sinks into the bottom of the heater. In time, all the air in the room is warmed as it circulates through the heater.

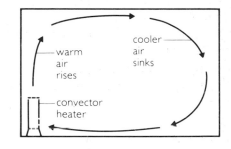

Convection in a refrigerator   Cold air is circulated round the food in a refrigerator by convection. The freezer compartment is placed near the top of the refrigerator so that cold air sinks away from it. Warmer air rises to the top of the refrigerator where it is cooled by the freezer compartment.

Land and sea breezes   Convection causes the onshore and offshore winds which sometimes blow on the coast during the summer.

In hot sunshine, the land heats up more quickly than the sea. Warmer air rises above the land and cooler air blows in from the sea to replace it.

At night, the land loses heat more rapidly than the sea. Warmer air now rises above the sea, causing cooler air to blow out from the shore.

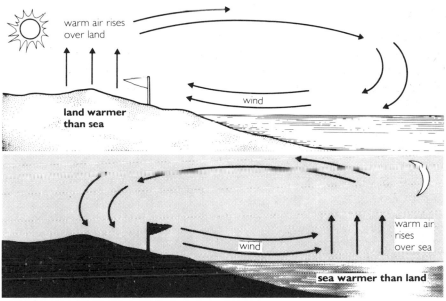

Questions

1. In a beaker containing both hot and cold water, what happens to
   a) the hot water; b) the cold water?
2. Why is a header tank fitted to a hot water system? Where is hot water from the boiler stored?
   Why is an expansion pipe necessary?
3. How does a 'radiator' distribute most of its heat?
4. Why is the freezer compartment placed near the top of a refrigerator?
5. Which heats up most rapidly during the day, land or sea? Which way do coastal breezes blow in the daytime? Why? Why do they blow in the opposite direction at night?

Questions on Chapter 5

1 How are the movements of molecules in a gas different from those in a solid?

2 What happens to the molecules in a material when the temperature falls?

3 −373 °C, −273 °C, −20 °C, 0 °C, 23 °C, 37 °C, 90 °C, 100 °C, 200 °C
From the above list, select:
   a the temperature at which water freezes
   b the temperature at which water boils
   c absolute zero
   d the temperature on a warm sunny day
   e the average temperature of the human body

4 Drop ink into water and the colouring soon spreads throughout the water.
Explain why this happens.
What is the process called?

5 If, through a microscope, you were to observe tiny particles of smoke floating in air, what would you see and why?

6 What is a semi-permeable membrane? Give an example.

7 By what process do living cells absorb water?

8 With the aid of a diagram, describe an experiment you could carry out to demonstrate capillary attraction.

9 Why do small amounts of water try to form into round droplets?

10 Why do materials such as cotton wool and blotting paper 'soak up' water?

11 How is 'rising damp' prevented in the walls and floors of a modern house?

12 Most materials expand when heated.
   a When is expansion a nuisance?
   b What use can be made of expansion?
   Give one example in each case.

13 The diagram below shows a bimetal strip

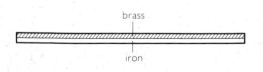

a Draw another diagram to show what will happen to the bimetal strip when it is heated.
b Name two devices which make use of a bimetal strip.

14 In what way is the expansion of water different from that of most other substances?

15 If the surface of a freshwater lake has just started to freeze, what will be the temperature of the water at the bottom of the lake?

16 Name two liquids commonly used in thermometers.
Which of the liquids would be used in a thermometer designed to measure very cold arctic temperatures? Why?

17 *Copper, iron, glass, water, air*
In the above list:
   a Which is the best conductor of heat?
   b Which is the poorest conductor of heat?

18 The metal end of a spade feels cold to touch, yet the wooden handle feels warm. Explain.

19 Describe three ways in which the loss of heat from a house can be reduced.

20 A beaker of water is placed over a bunsen flame. Explain how the water at the top of the beaker becomes hot.

21 Why is the heating element in an electric kettle placed near the bottom of the kettle rather than higher up?   SREB

22 During the summer, coastal breezes are very common. Copy and complete the diagrams below to show the direction of the winds during the daytime and at night.

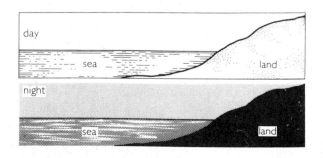

Explain in each case why the winds blow in the direction they do.

Chapter 6

Forces and Energy

What makes a car stop when it runs out of petrol?

. . . . . . is being used to create a . . . . that
accelerates the dragster . . .

6.1 Force, mass and weight

Most people think they know what a force is—but what is the difference between mass and weight? This section explains this but they would never believe you in the local supermarket.

Force
Force is an amount of push or pull and it is measured in *newtons* (N for short).

As forces go, a force of 1 newton (1 N) is very small. The astronaut in the diagram will use a force of about 20 newtons to pull the ring off the top of his can of coke.

The rocket motor in his spacecraft will produce a force of about 50 000 newtons.

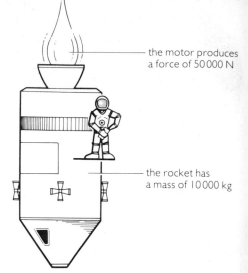

the motor produces a force of 50 000 N

the rocket has a mass of 10 000 kg

Mass
Mass is the quantity of matter in an object and it is measured in *kilograms* (kg for short)

The can of coke has a mass of less than ½ kilogram.
The astronaut has a mass of about 70 kilograms.
His spacecraft might have a mass of about 10 000 kilograms.
The mass of the Earth is a staggering
6 000 000 000 000 000 000 000 000 kilograms!

How masses behave   All objects have mass. This affects the way they behave in two ways:

Large masses are more difficult to speed up or slow down than small masses.

If the astronaut pushes his can of coke it speeds up easily—the same would not be true if he tried to push his spacecraft. The behaviour of moving masses is described in the next section.

All masses attract each other
No one has yet discovered why.

The *mass* of the sugar is one kilogram.

Gravitational force
The force of attraction between masses is known as *gravitational force*. The larger and closer the masses, the greater is the pull between them.

The gravitational force between the Earth and the Sun holds the Earth in orbit around the Sun; the gravitational force between the Moon and the Earth holds the Moon in orbit around the Earth.

The gravitational force between two everyday objects is too weak to measure but it becomes quite strong if one of the objects has as much mass as the Earth—strong enough for example to hold the astronaut firmly on the Earth's surface. If he drops his can of coke, gravitational force will quickly pull it towards the Earth.

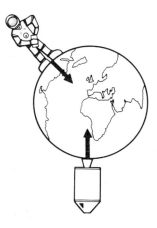

Weight

Weight is the common name for the gravitational force on an object and it is measured in newtons like all other forces.

On Earth, the astronaut has a weight of 690 newtons—that is the strength of the Earth's gravitational pull on his 70 kilograms of mass.

Moon

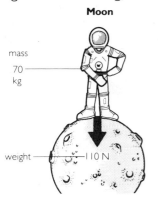

mass
70
kg

weight —— 110 N

Earth

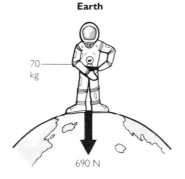

70
kg

690 N

Jupiter

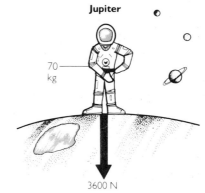

70
kg

3600 N

If the astronaut stands on the Moon, his weight will be much less because the Moon has less mass to attract him with. On a massive planet like Jupiter the astronaut would weigh more than five times as much as he does on Earth.

The astronaut's weight may vary but he still has the same amount of matter in him. Wherever he stands, his mass will still be 70 kilograms.

Measuring weight and mass

If you put a one-kilogram bag of sugar on a set of scales, it is the gravitational pull on the sugar which forces the scale pan downwards—the scales respond to weight.

Some sets of scales are marked in newtons but most give a reading in mass units such as kilograms or grams (there are 1000 grams in each kilogram). Readings in mass units present no problem to manufacturers of scales because an object of large mass also has a large weight on Earth.

As for the one-kilogram bag of sugar:
it has a *mass* of 1 kilogram and a *weight* on Earth of 9.8 newtons, but try telling them that at the supermarket!

The *weight* of the sugar is 9.8 newtons.

Questions

1. In what units are forces measured?
2. In what units are masses measured?
3. Give two ways in which large masses differ from small masses.
4. What is the common name for gravitational force?
5. Why does an astronaut weigh less on the Moon than the Earth? How is his mass affected if he moves from the Earth to the Moon?
6. How many grams are there in 1 kilogram?
7. Why is it wrong to say that a bag of sugar 'weighs' 1 kilogram? What is the weight of the sugar on Earth?

6.2 Force and movement

There are all sorts of forces acting on things which move on the surface of the Earth. This caused confusion for all scientists from ancient Greek times onwards. In 1687, Sir Isaac Newton sorted most of the muddles out—this section tells you about the modern version of his findings.

Movement without force

Without a force on it a stationary object will simply stay where it is. This is obvious to everyone.

Not quite so obvious is the fact that a moving object *keeps moving* if there is no force on it. With its motor turned off, the spacecraft shown below has no force acting on it, yet it will continue to travel at a steady speed in a straight line.

rocket
motor off

steady speed in a straight line

no force

The effect of a single force

When the rocket motor is fired the force will make the spacecraft gain speed—the spacecraft will *accelerate*. How rapidly it accelerates will depend on its mass.

In the diagram below the forces on the two spacecraft are equal but one spacecraft has much more mass than the other. It is the spacecraft with least mass which accelerates most rapidly.

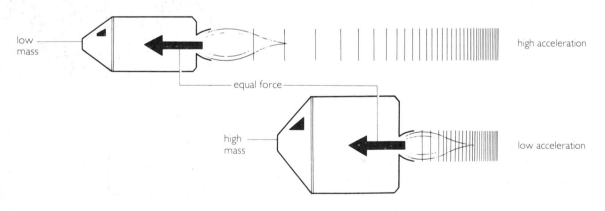

low
mass

high acceleration

equal force

high
mass

low acceleration

To summarize:

If no force acts on an object, its speed stays the same. A force can change the speed of an object—the speed of a small mass will change more than the speed of a large mass.

Friction

An unpowered craft may move at a steady speed in space but on Earth a moving car will begin to slow down the instant its engine is switched off. It is slowed by friction, the force which exists between all materials which rub against each other.

Air resistance is one type of frictional force. The resisting force from the air flowing past a fast moving car may be 2000 newtons or more.

In the diagram on the right, another type of frictional force is acting—that between two solid surfaces pressed together. The car body is difficult to move because of friction between its bottom surface and the ground.

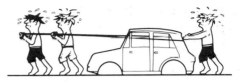

Overcoming friction   Man solved the problem of friction from the ground by putting vehicles on wheels.

Even a wheel produces some friction where it rubs against its shaft. Oil reduces the friction by helping the surfaces slide across each other more smoothly.

To reduce friction still further, wheels on vehicles are usually mounted on ball or roller bearings.

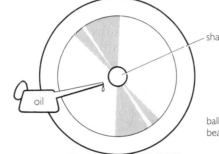

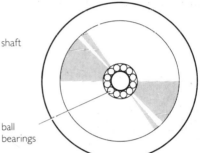

shaft

oil

ball bearings

Using friction   Friction does have its uses. If there were no friction between car tyres and the ground, the wheels of the car might spin but the car would stay where it was. Car tyres are designed to give as much friction as possible in all weather conditions.

Friction is also used to slow moving vehicles. In a disc brake, a steel disc attached to the car wheel spins between two small brake pads. When the brakes are applied the pads press against the disc and the frictional force slows the disc down.

Questions
1. What happens to a moving spacecraft with no force on it?
2. What happens to the spacecraft on the right if it fires its rocket motor? How would the result be different if the spacecraft had more mass?
3. Why does a fast car slow down if its engine is switched off?
4. Give two ways in which the friction between a wheel and a shaft can be reduced.
5. Where on a wheel is as much friction as possible needed? Why? Give one other use of friction.

Forces for rockets and jets

You can't make a force unless there's something to push against.
But what does a rocket push against in space?

Reaction forces

The astronaut and the rock shown on the right are 'floating' together in space. When the astronaut pushes the rock with his boot, the rock moves to the left and he moves to the right—he cannot push on the rock without it pushing equally hard on him.

When any force acts there is an opposite reaction force of the same strength.

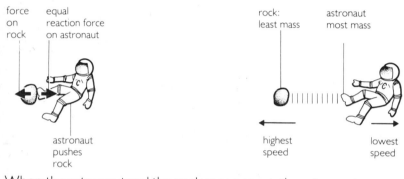

force on rock — equal reaction force on astronaut

astronaut pushes rock

rock: least mass — astronaut most mass

highest speed — lowest speed

When the astronaut and the rock move apart, the astronaut moves more slowly than the rock—he has the greater mass and is not so easily moved by a force. To move at a higher speed, the astronaut would either have to push harder on the rock or push against a more massive rock.

The rocket motor

In pushing against the rock the astronaut has made himself into a simple rocket motor.

Rocket motors don't normally push rocks, they throw out a large mass of fast moving gas. In pushing the gas out, a rocket motor is pushed in the opposite direction by the reaction force.

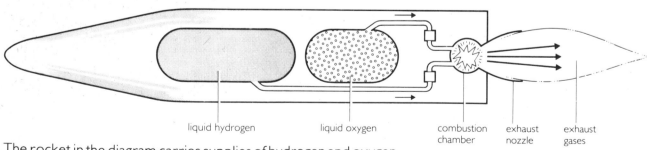

liquid hydrogen   liquid oxygen   combustion chamber   exhaust nozzle   exhaust gases

The rocket in the diagram carries supplies of hydrogen and oxygen stored as cold liquids so that they take up less room. In the combustion chamber the hydrogen burns violently with the oxygen and the gases formed expand rapidly in the intense heat. The expansion forces the gases out of the exhaust nozzle at high speed.

Jet engines

Like rocket motors, jet engines produce a forward force by pushing out large masses of gas behind them. Unlike rocket motors they will not work in space because they need a supply of air.

Why air is needed A jet engine needs air for two reasons.

First, air provides mass for the engine to push out. In large quantities air is heavy stuff—there are probably more than 100 kilograms of air just in your sitting room at home.

Second, air provides the oxygen needed to burn the kerosene fuel. Rockets have to carry their own bulky supply of oxygen with them.

How the engine works Large amounts of air are drawn in to the engine by the spinning blades of the compressor—the compressor looks like a series of gigantic fans:

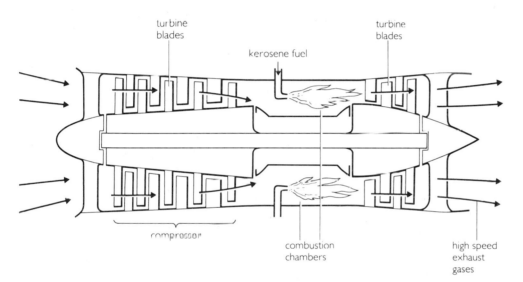

The compressor pushes air into the combustion chambers where kerosene (a type of paraffin) is squirted in. The kerosene burns fiercely in the air and the hot gases which form are forced out of the exhaust nozzle at high speed.

Before leaving the engine the gases pass through sets of turbine blades. The turbine blades are pushed round by the gas and the rotation is used to drive the compressor.

Questions

1. If the astronaut in the diagram on the opposite page pushes the rock with a 30 newton force, what reaction force acts on him? Why does he move more slowly than the rock?
2. Why are rocket fuels stored in liquid form?
3. A jet engine needs air for two reasons. What are they?
4. Describe what happens to the air as it passes through a jet engine. What drives the compressor round?
5. Give one advantage of a rocket motor over a jet engine.
6. Give one advantage of a jet engine over a rocket motor.

6.4 **Forces which turn**

How far can a bus be tilted before it falls over? What makes it fall over anyway? This section looks at the way forces make things turn.

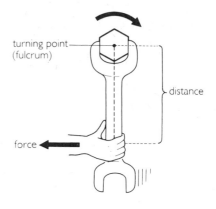

turning point (fulcrum)

distance

force

The turning effect of a force

The spanner in the diagram is being used to tighten a bolt. The force of the hand on the handle is producing a turning effect—the spanner and the bolt turn about a point known as a *turning point* or *fulcrum*.

There are two ways of producing a stronger turning effect, as shown by the diagrams in the margin. You can either pull with a greater force, or pull at the end of a longer handle. If you want it really tight, you might use both!

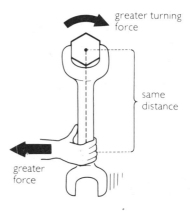

greater turning force

same distance

greater force

Moments The strength of the turning effect produced by a force is called a *moment*. It can be calculated as follows:

$$\text{Moment of a force} = \text{Force} \times \frac{\text{Shortest distance from the force to the turning point}}{}$$

If the force increases, or its distance from the turning point increases, its moment also increases.

Moments in balance

The plank in the diagram is balanced on a log of wood. The plank was balanced first, then bricks were placed on in positions that did not disturb the balance. Each of the bricks used weighs 20 newtons. Each set of bricks produces a turning effect—one moment tries to tip the plank to the left, the other tries to tip it to the right. The plank balances because both moments are equal:

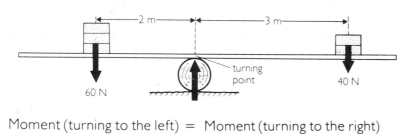

2 m   3 m

turning point

60 N   40 N

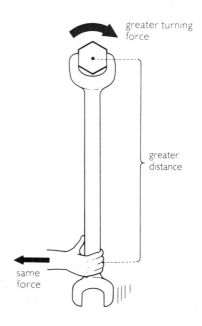

greater turning force

greater distance

same force

Moment (turning to the left) = Moment (turning to the right)

$$\text{Force} \times \frac{\text{distance}}{\text{from turning point}} = \text{Force} \times \frac{\text{distance}}{\text{from turning point}}$$

60 × 2 = 40 × 3

120 = 120

In each case, the turning moment is 120 Nm.

Centre of gravity

Lift a plank and it acts as if all its weight were concentrated at one point only. The point is known as the centre of gravity.

Support a plank at its centre of gravity and it will balance. Try to lift it at any other point and the turning effect of its weight will make it tip.

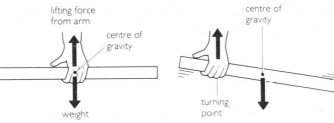

Stability

Some things topple over much more easily than others—it all depends on the position of the centre of gravity.

Push a box a little then release it and it will fall back to its original position—the box is in a *stable* position.

Push the box too far and it will topple. It starts to topple as soon as its centre of gravity has passed over the edge of its base —beyond this point its weight has a turning effect which tips the box even further.

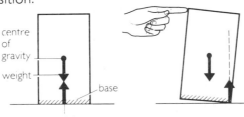

Factors affecting stability

A bus has a wide base. It has a low centre of gravity because its heavy mechanical parts are low down. These factors make it very stable— the bus has to be tilted a long way before it topples.

A coach is even more stable than a double-decker bus. It has a lower centre of gravity and can be tilted further before it topples.

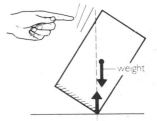

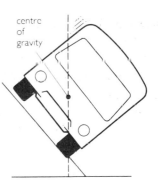

Questions

1. How can you produce a strong turning effect on a bolt?
2. What is a *moment*? How is the moment of a force calculated?
3. What weight is needed to balance the beam in the diagram?
4. Why is it easiest to carry a plank by holding it at its centre of gravity?
5. Which of the two boxes on the right is the most stable? Which two factors make it the most stable? Draw a diagram of each box tilted to the point at which it is about to topple.

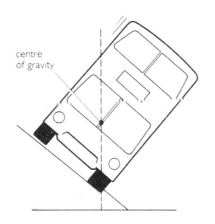

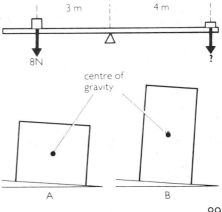

6.5 Work and energy

When is a jumbo jet like 5000 chocolate biscuits? Which releases most energy—eating a chocolate biscuit, throwing it, or dropping it?

Work

You do work when you climb the stairs, or lift a suitcase, or kick a football. Cranes do work when they lift a load and jet engines do work as they push aircraft through the air.

Work is done whenever a force moves.

I joule (I J) of work is done when a force of I newton moves through a distance of I metre.

The work done when a force moves can be calculated using the equation:

Work = force × distance

A 3 N force moving 4 m does 12 J of work.

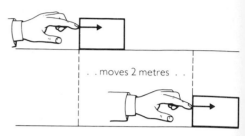

When a 3 newton force . . .

. . moves 2 metres . . .

. . . . 6 joules of work are done

Energy

Things have energy if they can do work.
Like work, energy is measured in *joules*.

There are many different forms of energy, though energy can change from one form into another.

Kinetic energy   Throw a stone and you give it energy. The moving stone has energy because it can do work—it does work if it smashes a window and it does work if it knocks something over. In doing work, the stone loses energy and slows down.

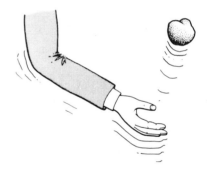

The energy of the moving stone is known as *kinetic energy*. The faster the stone is moving, the more kinetic energy it has. If two stones are thrown at the same speed, the stone with the greater mass has more kinetic energy.

Potential energy   An object has potential energy if it has been pushed or pulled into a position from which it can do work. A compressed spring has potential energy, so does a stretched rubber band—both can do work when released.

Lift a stone above the ground and you give it potential energy. Work was done in lifting the stone and the stone will do work when it falls—by crushing anything underneath it. The heavier and higher the stone, the more potential energy it has.

Heat energy   Heat is a form of energy because it can be used to do work. Burning petrol is used to turn a car engine.

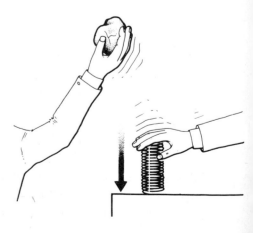

The heat energy put into a material often makes the molecules move faster—all the molecules gain extra kinetic energy.

Chemical energy   You need energy to throw a stone. The energy comes from food and it is released in your body when the food is combined with oxygen. The energy stored in food is called chemical energy.

Fuels like petrol and coal also contain chemical energy. When fuels burn in oxygen, chemical energy is changed into heat energy.

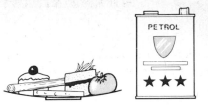

Electrical energy   The electric motor in the diagram is using electrical energy to do work. The energy carried to the motor by the electric current was originally stored in the battery as chemical energy.

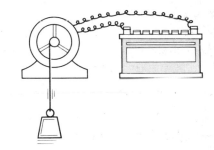

Other forms of energy   The list above is by no means complete. Light and radio waves carry energy, so do sound waves. Nuclear energy is stored in the nucleus of each atom.

Some typical energy values 1000 joules = 1 kilojoule (kJ) and 1 000 000 joules = 1 megajoule (MJ)		
The work you might do in lifting a building brick up above your head from the ground level	50 joules	(50 J)
The kinetic energy the brick might have if you throw it	75 joules	(75 J)
The work you might need to do to climb stairs	1500 joules	(1.5 kJ)
The energy you gain by eating a chocolate biscuit	300 000 joules	(300 kJ)
The energy gained by drinking a pint of beer	600 000 joules	(600 kJ)
The energy needed to boil a kettleful of water	700 000 joules	(700 kJ)
The energy you gain from a large helping of chips	1 000 000 joules	(1 MJ)
The energy stored in a car battery	2 000 000 joules	(2 MJ)
The energy gained from all the food you eat in one day	11 000 000 joules	(11 MJ)
The energy released by burning a gallon of petrol	160 000 000 joules	(160 MJ)
The kinetic energy of a jumbo jet as it takes off	1 500 000 000 joules	(1500 MJ)

Questions
1. When is work done? How much work would you do if you pushed a lawnmower 3 metres with a force of 20 newtons?
2. Give an example of something which has kinetic energy.
3. Give two examples of things which have potential energy.
4. What type of energy is stored in   a) food   b) fuels?
5. What device uses electrical energy to do work?
6. Some of the energy values in the chart can vary greatly. Which values will depend on:
   a) how heavy you are   b) how tall you are
   c) how strong you are   d) how fast something is moving?
   Which are examples of chemical energy?

6.6 Heat energy

A jumbo jet can't get energy from chocolate biscuits but many other energy changes are possible. Energy often changes from one form to another, but it usually ends up as heat energy.

Energy changes

When anything happens anywhere in the universe, energy changes from one form into another. Here are two simple examples:

A stone falling to the ground As a stone falls, it loses height and gains speed—its potential energy is changed into kinetic energy.

When the stone hits the ground, both the stone and the ground heat up slightly. The stone stops moving but the molecules in the stone and the ground move a little faster—the kinetic energy of the stone has been changed into heat energy.

A stone thrown across the ground As the man throws the stone, chemical energy in his muscles is changed into kinetic energy.

The stone skids across the ground, generating heat as it is slowed down by friction—its kinetic energy is changed into heat energy. In both of the examples above:

the total amount of energy at the end of each process is the same as it was at the beginning;

all the energy eventually ends up as heat energy.

These two statements remain true for all energy changes. All the different types of energy that there are, eventually turn into heat energy.

Absorbing heat energy

When a stone absorbs heat energy, its temperature rises.

The stones in the diagram are being heated up to the same temperature; both are absorbing heat from bunsen flames. More heat energy is needed to raise the temperature of the larger stone—there are many more molecules in it to be speeded up.

With more heat energy put into it, the larger stone has more heat energy to get rid of when it cools down. When the bunsens are turned off, the larger stone will continue to give off heat long after the smaller stone has cooled down.

Some materials are much better at storing heat than others:

a 1 kilogram stone made of granite needs to absorb only 840 joules of heat energy for its temperature to rise by 1 °C;
1 kilogram of water needs to absorb five times as much heat for its temperature to rise by the same amount.

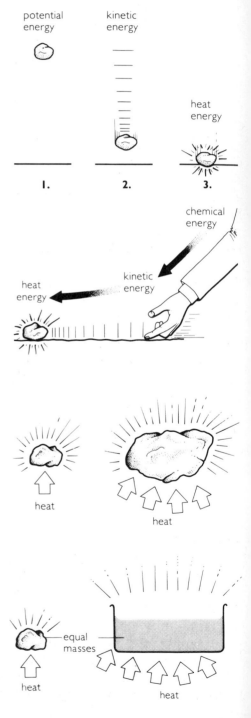

Specific heat capacity

The specific heat capacity of a substance is the heat energy needed to raise the temperature of 1 kilogram of the substance by 1 °C. It is measured in joules per kilogram per °C   (J/kg °C).

The table below gives the specific heat capacities of some common substances:

Specific heat capacities: J/kg °C

Energy in joules needed to heat 1 kilogram through 1 °C

Water	4200	Concrete	850	Steel	500
Sea water	3900	Granite	840	Copper	400
Meths	2500	Aluminium	900	Glass	670

Water has a particularly high specific heat capacity—it takes 4200 joules of energy to heat 1 kilogram of water through 1 °C. One kilogram of water will give out 4200 joules of heat energy if it cools down by 1°C. This makes water a useful substance for storing or carrying heat energy—examples are shown on the right.

Concrete has a lower specific heat capacity than water but a higher density—in the same space there is more mass. Concrete blocks are used in night storage heaters to store heat energy. Electrical heating elements heat the blocks overnight when electricity is cheaper to buy. The hot blocks continue to release their heat energy through the day as they slowly cool down.

Calculating heat energy changes

The heat energy gained or lost as the temperature of a substance rises or falls can be calculated using the equation:

$$\begin{array}{c}\text{Heat} \\ \text{energy} \\ \text{(J)}\end{array} = \begin{array}{c}\text{Mass} \\ \\ \text{(kg)}\end{array} \times \begin{array}{c}\text{Specific heat} \\ \text{capacity} \\ \text{(J/kg °C)}\end{array} \times \begin{array}{c}\text{Temperature} \\ \text{change} \\ \text{(°C)}\end{array}$$

For example, it would take 5400 joules of heat energy to increase the temperature of 3 kilograms of aluminium by 2 °C:

$$5400 = 3 \times 900 \times 2$$

Hot water bottles—good for storing heat.

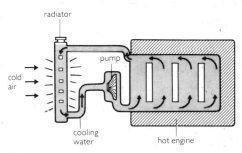

The cooling system of a car uses water to move a lot of heat quickly.

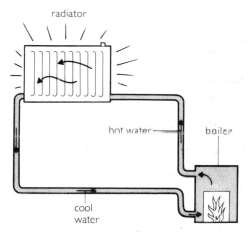

Central heating systems use water to spread heat around the home.

Questions

1. A falling stone hits the ground. What happens to its kinetic energy? What happens to its temperature?
2. Water has a high specific heat capacity. When can this be useful? Give examples.
3. Using the same heater, which would heat up most rapidly, a kilogram of sea water or a kilogram of ordinary tap water?
4. Copper has a specific heat capacity of 400 J/kg °C. What does this mean? Calculate how much heat energy is needed to raise the temperature of 3 kilograms of copper by 4 °C.

6.7 Latent heat

When the stones in the previous section lost heat energy, their temperature fell. Yet a pan of hot wax may lose heat for an hour or more without getting cooler. Something is happening to the wax even if its temperature isn't changing . . .

When a pan of hot liquid wax is removed from the heat, it starts to cool. If its temperature is measured every minute or so, a graph can be plotted as in the diagram:

The temperature of the liquid wax falls until the fat starts to turn solid. The temperature then stays unchanged for an hour or more. It does not start to fall again until the liquid wax has fully solidified.

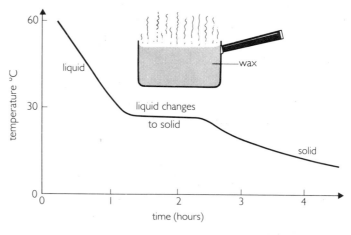

Latent heat of fusion

The wax gives off heat energy as it solidifies yet it does not get any cooler. There seems to be some hidden supply of heat energy inside it. The molecules themselves are the source of this hidden or *latent* heat. They lose some of their freedom and energy as they bind together in solid form, and it is this energy which is released as heat.

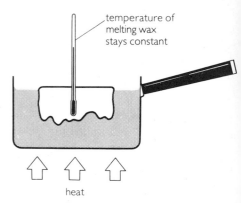

If the solid wax is heated it soon starts to melt. Its temperature stays unchanged as it melts. All the heat energy absorbed by the wax is used in giving the molecules enough energy to make them change from the solid to the liquid state.

The heat energy needed to change a solid into a liquid is known as the latent heat of fusion.

Latent heat of vaporization

A liquid must be supplied with heat energy if it is to change into a gas.

The heat energy needed to change a liquid into a gas is known as the latent heat of vaporization.

Water is turned into a gas every time a kettle is boiled. It takes nearly seven times as much heat energy to change a kilogram of water into steam as it does to change a kilogram of ice into water.

Evaporation

When a liquid changes into a gas, it is said to *evaporate*. Heating speeds up evaporation but a liquid evaporates whether it is heated or not. Wet clothes dry and rain puddles disappear even on a cold day because fast-moving molecules of water are constantly escaping from the liquid to form gas. Other than by direct heating, there are several ways of making a liquid evaporate more rapidly:

Increase the surface area of the liquid   Wet roads dry out quickly because the rain-water is spread over a large area. This gives the molecules a greater chance of escaping from the liquid.

Pass a stream of air through a liquid or across its surface   A liquid evaporates more rapidly if air is bubbled through it because it then has a larger surface area in contact with the air.
Air flowing across a liquid surface also helps evaporation: wet washing dries more quickly on a windy day.

Form the liquid into a fine spray   A spray is made up of millions of tiny liquid droplets and the total surface area of these droplets is very large. The liquid molecules escape easily from the highly curved surface of each droplet.

In the carburettor of a car engine, petrol evaporates rapidly as it is drawn into the airstream in the form of a fine spray. The petrol gas is sucked into the engine with the air and then burnt.

Cooling by evaporation

A liquid needs heat from somewhere in order to evaporate. If the liquid is not actually being heated, it must draw the heat energy it needs from some other source.

A little methylated spirit tipped on the back of your hand quickly evaporates. It extracts the latent heat that it needs from your hand, which feels very cold as a result.

If air is bubbled through ether as in the diagram, the latent heat needed to evaporate the ether is drawn from the glass test-tube. As the ether evaporates, the glass may get so cold that frost begins to form on it. (*Warning:* experiments with ether have to be carried out under very carefully controlled conditions).

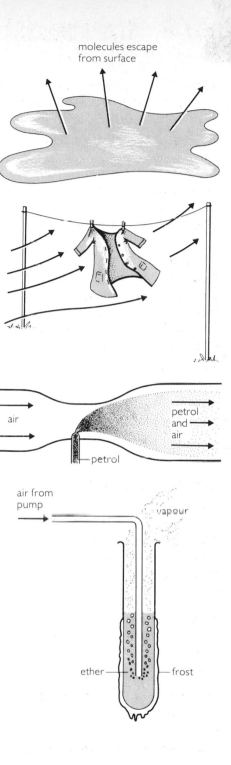

Questions

1. What happens to the temperature of hot wax as it cools?
2. Why is heat energy needed to melt a solid? What is this heat energy called?
3. What is latent heat of vaporization?
4. Why do wet roads dry so quickly after a shower of rain?
5. Why does wet washing dry best on a windy day?
6. Petrol enters the airstream through a carburettor in the form of a fine spray. Why?
7. Why does your hand feel very cold when you tip a little methylated spirit over it?

More about evaporation

When a liquid evaporates, it draws heat from everything it touches. A refrigerator uses the cooling effect of evaporation, so does the human body—but it's more difficult to keep the body cool on a muggy day.

The refrigerator

The cooling effect in many refrigerators is produced when a liquid called Freon evaporates. Freon is a very *volatile* liquid—it evaporates easily.

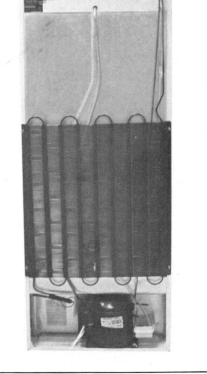

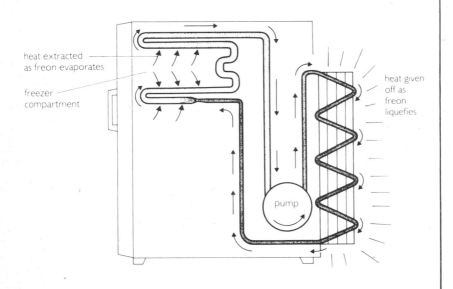

heat extracted as freon evaporates

freezer compartment

heat given off as freon liquefies

pump

The liquid Freon evaporates in the network of tubes in the freezer compartment. It does so as more and more Freon gas is drawn away by the electric pump. As the Freon evaporates, it draws the latent heat it needs from the food and the air next to the tubes—so everything in the freezer compartment cools down.

The pump compresses the Freon gas and forces it into the zig-zag pipe at the back of the refrigerator. Here the gas *condenses*—it changes back to liquid—and releases its latent heat. The unwanted heat is lost through the cooling fins around the pipe. The pipe feels hot if you touch it. The Freon, now liquid, is pumped round to the freezer tubes where it evaporates again.

Cooling the body

The human body produces a great deal of unwanted heat. It must get rid of this heat in order to stay at a steady temperature of about 37 °C. Much of the heat is lost by convection but some is lost as moisture on the skin evaporates. Moisture diffuses through the skin all the time. As it evaporates, it draws the latent heat it needs from the body which is cooled as a result.

Sweating   You start to sweat if your blood temperature rises more than about ½ °C above normal. The sweat is largely made up of water and it comes from *sweat glands* just under the surface of the skin. The sweat emerges through tiny holes in the skin called *pores*. As it evaporates, it takes heat away from the body.

Sweating also starts if the temperature outside your body rises above about 30 °C.

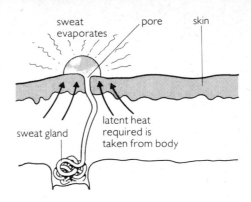

Humidity

When air is humid, it is heavily laden with water in gas form—the gas is called *water vapour*. Water evaporates slowly in humid air because molecules from the water vapour condense back into the water almost as fast as those in the water escape into the air.

Sweat tends to stay on your skin on humid or 'close' days. You feel hot and uncomfortable because the sweat cannot evaporate. A breeze helps to cool you because it aids evaporation.

Saturated air   Air is said to be *saturated* when it is holding the maximum possible amount of water vapour.

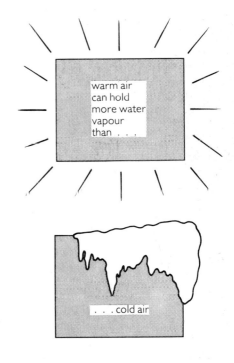

Warm air can hold more water vapour than cold air. If warm saturated air is cooled, some of its water vapour must condense back to liquid form. The water may appear as dew on the ground, or millions of tiny droplets in the air—we see these water droplets as mist or clouds.

Cold surfaces cool the air which touches them and water vapour may condense as a result. Condensation on cold windows and cold water pipes is caused in this way. When condensation freezes, it forms frost.

Questions
1. What do the tubes around the freezer compartment of a refrigerator contain? What makes these tubes so cold?
2. A refrigerator gives off heat energy. Where? *Why* is heat energy released?
3. When does the human body start to sweat? Where does the sweat come from?
4. Why do you lose heat when you sweat?
5. Why does a breeze help to keep you cool?
6. What is humid air?
7. Why does condensation form when warm, wet air is cooled?

6.9   **The four stroke petrol engine**

It converts the chemical energy in petrol into kinetic energy, it uses up valuable resources, but life wouldn't be the same without it.

The four-stroke cycle

The diagram below shows a single cylinder petrol engine in action. The crankshaft of the engine is pushed round every time the piston is forced down in the cylinder by the explosion of an air and petrol mixture. For each explosion that takes place there are four down and up movements of the piston—the engine moves through a *four-stroke cycle*:

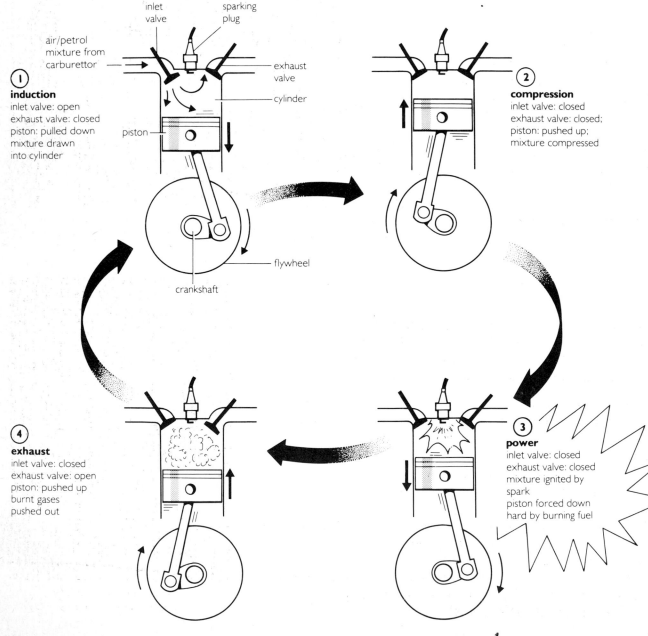

inlet valve

sparking plug

air/petrol mixture from carburettor

exhaust valve

cylinder

piston

crankshaft

flywheel

1 induction
inlet valve: open
exhaust valve: closed
piston: pulled down
mixture drawn
into cylinder

2 compression
inlet valve: closed
exhaust valve: closed;
piston: pushed up;
mixture compressed

4 exhaust
inlet valve: closed
exhaust valve: open
piston: pushed up
burnt gases
pushed out

3 power
inlet valve: closed
exhaust valve: closed
mixture ignited by
spark
piston forced down
hard by burning fuel

The carburettor supplies the cylinder with air and petrol mixed in the correct proportions for an explosion.

The sparking plug ignites the mixture with a high voltage spark produced by an *ignition coil*.

The flywheel gains enough kinetic energy during power strokes to keep the engine turning through the other strokes.

A system of chain wheels, shafts and levers opens each valve at the right time and makes the ignition coil produce its spark at the right moment.

Four cylinder engines Most car engines contain four cylinders with all the pistons turning the same crankshaft.

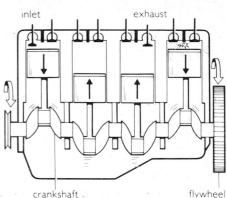

The sparks from the ignition coil are fed to each of the four sparking plugs in turn by a *distributor*. The timing of the sparks and the valve openings is arranged so that each cylinder is always on a different stroke from the others. In this way, there is always one cylinder on a power stroke and the crankshaft is pushed round more smoothly.

General view of the Austin Princess engine. The carburettor, spark plugs, and ignition coil are all visible.

Energy from petrol

When petrol burns in the cylinders of a car engine, energy is released as the exhaust gases are formed:

petrol + oxygen→carbon + some carbon + water + energy
               dioxide   monoxide   (steam) (heat)

Only about a quarter of the energy released from the petrol actually reaches the wheels of the car. Of the rest, some is used in turning the engine through the strokes which don't produce power, and some is used in overcoming friction.

All this wasted energy ends up as heat, and much of it has to be carried away by the cooling system surrounding the engine.

Questions

1. What does a carburettor do?
2. Why are engines fitted with flywheels?
3. Most car engines have four cylinders or more. Why?
4. Study the diagram of the 4-cylinder engine near the top of the page. Each cylinder is at the beginning of a stroke. Write down which stroke each is on.
5. During which stroke is energy released from the petrol? What happens to most of this energy? What exhaust gases are produced as the petrol burns?

A cut-away view of the same engine. How many of its components can you identify?

6.10 Machines

Pulleys, scissors and gearboxes are machines—so are human arms. You never get more work out of a machine than you put into it, but it does enable the work to be done more conveniently.

Levers

The lever shown below is a simple machine which makes it easier for the man to lift the load. The man's downward force, or *effort*, has twice as much turning effect on the lever as the load, so an effort of 40 newtons is all that is needed to lift the 80 newton load up off the ground.

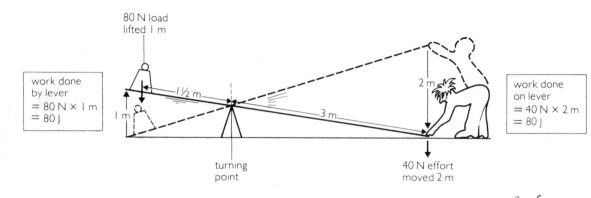

80 N load
lifted 1 m

work done
by lever
= 80 N × 1 m
= 80 J

1½ m

1 m

3 m

2 m

work done
on lever
= 40 N × 2 m
= 80 J

turning
point

40 N effort
moved 2 m

Mechanical advantage   Comparing the load moved with the effort required gives the *mechanical advantage* of a machine:

$$\text{Mechanical advantage of a machine} = \frac{\text{load}}{\text{effort}}$$

The lever shown above has a mechanical advantage of 2. The lever would have an even higher mechanical advantage if the load were nearer the turning point or the effort further away.

The wheelbarrow and the scissors on the right are both machines with a mechanical advantage greater than one—in other words, a large load is overcome with a small effort. But there is a price to pay for this gain in force: the effort has to move further than the load.

In the human arm, the load lifted at the end of the arm is much smaller than the effort produced by the muscle. The arm may lose in lifting ability but it gains in moving ability—only a small movement of the muscle is needed to move the end of the arm through a large distance.

Doing work   The work done by any force can be calculated by multiplying the force by the distance it moves. In the diagram above, the load is twice as large as the effort but it only moves half as far. As the calculations on the diagram show:

The work done by the lever = the work done on the lever

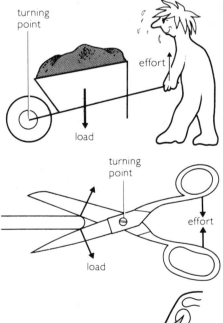

turning
point

effort

load

turning
point

effort

load

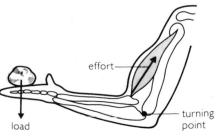

effort

load

turning
point

Pulleys

The pulley on the right is being used to lift up an engine—pulley wheels are usually mounted side by side in the pulley blocks but it is easier to draw them one above the other.

The mechanic pulls with an effort of 100 newtons to lift the 300 newton load: the pulley has a mechanical advantage of 3.

Velocity ratio   For the load to be lifted 1 metre, each of the numbered ropes has to shorten by 1 metre. Each rope is of course part of the one long rope, so the mechanic has to pull this rope down a total of 4 metres.

This means that the effort moves 4 times further than the load—the pulley has a *velocity ratio* of 4.

$$\text{Velocity ratio of a machine} = \frac{\text{distance moved by effort}}{\text{distance moved by load}}$$

Efficiency   Most machines waste energy because of friction, so more work has to be put into a machine than is got out. The *efficiency* of a machine can be worked out as follows:

$$\text{Efficiency} = \frac{\text{work done by a machine}}{\text{work done on a machine}}$$

The mechanic in the diagram does 400 joules of work on the pulley rope; the pulley only does 300 joules of work on the load. The pulley is ¾ efficient—only ¾ of the work done on the pulley is actually used to lift the load; the rest is wasted.

The efficiency of a machine can be worked out in another way:

$$\text{Efficiency} = \frac{\text{mechanical advantage}}{\text{velocity ratio}}$$

The pulley in the diagram has a mechanical advantage of 3 and a velocity ratio of 4—figures again giving an efficiency of ¾.

If a machine has an efficiency of 1, it does not waste any energy. Its mechanical advantage (comparing forces used) is equal to its velocity ratio (comparing distances moved).

Questions

1. How is the mechanical advantage of a machine calculated?
2. Name two machines with a mechanical advantage greater than 1.
3. Name a machine in which the effort is greater than the load.

The remaining questions refer to the pulley on the right:

4. If the load is to be lifted 1 metre, how far must the rope be pulled? What is the velocity ratio of the pulley?
5. The pulley has an efficiency of one. What does this mean?
6. What is the mechanical advantage of the pulley? What a load can the pulley lift with an effort of 50 newtons?

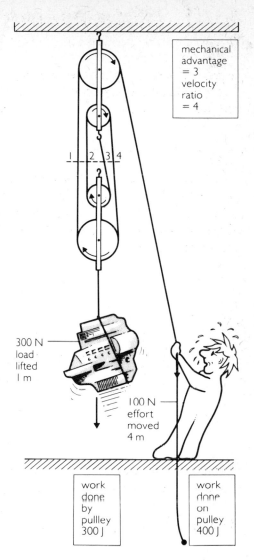

mechanical advantage = 3 velocity ratio = 4

1 2 3 4

300 N load lifted 1 m

100 N effort moved 4 m

work done by pullley 300 J

work done on pulley 400 J

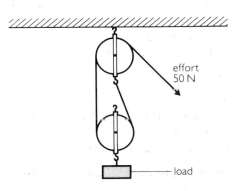

effort 50 N

load

6.11 The human engine

A petrol engine burns petrol, a human engine 'burns' food. Like other engines, the human body can do work when it releases the energy stored in its fuel.

Food fuels

Nearly all the energy obtained by the human body comes from three types of food—*carbohydrates*, *fats* and *proteins*.

Carbohydrates   These come from foods such as bread, flour and other cereals, sugar, and potatoes. They provide you with about 50% of your energy.

Carbohydrates are compounds of carbon, hydrogen and oxygen which break down when digested into substances like *glucose* (a simple sugar).

carbohydrate

Glucose is carried round the body in the bloodstream. Some is changed into *glycogen*, which is stored in the liver and muscles and can be converted back to glucose whenever its energy is needed. Energy is released when glucose is combined with oxygen in the cells of the body:

glucose + oxygen → carbon dioxide + water + energy

glucose

This is a process of slow combustion without the explosions and flames found in a petrol engine but it does provide the energy needed to move the muscles of the body. We breathe in air to get the oxygen needed for combustion, and we breathe out carbon dioxide and water vapour as our exhaust gases.

If the body takes in more carbohydrate than it needs to produce energy, the surplus is converted into body fat.

Fats   Main sources of fats are foods such as butter, meat, milk and margarine. The fats you eat supply you with about 40% of your energy.

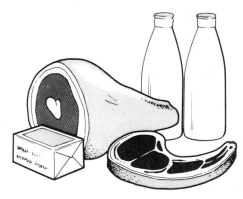

Like carbohydrates, fats are made up of carbon, hydrogen and oxygen and they release energy when combined with oxygen.

As the body can store fats, they act as a useful reserve supply of energy. Nonetheless, most doctors think that people would be less liable to heart and bowel disease if the amount of fat in their diet was reduced.

Proteins   Animals are largely made of substances called proteins, and plants are partly made of them.

The body needs protein for the growth and repair of body tissues but any spare protein is used as fuel.

You obtain most of your protein from foods such as bread, milk, eggs, cheese, meat, and fish.

Energy from food

The table on the right shows the amounts of energy that can be obtained from a number of different foods. Fats are the most concentrated source of energy.

Energy needs   The energy needs of average 16 year-olds are:

females – about 9 500 kilojoules (kJ) every day;
males – about 12 500 kilojoules (kJ) every day.
(1 kilojoule = 1000 joules)

If you are sixteen and female, 3 kilograms of boiled potatoes would probably provide you with all the energy you needed in one day—though they would not give you all the other essential nutrients necessary for good health.

Energy use   About half the energy you gain from your food is used to drive essential processes in the body—energy is needed for breathing, circulating blood and maintaining body temperature. The rest of the energy gained from food is needed so that your muscles can do work.

When you use up energy to move your muscles, only about 15% of it is converted into work. The other 85% is released as heat energy—which is why physical exercise makes you sweat.

energy stored in 100 grams of food (about ¼ lb)	
lard	3700 kilojoules
sugar	1600 kilojoules
corn flakes	1500 kilojoules
bread	1000 kilojoules
boiled potatoes	330 kilojoules
celery	35 kilojoules
(1 kilojoule = 1000 joules)	

Sources of food energy

All the food which you eat comes from plants, or animals which feed on plants.

Green plants use the Sun's energy to build up carbohydrates, fats and proteins from carbon dioxide, water, and minerals in the soil—the process is called *photosynthesis*.

The Sun is therefore the source of all energy stored in your food.

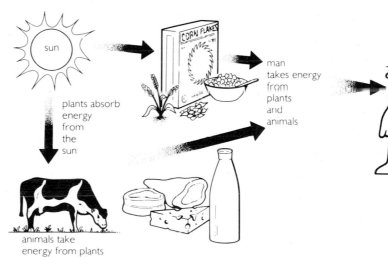

plants absorb energy from the sun

animals take energy from plants

man takes energy from plants and animals

Questions

1. Which types of food supply us with most of our energy?
2. What substance is formed when carbohydrates are digested? Where can the body store this substance and in what form?
3. Energy is released when glucose is combined with oxygen. What else is produced?
4. Which types of food are the most concentrated source of energy?
5. Which stores most energy—100 grams of cornflakes or 100 grams of lard?
7. Why do you sweat when you do physical work?
8. Where does all the energy in food originally come from?

What type of food is each of these?

Questions on Chapter 6

1 *metre, newton, joule, kilogram, watt*
From the above list, name:
    a a unit of mass
    b a unit of force
    c a unit of energy
    d a unit of weight

2 An object is moved from the Earth to the Moon. How does this affect:
    a its mass **b** its weight?

3 In the following cases state whether the friction between the surfaces is an advantage or a nuisance:
    a friction between a wheel and its shaft
    b friction between brake pads and the disc on a car wheel
    c friction between shoes and the ground
    d friction between the pistons and the cylinders in a car engine
    e friction between car tyres and the ground.

4 As its fuel burns, a rocket motor is pushed forwards by a high force. What causes this force?

5 Why is a rocket motor able to work in space but a jet engine not?

6 Why is it an advantage for buses and lorries to have as low a centre of gravity as possible?

7 How much work would you do in lifting a stone weighing 20N through a vertical distance of 2 m? What type of energy does the stone gain as it is being lifted up?
What happens to this energy if the stone is dropped?

8 Copy out and complete the following:
    a In an electric kettle, electrical energy is changed into . . . . energy
    b In a . . . . electrical energy is changed into sound energy
    c In a . . . ., chemical energy is changed into kinetic energy

9 The specific heat capacity of water is nearly five times as much as that of aluminium. What does this mean?

10 Write down three ways, other than by direct heating, in which a liquid can be made to evaporate more rapidly.

11 Once the water in an electric kettle begins to boil, the temperature stops rising. If the kettle is left switched on for a minute or so, what happens to all energy supplied?

12 You are likely to chill quickly if you stand out in the wind in wet clothes. Why?

13 How is the cooling effect produced in a refrigerator?

14 Why do you feel more uncomfortable on a humid day than on a dry day?

15 Copy and complete the table below to show the valve and piston movements in one cylinder of a four-stroke petrol engine.

Stroke	Inlet valve	Outlet valve	Piston
Induction Compression Power Exhaust			

ALSEB

16 The lever in the diagram is being used to lift a small load:

    a Copy the diagram, marking on the load, the effort and the turning point.
    b What downward force is needed (X) to lift the load?
    c What is the mechanical advantage of the lever?
    d What is its velocity ratio?
    e How could the mechanical advantage of the lever be made even greater?

17 Draw a diagram of a pulley system with a velocity ratio of 2.

18 Copy out and complete the following passage:
In a petrol engine, energy is released when . . . . is combined with oxygen. In the human body, energy is released when food is combined with . . . . Both processes produce unwanted . . . . and . . . . These substances are released into the atmosphere.

Chapter 7

Density
and Pressure

Some things float and some things don't.
What makes the difference?

Ignore the man in the photo. He's breaking
the rules!

7.1 Density

Which weighs more, a tonne of coal or a tonne of feathers? Which weighs more, a cubic metre of coal or a cubic metre of feathers?

Everybody knows that feathers are 'lighter' than coal . . . but are they?

The pile of feathers in the rather unlikely experiment on the right is just as heavy as the pile of coal.

The feathers are of course taking up far more space than the coal—they have a larger volume. A fairer test might be to compare *equal volumes* of coal and feathers.

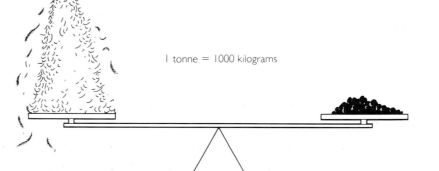

1 tonne = 1000 kilograms

Density

All the substances shown in the chart below have the same volume. Each box has a volume of 1 cubic metre and the mass of material that fills it is marked in kilograms (kg).

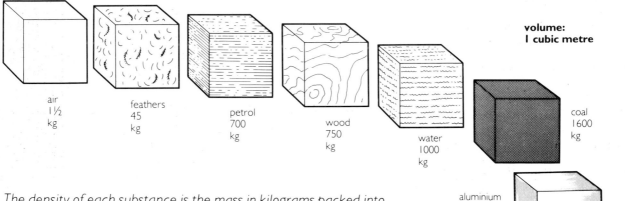

air
1½ kg

feathers
45 kg

petrol
700 kg

wood
750 kg

water
1000 kg

volume:
1 cubic metre

coal
1600 kg

aluminium
2700 kg

steel
7800 kg

lead
11300 kg

The density of each substance is the mass in kilograms packed into each cubic metre. It is measured in *kilograms per cubic metre*—sometimes written kg/m³ for short.

Some examples from the chart:
The density of lead   11 300 kilograms per cubic metre.
The density of coal   1600 kilograms per cubic metre.
The density of water   1000 kilograms per cubic metre.
The density of the feathers   45 kilograms per cubic metre.

So feathers are not 'lighter' than coal, they are *less dense.*

Other density units Density values are sometimes given in grams per cubic centimetre (g/cm³). Water for example has a density of one gram per cubic centimetre—one cubic centimetre of water has a mass of one gram.

Measuring density

Unfortunately, materials are not usually found in exact cubic metre chunks. Densities have to be measured using more awkward shapes and volumes.

The density of a substance can be worked out once the mass and volume are known:

If 6 cubic metres of water have a mass of 6000 kilograms,
1 cubic metre of water has a mass of 1000 kilograms.
The density of the water is 1000 kilograms per cubic metre—the figure is worked out by dividing the number of kilograms by the number of cubic metres. So:

$$\text{Density} = \frac{\text{mass}}{\text{volume}}$$

Measuring mass The mass of a substance can be found using a mass balance or a set of scales marked in kilograms (or grams).

Measuring volume The volume of a liquid can be found by pouring the liquid into a measuring cylinder and reading the level on the scale.

The volume of a small solid can be found by lowering the solid into a measuring cylinder partly filled with a liquid such as water. When the solid is fully immersed, the rise in liquid level on the scale gives the volume of the solid.

If the solid is in the shape of a simple block with square corners, its volume can be calculated:

$$\text{Volume} = \text{length} \times \text{width} \times \text{depth}$$

Relative density

Sulphur has a density of 2000 kg per cubic metre; water has a density of 1000 kg per cubic metre. Sulphur is therefore twice as dense as water—it has a relative density of 2.

$$\frac{\text{Relative density}}{\text{of a substance}} = \frac{\text{density of substance}}{\text{density of water}}$$

Water itself has a relative density of 1.

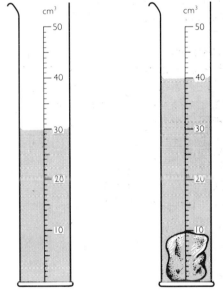

scale marked in
cubic centimetres

Questions

1. What does the density tell you about a substance?
2. Write down the densities of the following substances: lead, coal, air, petrol, aluminium, water, steel.
3. What is the volume of the liquid in the measuring cylinder on this page? What is the volume of the small solid placed in it?
4. Sulphur has a relative density of 2. What does this mean?
5. In the diagram on the right, which substance has the greatest mass—A, B, C or D? Which has the greatest volume? Work out the density of each substance. Use the chart on the opposite page to help you decide which substance each might be.

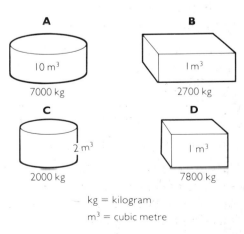

A
10 m³
7000 kg

B
1 m³
2700 kg

C
2 m³
2000 kg

D
1 m³
7800 kg

kg = kilogram
m³ = cubic metre

7.2 Pressure

Some forces are much more concentrated than others . . . . .

Pressure

Push a drawing pin into a piece of wood and the force on the wood is concentrated onto a small area. Push on the wood with your finger and the same force is spread over a much larger area.

The word *pressure* describes how concentrated a force is—the more concentrated a force, the higher the pressure.

Under the tip of the drawing pin the pressure is very high because the force acts on a very small area.

Under the finger the pressure is much lower because the force is spread over a much larger area.

Calculating pressure To scientists, pressure has a very exact meaning—it is the force in newtons that would act if the pressure was exerted over one square metre of a surface.

Surfaces do not usually have an area of exactly one square metre but pressures can be calculated using the equation:

$$\text{Pressure} = \frac{\text{force}}{\text{area}}$$

E.g. A 12 newton force pushing on an area of 2 square metres produces a pressure of 6 newtons per square metre (6 N/m²).

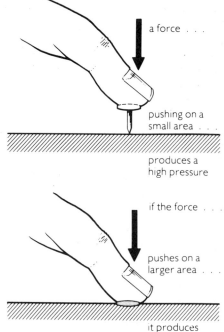

a force . . .

pushing on a small area . . .

produces a high pressure

if the force . . .

pushes on a larger area . . .

it produces a lower pressure

Pressure in liquids

The force of gravity tries to pull a liquid downwards in its container. This causes pressure on the container and pressure on any object put into the liquid.

Pressure increases with depth

The deeper the liquid the greater the weight of liquid pushing on the bottom of the container. Dams are thicker at the base than at the top because they have to withstand a much higher pressure from the water at the bottom of a lake.

pressure increases with depth

pressure acts in all directions

Pressure acts in all directions A liquid under pressure pushes on every surface in contact with it no matter which way the surface is facing.

Pressure depends on the density of the liquid Petrol is less dense than water. If petrol filled the lake instead of water the pressure at all points in the lake would be less.

The pressure does not depend on the width of the container
The pressure at the bottom of each glass due to the weight of the liquid is exactly the same for each of them. The wider mug does have a greater *weight* of beer to support but the downward force from the beer is spread over a larger area.

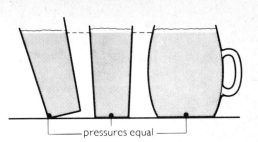
pressures equal

Hydraulics

Hydraulic machines make use of liquids under pressure rather than levers and wheels. Liquids have two important properties which make such machines possible:

1. Liquids cannot be squashed—they are virtually incompressible.
2. Press on a trapped liquid and the pressure is felt right through the liquid.

Car brakes are operated hydraulically, so too are some car jacks.

The hydraulic jack   The diagram below shows a simple working model of a hydraulic jack:

The idea behind the jack looks simple enough—if you push the smaller piston down, the oil is pushed through the pipe and the larger piston is forced upwards.

But the system has another important feature. A small downward force from your thumb is all that is needed to make the heavy brick move upwards.

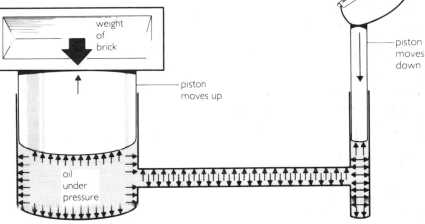

weight of brick

piston moves up

oil under pressure

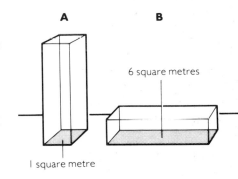

piston moves down

When the smaller piston is pushed down it puts the oil under high pressure since the force is only being applied to a very small area. High pressure oil pushing on the much larger area of the other piston produces a large upward force—the force is strong enough to overcome the weight of the brick so the brick is pushed upwards.

The upward *force* on the larger piston may be large but the upward *movement* is not. The smaller piston has to be pushed down a long way to lift the brick even a short distance.

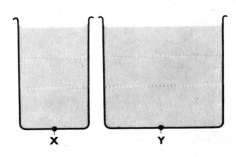

A   B

6 square metres

1 square metre

Questions

1. In the diagram on the right both blocks weigh 12 newtons. Which block exerts most pressure on the ground? Why? Calculate the pressure under each block.
2. Why are dams thicker at the base than at the top?
3. The two cans on the right are filled with petrol. How does the pressure at X compare with the pressure at Y? If the petrol were replaced by water, how would this affect the pressures at X and Y?
4. What two properties of a liquid are used in a hydraulic jack?

X   Y

7.3 Floating and sinking

A steel boat floats in water, yet a lump of steel sinks. What makes things float? Why do some things float but not others?

Upthrust
A boat is kept afloat by an upward force from the water. The force is called an *upthrust* and it is caused by the pressure of the water pressing on the bottom of the boat.

Archimedes' Principle The boat in the diagram takes up space previously filled with water—the boat has displaced water. Experiments show that:

the upthrust on the boat = the weight of water displaced

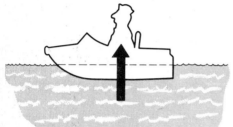

the upthrust on a boat is 9000 newtons   if the boat displaces water weighing 9000 newtons

This principle was discovered by Archimedes more than 2000 years ago. It applies to all objects in any liquid or gas, whether the objects are floating or not.

Floating
When a boat is first lowered into the water, the upthrust on it rises as more and more water is displaced. The boat stops sinking down into the water when the upthrust is just large enough to support the weight of the boat. When the boat is floating:
The upthrust on the boat = The weight of the boat

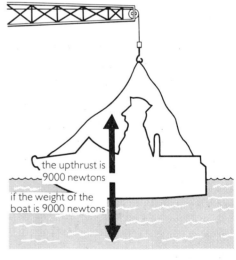

the upthrust is 9000 newtons

if the weight of the boat is 9000 newtons

The Law of Floating   If you study the forces in the diagrams above and on the right, you will see that:

the weight of the boat = the weight of water displaced

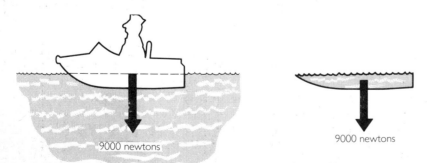

9000 newtons

9000 newtons

This principle applies to all objects floating in any liquid or gas and it is known as the *Law of Floating*.

Levels of floating

Two factors affect how low in the water a boat will float:

The weight of the boat and its load   If a boat carries a heavy load, more upthrust is needed to support the extra weight. The boat displaces more water by floating lower down in the water. If the load is too heavy, the upthrust cannot support the weight and the boat sinks.

The density of the water   Freshwater in a river is less dense than the salt water in the sea, and warm water is less dense than cold water—when water expands, its mass is more spread out.

This means that a boat must float lower in less dense water in order to displace the same weight of water. A boat floats lower in freshwater than it does in salt water, and a boat floats lower in warm water than it does in cold water.

To avoid the problem shown in the diagram, ships have a series of maximum loading levels ('Plimsoll' lines) marked on their sides to suit the different types of water in which they float.

The hydrometer

A hydrometer is a small float used for measuring the relative densities of liquids. Like a boat, a hydrometer floats lower in liquids of lesser density.

The stem of a hydrometer has a scale marked on it. The relative density of a liquid is found by reading the scale at the point where the liquid surface touches it.

The density of floating materials

You can tell whether a material will float or sink in a liquid by comparing its density with that of the liquid.

Ice is less dense than water—ice floats in water.
Warm water is less dense than cold water—warm water floats upwards through cold water.
Tar has the same density as water—tar just floats in water. Steel is more dense than water—steel sinks in water.

A steel ship floats in water because it is hollow—its average density is less than that of the water.

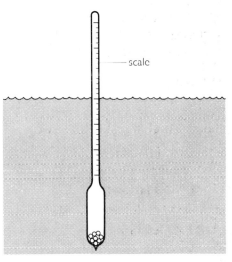

scale

Questions

1. What causes the upthrust on a boat?
2. A floating boat displaces water weighing 6000 newtons. What is the upthrust on the boat? What is the weight of the boat?
3. A girl climbs aboard a floating boat. What happens to the boat? What happens to the weight of water displaced? What happens to the upthrust on the boat?
4. Why does a boat float lower in freshwater than in salt water?
5. What is a hydrometer? What does it measure?
6. Steel sinks in water, yet a steel boat floats. Why?

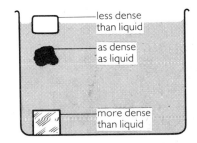

less dense than liquid

as dense as liquid

more dense than liquid

7.4 Pressure from the atmosphere

We live at the bottom of a deep ocean of air called the atmosphere. The air around us is at very high pressure—without this pressure you couldn't even make a decent cup of tea.

Atmospheric pressure

In some ways, the atmosphere is like a liquid—its pressure acts in all directions and its pressure gets less as you rise up through it. Unlike a liquid however, the atmosphere is much more dense at lower levels—the atmosphere stretches hundreds of kilometres into space yet most of the air lies within about ten kilometres of the Earth's surface.

Atmospheric pressure at sea level Down at sea level, the air pressure is about 100 000 newtons per square metre— that's equivalent to the weight of ten cars pressing on each square metre.

We do not normally feel the effect of this crushing pressure. Like the undamaged oil can below, we have high pressure air inside us as well as outside:

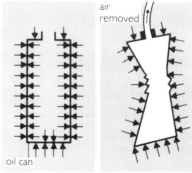

When the can is full of air, the air pressure inside the can balances the air pressure outside.

Remove the air in the can with a vacuum pump, and the sides of the can are pushed in by the pressure of the atmosphere.

Measuring atmospheric pressure

Instruments which measure atmospheric pressure are called *barometers*.

A simple barometer can be made by filling a long glass tube, sealed at one end, with a very dense liquid metal called mercury. The tube is put open end downwards into a dish of mercury and the level of the mercury in the tube starts to fall. The level stops falling when the pressure from the mercury left in the tube is balanced by the pressure of the atmosphere acting on the mercury in the dish. Atmospheric pressure is found by measuring the height of the mercury column on the scale—the result is usually expressed in 'millimetres of mercury'.

At sea level, atmospheric pressure is about 760 millimetres of mercury, though this varies slightly according to weather conditions. Rain clouds form in large areas of lower pressure air called depressions, so a fall in the barometer reading often means that bad weather is on the way.

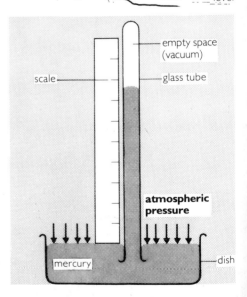

Using atmospheric pressure

The pressure of the atmosphere can be used in a variety of ways. Here are just two examples:

Rubber suckers   Push a rubber sucker against a piece of glass and you squeeze out most of the air from under the sucker. Try to pull the sucker away from the glass and the pressure of the trapped air drops as the air spreads to fill a larger space. With high pressure air outside it and low pressure air underneath it, the sucker is held firmly against the glass.

Drinking straws   When you 'suck' on a straw, you lower the air pressure in the straw by expanding your lungs.

Atmospheric pressure pressing down on the drink pushes the liquid up the straw and into your mouth.

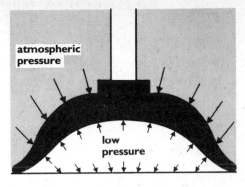

Atmospheric pressure and boiling

At sea level, water boils at about 100 °C. At the top of Mount Everest, water boils at only 70 °C. It becomes impossible to make a good cup of tea! The lower boiling temperature is a result of the lower atmospheric pressure at the top of the mountain.

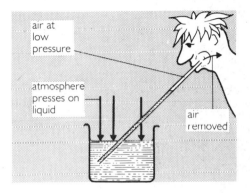

If you watch water being heated, you can see small bubbles forming as the liquid starts changing into a gas. The pressure of the atmosphere on the water stops these bubbles growing in size, but the pressure in the bubbles grows stronger as the water gets hotter.

The water boils when the pressure in the gas bubbles is high enough to overcome atmospheric pressure. The gas bubbles grow rapidly and erupt on the surface of the water. If atmospheric pressure is low, the gas bubbles do not need to be so hot for this to happen—the water boils at a lower temperature.

Questions

1. Moving up through the atmosphere, what happens to:
   a) the pressure of the air   b) the density of the air?
2. Why does an old oil can not normally collapse under the pressure of the atmosphere? What would make the can collapse?
3. What instrument is used to measure atmospheric pressure?
4. Give the approximate pressure of the atmosphere at sea level in
   a) newtons per square metre   b) millimetres of mercury
5. Why is it difficult to pull a rubber sucker away from a window?
6. What happens to the boiling temperature of water if atmospheric pressure falls?

7.5 Pumps and gauges

Pumps are used to move liquids and gases, gauges are used to measure their pressures. This section looks at a few of the more common examples of pumps and gauges.

Pumps

The force pump   The hand pump used to squirt water onto a car windscreen is known as a *force pump*. It contains a *piston* which is a water-tight fit in a *cylinder*, and two *valves*. Each valve allows water to flow through in one direction only. Flowing in one direction, the water opens the valve by pushing the ball bearing out of the gap. If water starts to flow in the opposite direction, the valve closes—the ball bearing is pushed into the gap and the flow is stopped.

The pump is worked by moving the piston outwards and inwards over and over again:

When the piston is pulled outwards, the outlet valve closes, the inlet valve opens, and atmospheric pressure forces water from the bottle up into the cylinder.

When the piston is pushed inwards, the inlet valve closes, the outlet valve opens, and water is forced out of the cylinder and up to the windscreen.

plunger pushed in and out

ball bearing   outlet valve

piston   cylinder

inlet valve

water

bottle

The bicycle pump   The bicycle pump works in a similar way to the pump described above. The valve fitted to the tyre acts as the outlet valve. The cup-shaped washer acts both as a piston and as an inlet valve.

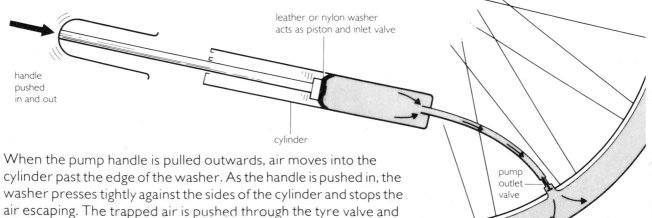

leather or nylon washer acts as piston and inlet valve

handle pushed in and out

cylinder

pump outlet valve

When the pump handle is pulled outwards, air moves into the cylinder past the edge of the washer. As the handle is pushed in, the washer presses tightly against the sides of the cylinder and stops the air escaping. The trapped air is pushed through the tyre valve and into the tyre.

Pressure gauges

The manometer   The pressure of a gas or liquid can be measured using a manometer like the one shown in the diagram.

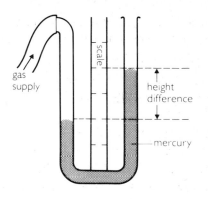

One end of the manometer tube is open to the atmosphere. To measure the pressure of the gas supply in a laboratory, the other end of the manometer tube would be connected to a gas tap with a piece of rubber tubing. When the gas tap is turned on, the gas pressure pushes the mercury round the tube and the mercury levels become different as in the diagram.

The height difference indicates how much higher the gas pressure is than atmospheric pressure. The pressure difference is often measured in 'millimetres of mercury' though the scale can be marked in 'newtons per square metre'.

The aneroid barometer   This instrument measures the pressure of the atmosphere. It is more portable than a mercury barometer and its dial scale makes it easier to read.

The main feature of the aneroid barometer is the small sealed metal box containing air at low pressure. Atmospheric pressure tries to squash this box—the box is corrugated to make it more flexible in the middle.

If the atmospheric pressure rises, the top and bottom of the box become even more squashed in. The movement of the box is magnified by a lever: the lever pulls a chain which moves the pointer further across the scale.

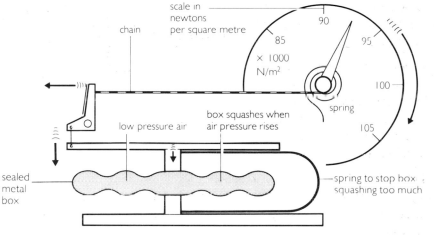

Questions
1. A force pump contains two valves. What does a valve do?
2. When does the inlet valve in a force pump open? When does the outlet valve open?
3. Where is the inlet valve in a bicycle pump? Where is the outlet valve?
4. What is the instrument on the right called? What is the pressure reading on it in millimetres of mercury?
5. What advantages does an aneroid barometer have over a mercury barometer? Why does the pointer on an aneroid barometer move when atmospheric pressure rises?

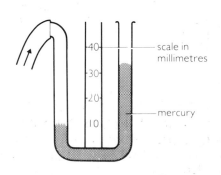

Questions on Chapter 7

1 Lead is more dense than aluminium. What does this mean?

2 How would you measure the volume of a rubber bung?

3 Petrol has a density of 700 kg/m³. What is the mass of 3 cubic metres of petrol?

4 a What volume of air is there in a room 5 metres long, 5 metres wide, and 2 metres high?
b If the density of air is 1.5 kg/m³, what is the mass of the air in the room?

5 When you press a drawing pin into wood, why is the pressure on the wood very much greater than the pressure from your thumb?

6 Draw a diagram of a simple hydraulic jack. Why is the area of the piston lifting the load much larger than the area of the piston moved by the effort?

7 a What is the instrument in the diagram called?
b If 1 millimetre in the diagram represents 1 centimetre on the actual apparatus, what is the pressure of the atmosphere in centimetres of mercury?
c In what way would the reading change if the instrument were taken up a mountain?

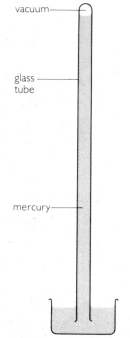

8 The pressure inside a pressure cooker is higher than the air pressure outside. How does this affect the boiling point of the water in the pressure cooker?

9 Describe two ways in which the pressure of the atmosphere can be put to practical use.

10 Draw a diagram of the instrument you would use to measure the pressure of the gas supply in a laboratory. What is the instrument called?

11 The force pump in the diagram below is being used to pump water from tank A to tank B.

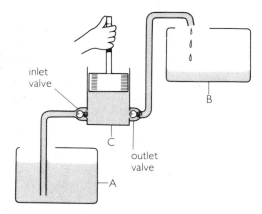

Copy and complete the following table to show the action of the pump:

Stroke	Inlet valve *open or shut?*	Outlet valve *open or shut?*	Movement of water
Piston pulled upwards			Water moves from ...... to ......
Piston pushed downwards			Water moves from ...... to ......

12 Copy and complete the following:
a Lead sinks in water because it has a greater .... then water.
b Ice floats because ....
c There is an upward force on any object placed in a liquid. The force is called an .... and it is equal to ....
d When an object floats, the weight of the object is equal to ....
e A hydrometer floats lower in petrol than in water because ....
f An object which just floats in fresh water will .... in salt water.

116

Chapter 8

Plants and Animals

What's the difference between animals and plants?
What are they both made from?

8.1 Living organisms

Animals and plants are living organisms. They are alike in many ways but there are differences in the substances they contain and the ways in which they get their food. Food supplies animals and plants with the energy they need to live.

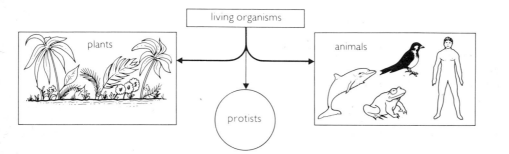

protists are simple organisms which are difficult to class as either animals or plants

Similarities between animals and plants

The following are features of all living things:

Feeding   Animals take in food. Plants take in materials to make their food.

Respiration   Animals and plants need energy to move, to grow and to maintain life. Usually, they get the energy they need by combining their food with oxygen.

Excretion   Animals and plants produce waste materials which they must get rid of in some way. Human beings do so in breathing out, sweating, and using the lavatory.

Growth   Animals and plants may grow bigger. They may also grow more complicated in their structure.

Movement   Animals and plants are able to move, though animals usually make more obvious movements than plants.

Reproduction   Animals and plants can produce others of their own kind. Human beings have children, a simple organism may just split into two. Life goes on even though individuals die.

Sensitivity   Living things react to the outside world. A plant may search for water or light, an animal may seek warmth. Animals usually respond to a stimulus much more quickly than plants.

Differences between animals and plants

Animals and plants differ in many ways. These differences include:

Cellulose   Plants are partly built from a substance called cellulose. Animals do not use cellulose for body-building.

Chlorophyll   Most plants contain a green substance called chlorophyll. Plants use chlorophyll to absorb energy from sunlight.

Eating sunshine, or eating plants?

Green plants make their own food from carbon dioxide, water and other simple materials. They can only do this by using energy from sunlight to turn these substances into new plant tissue and food for storage. The process is called *photosynthesis* and oxygen is "breathed out" from plants as it takes place.

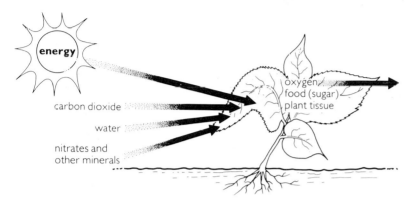

Animals cannot obtain energy directly from sunlight. They take in food which has been made and stored in plants. Some animals feed directly on green plants, others feed on animals which eat green plants.

Energy for living

Like plants, animals get the energy they need by combining their food with oxygen during a process called *respiration*. They breathe in oxygen so that respiration can take place in the tiny cells which make up their bodies. As it takes place carbon dioxide and water are formed.

How many "signs of life" can you spot in this quiet rural scene?

Questions

1. What are the seven features common to all living things?
2. What substance makes plants green? How do plants use it? What other substance is found in plants but not animals?
3. What substances do plants take in to make their food? Where does the energy come from to make the food? What is the process called? What gas does it produce?
4. What is respiration? Where does it take place?
5. Energy is released during respiration. What else is produced?
6. What gases do you breathe in and out?

8.2 Living cells

All animals and plants are made up of tiny living units called cells. These cells come in many different shapes, sizes and types. Within them all the basic chemistry of living and growing takes place.

Cell structure: animals

Most cells are so small that many thousands would fit on the head of a pin. Not all cells are so small—a chicken's egg is one single cell.

A thin skin called a *membrane* surrounds each cell. Within it are the jelly-like *cytoplasm* and *nucleus*.

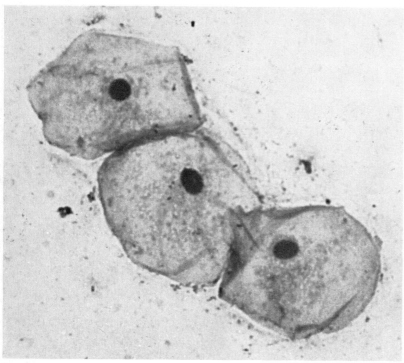

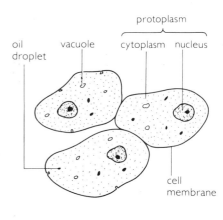

Typical animal cells. The photograph shows cells from the lining of the cheek.

Cell membrane   This thin skin controls the flow of all the substances which pass in and out of the cell.

Cytoplasm   This is the chemical factory of the cell. Here, new substances are built up from materials taken into the cell and energy is released and stored. Sometimes the cytoplasm contains tiny droplets of liquid—these are known as *vacuoles*.

Nucleus   The nucleus controls all the chemical reactions that take place in the cell. Thread-like *chromosomes* in the nucleus store the chemical instructions used to build the cell.

All the living matter in a cell is known as *protoplasm*.

Cell structure: plants

Plant cells also have a *cell membrane*, *cytoplasm* and *nucleus* but they differ from animal cells in several ways.

Cell wall   Plant cells are surrounded by a firm wall of *cellulose*. Cell walls hold plant cells together and give plants much of their strength.

Chloroplasts   Many plant cells contain tiny structures called *chloroplasts*. Within them is the green substance called *chlorophyll* which absorbs energy from sunlight.

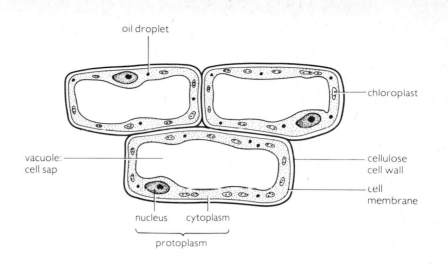

Cell-sap   Plant cells contain a large central droplet of watery liquid (a *vacuole*) called *cell-sap*. Osmotic pressure from this liquid pushes on the outer parts of the cell keeping the cell firm or *turgid*.

Cell specialization

Advanced organisms (like you and me) are built up from many billions of cells. Different groups of cells have different jobs to do—the cells are *specialized*. For example, one group of cells form muscle to move the body; another group will be concerned with reproduction.

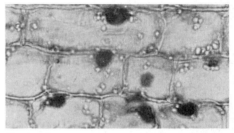

Plant cells.

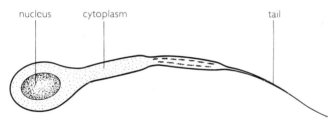

Sperm cell.

Groups of similar cells form *tissue*. Tissues grouped together to do one particular job form an *organ*. Muscles are organs, so are eyes and lungs.

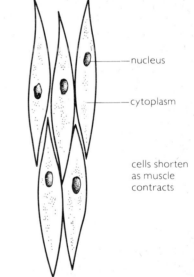

Muscle cells.

Questions

1. What controls the flow of substances in and out of a cell?
2. Which part of a cell controls all chemical reactions taking place in the cell?
3. Where do the main chemical reactions in a cell take place?
4. How is the outside of a plant cell different from that of an animal cell?
5. What do chloroplasts contain? Why?
6. What do the large liquid droplets in a plant cell contain? What are they called?
7. What is tissue? What is the name given to a group of tissues which do one particular job?

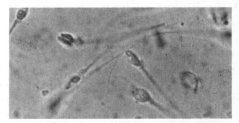

Human sperm cells, enlarged 1500 times.

8.3 Cells and more cells

The amoeba is a tiny single-celled creature which reproduces by dividing to form two new cells. Advanced plants and animals reproduce by joining together a male and female cell to form a single new cell. By dividing over and over again, in different ways, the single cell becomes the many different types of cell needed to make up the new plant or animal. This incredible dividing process is controlled by chromosomes in the nucleus of each cell.

The amoeba

The single-celled amoeba lives in ponds and damp soil and feeds on microscopic plants. It grows bulges around small pieces of food which it then takes into its cytoplasm in the form of small liquid droplets (vacuoles). Digested food is absorbed into the cytoplasm. Undigested waste is left behind as the amoeba 'flows' on its way.

Binary fission   The amoeba reproduces itself by a process called *binary fission*. The nucleus of the cell divides in two and the cytoplasm then separates to form two new cells. These *daughter* cells are copies of the original *parent* cell.

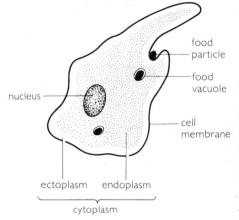

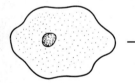 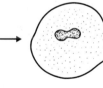 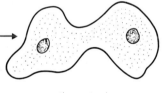 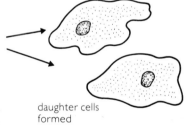

parent cell   nucleus divides ...   ... then cytoplasm   daughter cells formed

Reproduction in cells

Asexual reproduction   Like the amoeba, many organisms reproduce by dividing to form new organisms. Reproduction of this kind is described as *asexual*.

A tulip reproduces asexually when new bulbs grow on the side of the original bulb and then separate from it.

Sexual reproduction   A new human life starts when a *sperm cell* from a man combines with an *egg cell* in a woman to form a single new cell called a *zygote*. This new cell divides over and over again to form the billions of cells in a baby's body. The body has many different parts—every "daughter" cell does not end up an exact copy of its parent cell.

This process is called *sexual reproduction* and it is used by the more advanced plants and animals. Many common plants can reproduce both sexually and asexually.

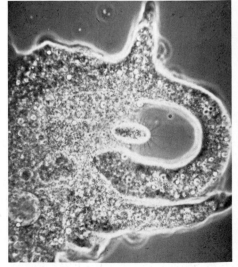

This amoeba has just finished bulging round its prey, taking in some liquid with it.

Chromosomes: building new cells

Cells are made up of molecules, some of which contain many thousands of atoms. Cells build new molecules by rearranging the atoms of incoming material.

The chemical building instructions are stored in each nucleus in coded form by molecules of deoxyribonucleic acid (*DNA*). These DNA molecules can produce exact copies of themselves, so their building instructions can be passed on to any new cells that form.

DNA is stored in the nucleus of a cell in structures called *chromosomes*. Our own cells each contain 46 chromosomes which between them store the chemical instructions for building the complete human body.

Mitosis   Before a cell divides, copies of each chromosome form alongside the originals and then separate from them. As the cell divides, a full set of chromosomes collects at each end to form part of two new nuclei. The process is called *mitosis:* it ensures that full chemical building instructions are passed on to the new cells.

Human cells are built mainly from:

oxygen, carbon and hydrogen

with some

nitrogen, calcium, phosphorus, potassium, sulphur, sodium, chlorine

and traces of

iron, iodine, copper, zinc cobalt, magnesium and manganese.

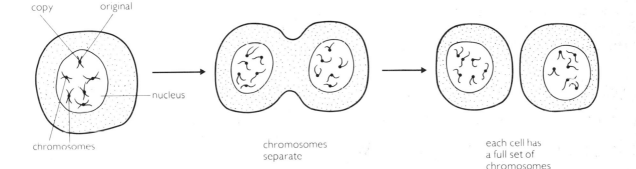

copy   original

nucleus

chromosomes

chromosomes separate

each cell has a full set of chromosomes

Meiosis   The cells that go to form reproductive tissue—sperm in males, and eggs in females—split so as to have only 23 chromosomes each. This type of splitting is called *meiosis.* In the original cell from which you grew, called the *zygote*, 23 chromosomes come from your father, and 23 from your mother. With luck, you inherited both your father's good looks and your mother's intelligence.

Questions

1. How does an amoeba take in and then store its food?
2. The cytoplasm of an amoeba is divided into two regions: what are they called?
3. How does an amoeba reproduce itself? What is the process called?
4. What 3 types of atom are human cells mainly built from?
5. What structures in the nucleus of a cell store its chemical building instructions? What happens to these structures before a cell divides? What substance carries the instructions in coded form?

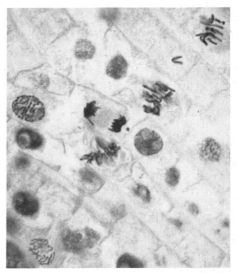

This photo is of the very tip of an onion root. The cells are dividing by mitosis.

8.4 Green plants: making and using food

Like other living things, green plants need food in order to live and grow. They take in simple materials from the soil and the atmosphere and turn these into food by using the energy in sunlight.

Transpiration and photosynthesis

Transpiration   Large amounts of water evaporate from the leaves of a plant though the leaf cells do have some control over the rate at which water is lost. This loss of water by evaporation is known as *transpiration* and it draws new water and vital minerals from the soil, up through the plant, to the leaves.

The upward flow of water through a plant is called a *transpiration stream*. In a large tree the flow of water may be more than 100 litres every day.

Although most of this water evaporates, some is kept in the plant and used in the food-making process called *photosynthesis*.

light energy

water evaporates (transpiration)

photosynthesis

oxygen

carbon dioxide

food to storage areas and growing points

stem

transpiration stream

water

root

water and minerals from soil

Photosynthesis   This is the process by which energy from sunlight is used to turn simple materials into food. It mainly takes place in the leaves of green plants.

The leaves draw water from the transpiration stream and carbon dioxide gas from the atmosphere—the gas is taken in through tiny pores called *stomata*.

Chlorophyll in the leaves absorbs energy from sunlight and cells use this energy to turn the carbon dioxide and water into foods such as sugar:

carbon dioxide + water + energy → food (sugar) + oxygen

Oxygen released by this chemical reaction passes out into the atmosphere through the tiny pores in the leaves.

One of the simplest foods made by plants is a type of sugar called *glucose*. Chains of glucose molecules form the tough substance called *cellulose* of which plants are largely made.

Stored food   Much of the food made in a leaf is carried away in solution to other parts of the plant. Some goes to points of new growth where it is used in building the plant—some goes to storage areas in the roots, stem or leaves. Stored food can later be used as a source of energy.

Energy from food: respiration

Plants need energy to drive all the chemical reactions which enable them to live and grow. *Respiration* is the process by which plants release energy from their food:

food + oxygen → carbon dioxide + water + energy

Respiration takes place all the time, so plants need a steady supply of oxygen.

During daylight hours, plants produce more oxygen by photosynthesis than they can use. They therefore give out oxygen into the atmosphere.

Photosynthesis stops at night—plants must then draw the oxygen they need for respiration from the atmosphere.

Overall, plants produce more oxygen than they can use. Animals use up this oxygen, so the amount of oxygen in the atmosphere remains steady.

Testing for starch

During the daytime, photosynthesis may produce sugar at a faster rate than it can be used or carried away from the leaf. Many plants convert this extra sugar into *starch* which is temporarily stored in their leaves. The diagram shows a simple test you can perform on a leaf to find out whether or not starch is present.

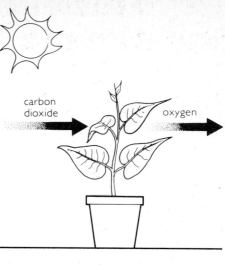

carbon dioxide   oxygen

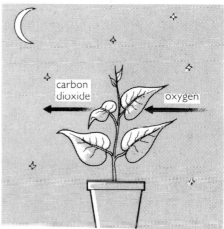

carbon dioxide   oxygen

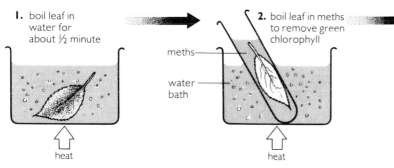

1. boil leaf in water for about ½ minute

heat

2. boil leaf in meths to remove green chlorophyll

meths

water bath

heat

3. dip leaf in boiling water to soften it

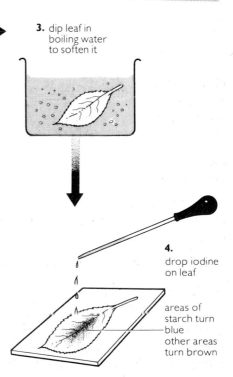

4. drop iodine on leaf

areas of starch turn blue
other areas turn brown

Questions

1. By what process is water drawn up through a green plant?
2. Where in a plant does food-making mainly take place? Why does it only take place during daylight hours?
3. What happens to the food made in a plant?
4. Why do plants need energy?
5. What gas do plants need to release the energy from their food?
6. When does a green plant give out oxygen?
7. When does a green plant take in oxygen?
8. Why does the oxygen in the atmosphere remain steady?
9. Why may starch build up in a leaf during the daytime?

8.5 Flowering plants: structure and growth

Plants have a structure which enables them to work as efficient food makers. The food supplies the plant with energy—it also supplies it with the materials it needs in order to grow.

Structure of a flowering plant

A typical flowering plant has a *root* in the ground and a stem which supports leaves, buds and flowers. The upward growing stem with its leaves, buds and flowers is known as a *shoot*.

Leaf   Leaves are the "food factories" of a plant. They are supplied with simple materials from the atmosphere and the soil. They use the energy in sunlight to turn these materials into food.

The upper surface of a leaf is often covered with a waxy layer called *cuticle* which stops the leaf losing too much water by evaporation. Just under this layer are the food-making cells which absorb energy from sunlight.

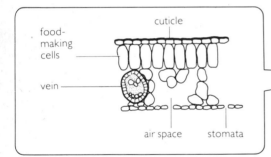

The food-making cells get their supply of carbon dioxide through tiny pores *(stomata)* which are mainly on the underside of the leaf. Both oxygen and evaporating water leave the leaf through the same pores.

A system of narrow tubes brings water and minerals to the food-making cells and takes dissolved food away. The tubes are bunched together to form *veins*—each leaf contains a network of veins which meet to form a *main vein* through the centre of the leaf.

Stem   The stem supports and spaces out the leaves so that they can receive as much light as possible. Food-tubes and water-tubes run through the stem. They connect the food- and water-tubes in the leaves with those in the roots.

Roots   Roots fix a plant firmly in the soil. They take in water and minerals from the soil through tiny tubes called *root hairs*. In many plants, the roots act as a store for much of the food made in the leaves.

New growth

Some of the materials made and stored in a plant are carried through the food-tubes to points of new growth. Here, new plant tissue is built up as rapid cell division takes place.

Growth in roots   There is a *growing point* at the tip of each root where new root tissue is rapidly built up. As the root tip grows, the root pushes itself further into the soil in search of water.

Growth in buds   In a bud, young, folded leaves are packed around a short stem and protected by tough outer leaves called *bud scales*. At the end of the short stem there is a flower, or a growing point where a new bud will form.

The bud at the top of the main shoot is called the *terminal bud*. In the springtime, the leaves in this bud unfold and space out as the stem pushes upwards. If the terminal bud produces a flower, no growing point is left when the flower finally falls away. Growth in the following season then takes place in the side or *axillary* buds.

Thickening in the stem   As a plant grows its stem thickens in order to support the extra weight above it.

New cells are made in a thin layer called the *cambium* which lies between the food-tubes and the water-tubes in the stem. The cambium moves outwards as new food-tubes are formed on the outside of the layer and new water-tubes on the inside.

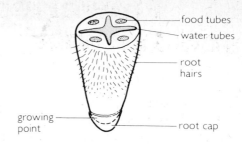

A plant root.

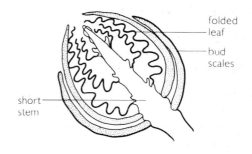

A plant bud.

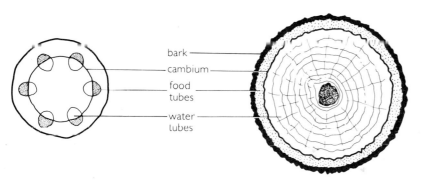

Questions

1. Why do some leaves have a waxy layer on their upper surface? What is this layer called?
2. Where in a leaf are the food-making cells?
3. How does carbon dioxide get into a leaf?
4. What are veins? Why does a leaf contain them?
5. Give two reasons why a plant needs a) a stem b) roots.
6. Where in a root is the growing point?
7. What does a bud contain?
8. Why does the stem of a plant thicken as the plant grows?
9. Stems grow thicker as a result of cell division. Where does this take place?

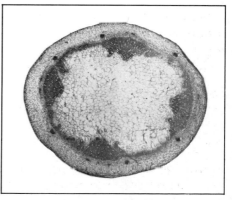

Cross section through the stem of a sunflower.

8.6 Reproduction in flowering plants (1)

Plants which flower do so in order to reproduce themselves. Flowers contain the tiny male and female cells which, when combined, grow into seeds. These seeds are scattered over a wide area. Some survive to grow into new plants.

Flower structure

Some flowers contain male cells, some contain female cells but many contain cells of both types. The male and female cells are stored in the *stamens* and *carpels* which stand in rings around the centre of a flower.

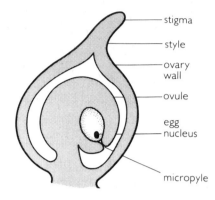

Carpel: before fertilization.

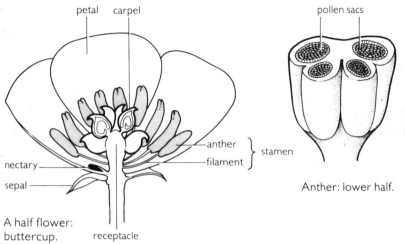

A half flower: buttercup.

Anther: lower half.

Stamens These hold the grains of *pollen* which contain the male cells. The pollen is stored in *pollen sacs* in the bulge at the end of each stamen. Pollen is exposed when this bulge (the *anther*) ripens and splits.

Carpels Each carpel has a hollow in its base called an *ovary*. From the walls of this hollow grow tiny round *ovules* which each contain one female cell—an *egg-cell*. When the tip of a carpel is ripe, it is ready to receive and nourish grains of pollen.

Pollination and fertilization

For a male cell to combine with a female egg-cell, pollen grains must first be transferred to the tip of a carpel. This process is called *pollination*.

Cross-pollination This is the transfer of pollen grains from one plant to carpels on another plant of the same type. In some cases the pollen grains are carried by wind, in others by insects such as bees which move from flower to flower. Flowers are often brightly coloured to attract insects. The insects visit them in search of the sugary nectar in the nectaries and pick up grains of pollen on their bodies as they do so.

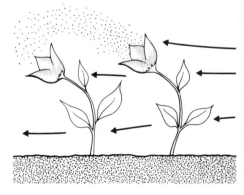

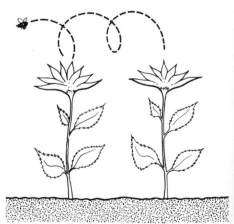

Pollination by wind and insects.

Self-pollination   This is the transfer of pollen grains from stamens to carpels in the same plant.

Most plants arrange things so that self-pollination is not very likely to happen. Self-pollinated plants have much less chance of producing variations that will help future plant generations in their struggle for survival. Pollen sacs and carpel tips may ripen at different times to prevent self-pollination taking place.

Fertilization   When ripe, the tip of a carpel will nourish grains of pollen which stick to it. Each pollen grain then grows a long *pollen tube* which pushes down towards an ovule. A nucleus from a male cell passes down this tube and combines with the nucleus in the female egg-cell—the egg-cell is then *fertilized*. After fertilization of the egg-cells has taken place, much of the outer flower shrivels up and falls off.

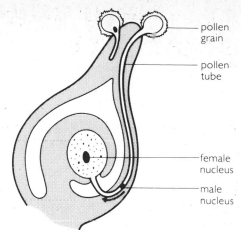

Carpel: during fertilization.

Seeds and fruits

Seeds   Within its ovule each fertilized egg-cell grows by cell division to form a seed. Each seed is a tiny new plant with a thick protective *seed coat* around it.

Fruits   Biologists describe the complete ovary after fertilization as a fruit—they do not use the term fruit in quite the same way as a greengrocer. Oranges are fruits but so too are tomatoes and bean pods.

When you eat an apple you are actually eating the *receptacle* which contains the ovary. This receptacle is often called a *false fruit.*

Dispersal of seeds and fruits   Plants scatter their seeds over a large area to give as many of them as possible a chance of surviving as new plants. Different plants use different methods to disperse their seeds.

Some seeds are carried by wind, some hook on to animals. Some seeds come from pods which pop and flick their contents across the ground. Some seeds remain in fruits which are then eaten by animals—the hard seeds pass out onto the ground with the faeces.

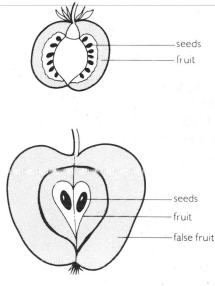

Two fruits: tomato and apple.

Questions

1. Where in a flower are the male cells of reproduction stored? Where are the female egg-cells stored?
2. What is the tip of a carpel called? What name is given to the bulge at the end of a stamen?
3. Give two ways in which cross-pollination can take place.
4. Why are some flowers brightly coloured?
5. What is self-pollination?
6. A pollen grain attaches itself to the tip of a carpel. How does fertilization then take place?
7. What is a seed? What is a fruit?
8. List the ways in which fruits and seeds can be dispersed.

8.7 Reproduction in flowering plants (2)

Given the right conditions, a seed will grow into a new plant. In time, this plant will build up the store of food it needs in order to reproduce itself. Some plants do not survive after they have reproduced but many types live on to reproduce over and over again.

Germination

Seeds are usually very dry when scattered from a plant. In this state some can remain alive but inactive for long periods—they are then *dormant*.

Growth begins when a seed is in the presence of water, oxygen and a temperature that suits it. When a seed begins to grow, it is said to *germinate*.

The germination of a broad bean seed is described below though many other seeds germinate in a similar way.

Germination of a broad bean seed   Inside the seed coat of a broad bean seed lies the beginnings (the *embryo*) of a new plant. A tiny leafy shoot is present, so too is a tiny root. These are joined to two *seed-leaves* which store the food needed for the first stages of growth.

Germination begins when the bean seed absorbs water, swells, and bursts through the seed coat:

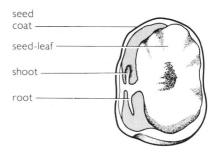

seed coat
seed-leaf
shoot
root

A broad bean seed.

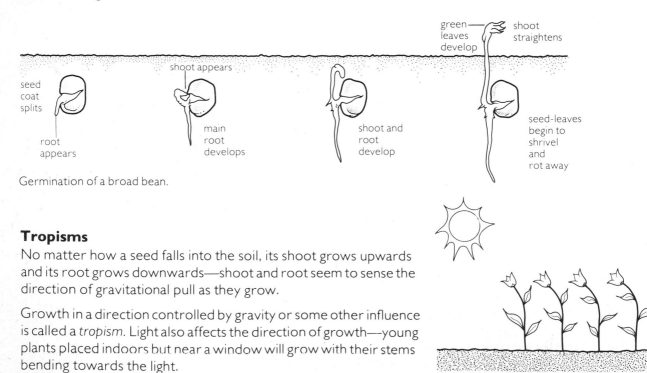

Germination of a broad bean.

Tropisms

No matter how a seed falls into the soil, its shoot grows upwards and its root grows downwards—shoot and root seem to sense the direction of gravitational pull as they grow.

Growth in a direction controlled by gravity or some other influence is called a *tropism*. Light also affects the direction of growth—young plants placed indoors but near a window will grow with their stems bending towards the light.

Life cycles

As it grows, a flowering plant passes through two distinct phases.

During its *vegetative phase* the plant gains in size and weight as it builds up a supply of stored food. During its *reproductive phase* the plant uses this stored food to produce flowers, seeds and fruits.

Some plants pass through each phase only once before they die. Some live through many cycles of growth and reproduction.

Annual plants (e.g. marigolds) These live through one growing season only. They reproduce once in the year and then die as their food reserves are exhausted.

Biennial plants (e.g. cabbages, carrots) These spend the growing season in their first year building up a store of food in their roots, stems or leaves. These food stores survive the winter, unless you eat them, and the food is used to produce flowers, seeds and fruits the following year. The plant then dies.

Herbaceous perennials (e.g. crocuses) These die away above ground level each autumn but build up enough stored food to flower every year or so. The food is stored in swollen stems, roots or leaves known as *bulbs, corms, rhizomes* or *tubers*.

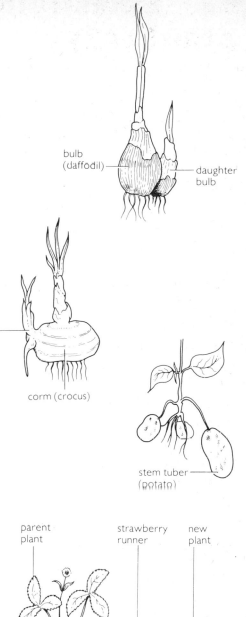

bulb (daffodil)

daughter bulb

daughter corm

corm (crocus)

stem tuber (potato)

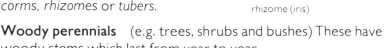

rhizome (iris)

Woody perennials (e.g. trees, shrubs and bushes) These have woody stems which last from year to year.

Vegetative reproduction

Although many plants form flowers in order to reproduce, some perennial plants are also able to reproduce by growing parts which separate from the parent plant to form new plants. Side buds in a daffodil bulb grow into bulbs which may separate from the parent bulb. Strawberry plants produce runners which take root to form new plants.

parent plant

strawberry runner

new plant

Reproduction of this type is known as *vegetative reproduction*—it is a form of asexual reproduction.

Questions
1. What does a seed need in order to germinate?
2. Describe the stages in the germination of a broad bean.
3. What are tropisms? Give two examples.
4. What two phases are there in the life cycle of a flowering plant? What happens during each?
5. Where do herbaceous perennials store their food?
6. How can a strawberry plant reproduce itself asexually?

8.8 Classifying living things

Scientists begin to classify living things by grouping them into *kingdoms.*

Most living things can be placed without too much difficulty in either the *plant kingdom* or the *animal kingdom.* Some do not fit easily into either—many scientists place these in a third kingdom, the *protista.*

The three kingdoms are each divided into smaller groups of organisms called *phyla,* some of which are shown in the charts below. The organisms in any one *phylum* will have several general features in common.

The smallest groups of living things are called *species.* Members of a species are so much alike that they can mate together and produce young like themselves. Humans are a species, so are barn owls, common meadow buttercups and guinea pigs. There are well over a million species of living organism on Earth.

The protista kingdom

Protozoa:
These single-celled organisms are microscopic in size.

amoeba

euglena

Fungi:
Some fungi live and feed on organisms which are living: some feed on the decaying remains of dead organisms.

mushroom

bread mould

yeast

Algae:
There are several phyla of algae. Green algae live in water or on damp land; brown algae live in the sea.

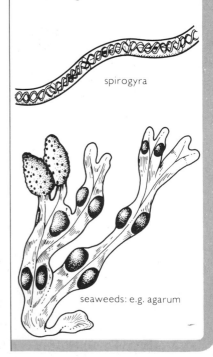

spirogyra

seaweeds: e.g. agarum

The plant kingdom

Bryophytes:
These plants live in damp places and have no true roots, stems or leaves though they possess structures which look rather similar.

The bryophytes include the **liverworts** and the **mosses**.

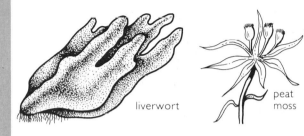

liverwort

peat moss

Ferns:
Ferns have roots, stems and leaves but they produce no flowers.

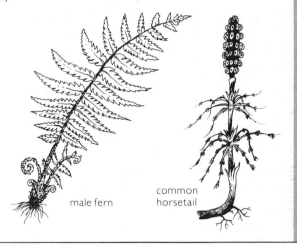

male fern

common horsetail

Seed plants:
The seed plants are the most advanced forms of plant life to be found on Earth.

Flowering seed plants:
These produce their seeds in ovaries which then form fruits.

Monocotyledons are narrow-leaved plants which contain only one seed-leaf in each seed.

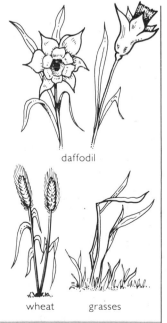

daffodil

wheat   grasses

Dicotyledons have broad leaves, and seeds which each contain two seed-leaves. They include:-

herbaceous plants e.g. buttercups and daisies;
shrubs e.g. woody hedges and bushes;
deciduous trees e.g. oak, ash and elm.

buttercup   oak

Non-flowering seed plants:
These include coniferous trees like the fir, pine and spruce.

The seeds are contained in cones rather than in fruits.

spruce

8.9 Classifying living things: the animal kingdom

Coelenterates:
Nearly all live in the sea.

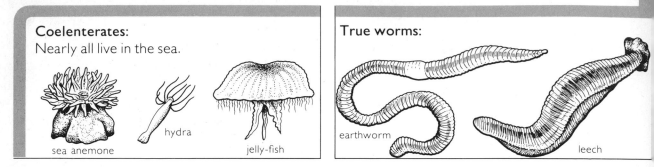

sea anemone

hydra

jelly-fish

True worms:

earthworm

leech

Arthropods:
This is the largest phylum in the animal kingdom. Arthropod bodies are in sections, with a strong outer case called an **exoskeleton**. Arthropod legs are in pairs and jointed.

Crustaceans:

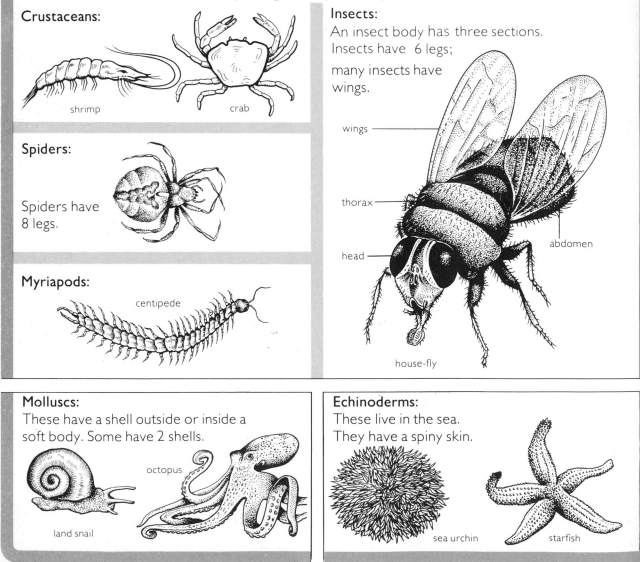

shrimp

crab

Insects:
An insect body has three sections.
Insects have 6 legs;
many insects have wings.

wings

thorax

abdomen

head

house-fly

Spiders:

Spiders have 8 legs.

Myriapods:

centipede

Molluscs:
These have a shell outside or inside a soft body. Some have 2 shells.

land snail

octopus

Echinoderms:
These live in the sea.
They have a spiny skin.

sea urchin

starfish

Vertebrates:

These animals have a backbone (a vertebral column).

Some animals have a body temperature which changes—'cold blooded' animals:

Fish:

Some fish have a cartilage skeleton.

shark

Some fish have a skeleton made of bone.

perch

Amphibians:

These live on land. They lay eggs, and produce young which live in the water at first.

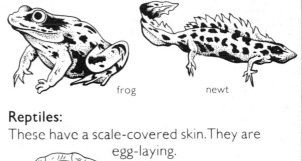

frog   newt

Reptiles:

These have a scale-covered skin. They are egg-laying.

tortoise   crocodile

Some animals have a constant, warm, body temperature—'warm blooded' animals:

Birds:

Birds are feather covered. Their front limbs form wings. Most, but not all, birds can fly.

robin

penguin

Mammals:

Mammals are hair covered. They suckle their young with milk from the mother. Primates (monkeys, apes, man) are the most advanced animals of all.

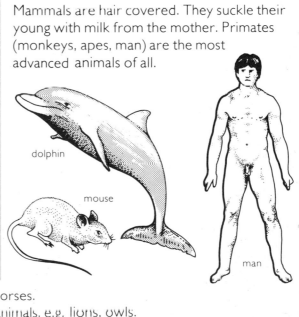

dolphin

mouse

man

Herbivores: animals which feed on plants. e.g. cows, horses.
Carnivores: animals which feed on the flesh of other animals. e.g. lions, owls.
Omnivores: animals which feed on plants and animal flesh. e.g. man.

8.10 Evolution

The first living organisms appeared on Earth more than 3000 million years ago. As generation followed generation these organisms slowly changed and in time they developed into the animals and plants of today. This process of gradual development is called evolution—an explanation of the process of evolution is offered by the theory of natural selection.

Evolution of the mammals

The diagram shows some of the stages in the evolution of the mammals which exist today.

The path of evolution has divided many times in the past. Where animals have begun to live and breed in separate groups, evolution has taken a different course with each group.

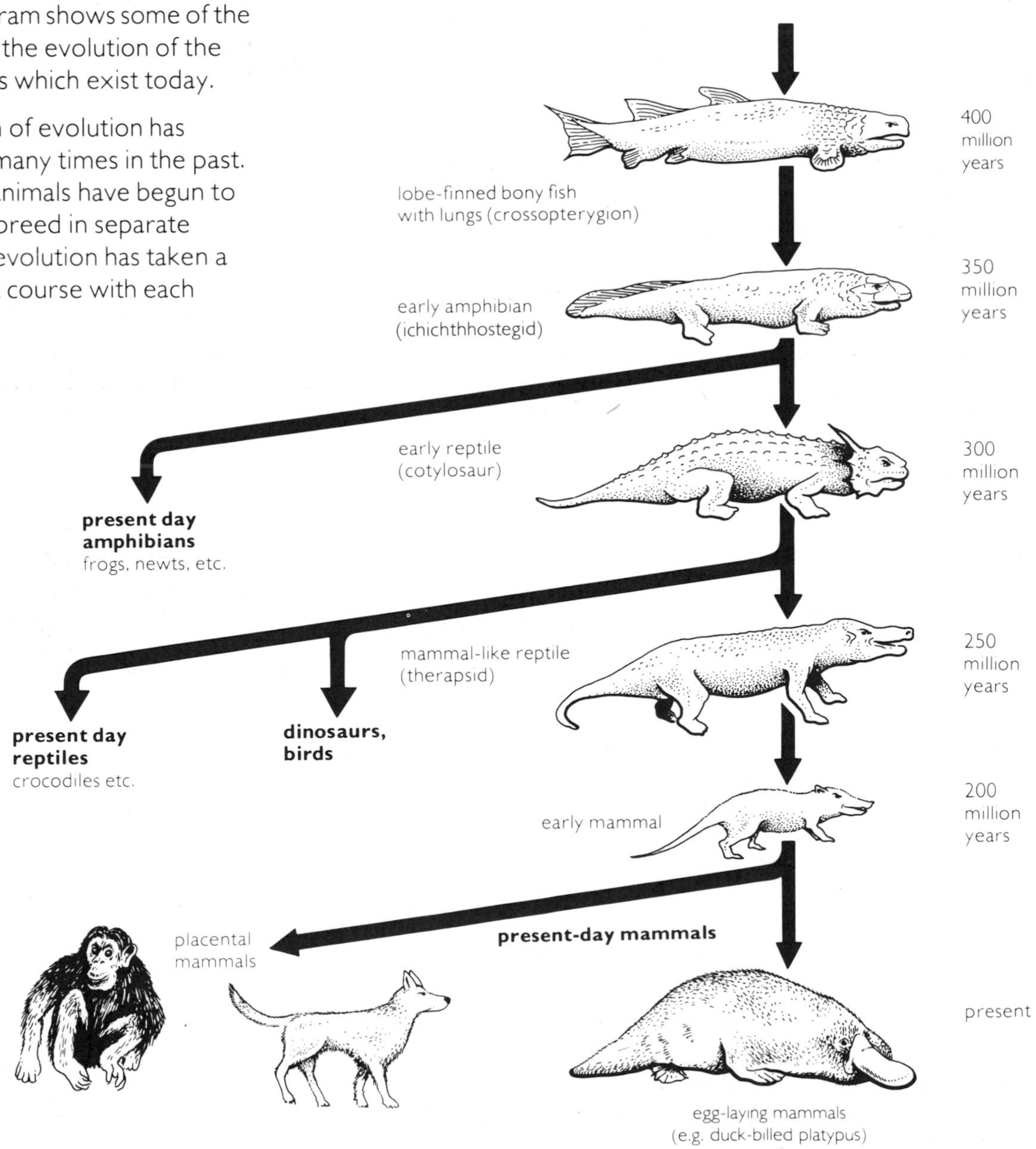

400 million years

lobe-finned bony fish with lungs (crossopterygion)

350 million years

early amphibian (ichichthhostegid)

300 million years

early reptile (cotylosaur)

present day amphibians
frogs, newts, etc.

250 million years

mammal-like reptile (therapsid)

present day reptiles
crocodiles etc.

dinosaurs, birds

200 million years

early mammal

present-day mammals

placental mammals

present

egg-laying mammals (e.g. duck-billed platypus)

The theory of natural selection

Charles Darwin suggested that evolution was the result of a process which he called *natural selection*. The *theory of natural selecton* is explained in stages below—for simplicity, the explanations deal only with animal life though the theory applies to the evolution of all forms of life.

Mutation in a moth.

Variations   No two animals are ever exactly alike. Small changes are always appearing in a species as animals produce their young. There are *variations* in colour, shape, weight, height and countless other features.

Now and again an animal may be born with a completely new feature—a colour change or a different skin surface for example. Such variations are called *mutations* and they happen because a mistake occurs in the chromosome copying within a cell. A mutation is normally harmful to an animal but just occasionally it may be useful.

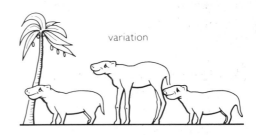
variation

Survival of the fittest   Animals are in a constant struggle for survival. They face difficult weather conditions, they may be hunted, and they must compete with each other for what little food is available. Of all the variations which appear in animals, some will help in the struggle for survival and some will not—some animals survive to reproduce but many do not. Nature 'selects' for survival those animals whose variations have survival-value.

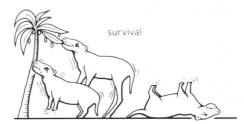
survival

Adaptation   As it is the survivors which reproduce, the variations which help an animal to survive are those most likely to be passed on to later generations. For example:

If long legs aid survival, long-legged animals are those most likely to live long enough to produce young—later generations will inherit their long legs.

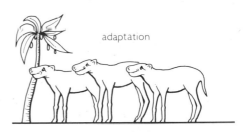
adaptation

By this process of natural selection each species evolves so that its members can best cope with their living conditions—they become *adapted* to their environment.

If the animals of one species begin to live and breed in isolated groups, evolution will take a different course with each group. Several new species will then evolve.

Questions

1. Which of the groups of animals on the opposite page evolved from early reptiles.
2. Write down two examples of variations which might be found between animals of the same species.
3. What is a mutation? Give an example.
4. Why are some variations more likely to be passed on to later generations than others?
5. Why may several species evolve from a single species?

8.11 Balance of nature

Scientific study of the way in which living things depend upon each other is called ecology. By the end of this section, you will understand why studying it is important.

Food chains

Grass grows by turning carbon dioxide, water and salts into food using energy from the sun. Cows cannot make their food in this way. They eat grass, converting it into their own body materials. We, in turn, drink milk and eat meat to produce our body cells. This is an example of a *food chain*.

Animals use only one tenth of their food intake for body building. The rest is used for keeping warm, or for keeping moving, or is undigested. The loss at each stage in the food chain is shown by a *pyramid* structure. It takes 1000 tonnes of the microscopic plants to support one tonne of shark through a food chain.

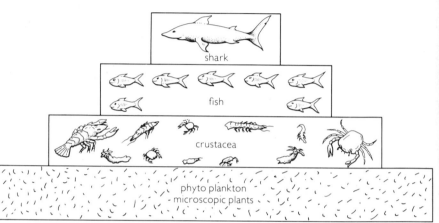

Food webs

Most animals eat more than one kind of food. A *food web* shows how creatures depend upon each other.

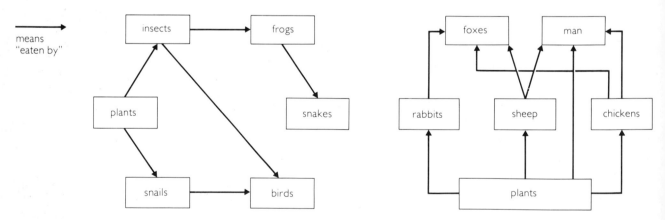

Anything that happens to one member of a food web will affect all the others.

When myxomatosis killed most of the rabbits in Britain, foxes were affected. They ate more domestic animals and reduced one source of man's food. Plants were also affected. Seedlings of trees and bushes on moors and grassland began to flourish because there were no rabbits to nip them off!

Predator to prey ratio

There is a natural balance between *predators* (animals which eat others) and their prey. The numbers remain about the same unless something happens to change living conditions, the *environment*.

The graph shows the balance between toads and slugs living near a stream. If, for some reason, too many toad tadpoles develop into adults, they will eat nearly all the slugs (1). Deprived of a major source of food the toads will die off (2). The plants which feed the slugs will flourish and the numbers of slugs will quickly increase again because they have plenty of food and few predators (3). The predator to prey ratio is restored (4).

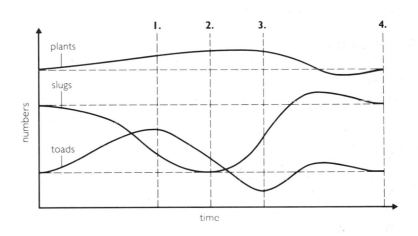

Disturbing the balance

Man often upsets the balance of nature. In doing things to tip the balance in his favour he affects other animals badly. He sometimes suffers in other respects himself.

For instance, more efficient methods of catching herring resulted in cheap fish at first. However, the number left in the sea became so small that they were no longer catchable. The growing of single crops in large areas, called *monoculture*, is an efficient way of producing food but it encourages the increase of particular parasites and pests. Mildly poisonous chemicals used to kill crop-destroying pests and disease-carrying insects, sometimes affect other animals. D.D.T. seemed to be a perfect insecticide until it was used to kill gnats in Clear Lake, California. Although very dilute in the water, the concentration built up through a food chain. It increased steadily in the plankton and fish until it was strong enough to kill the many water birds living on the lake.

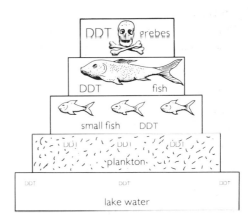

When excess chemical fertiliser washes into lakes, tiny plants called algae grow abundantly. Their decay uses up all the oxygen in the water so that fish die and a foul mud is formed.

Questions

1. Give an example of a food chain.
2. What fraction of food is used for body building?
3. Draw the food web between plants, insects, snails and birds.
4. State 3 different effects of the disease myxomatosis.
5. What is meant by 'predator' and 'environment'?
6. Explain why the predator to prey ratio is roughly constant.
7. Describe one harmful effect of the insecticide D.D.T.
8. How can excessive use of fertilisers cause lakes to foul up?

A victim of disturbing the balance.

8.12 **Elements present in cells**

*What are cells actually made of? Molecules, like everything else!
Molecules of living cells are based on long chains of carbon atoms
linked together. To these chains are joined many other atoms. As
plants and animals grow and die, these atoms are used over and over
again.*

Materials in cells

The basic materials of all living cells are compounds of carbon,
hydrogen, oxygen and nitrogen called *proteins*. Cells contain a lot of
water, and store energy-producing fuels called *carbohydrates*.
Carbohydrates contain carbon, hydrogen and oxygen only. Smaller
quantities of other elements are present in specialised cells: iron in
blood, for instance and calcium and phosphorus in bones.

Different things have different amounts of the materials listed. The
cell materials of worms are changed into bones and feathers when
eaten by birds. However, the 4 basic elements in all living things
come from carbon dioxide, water and nitrate salts.

The carbon cycle

Carbon atoms, the basis of all living cells, come from carbon
dioxide in the air and are recycled as shown.

compounds in cells	elements
water	hydrogen oxygen
proteins	carbon hydrogen oxygen nitrogen
carbohydrates sugars, starches, cellulose.	carbon hydrogen oxygen

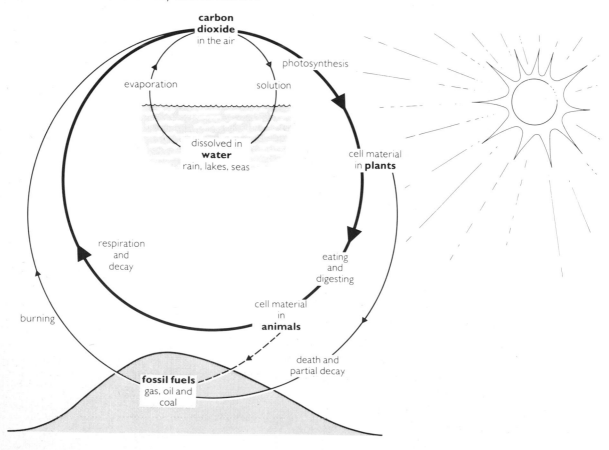

140

The nitrogen cycle

The nitrogen needed for cell-building proteins also comes from the air. Certain plants are able to absorb nitrogen from the air through lumps on their roots. Such plants are *leguminous*: they include peas, beans and clover. Farmers grow these crops every few years, ploughing parts of them back to enrich the soil with nitrogen compounds. Artificial fertilisers are made by converting nitrogen from the air into ammonium and nitrate salts. These dissolve in water when added to the soil and are absorbed by plants through their roots. Manure (animal excretion) and compost (rotting plants) are rich in nitrogen compounds and these are returned to the soil. Microscopic organisms called *bacteria* play an important part in the recycling of nitrogen.

Clover is often grown to increase the nitrogen content of the soil.

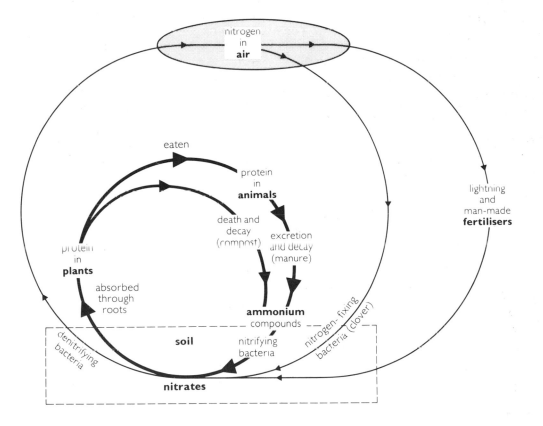

Questions

1. What are the molecules of living cells based on?
2. What are proteins? What elements do they contain?
3. What are carbohydrates? What elements do they contain?
4. Give 2 examples of other elements present in specialised cells.
5. Describe one route for the recycling of carbon atoms.
6. How do all plants absorb nitrogen? Where does the nitrogen come from in the first place?
7. What are leguminous plants? Give 2 examples.
8. Name 2 artificial and 2 natural fertilisers.

8.13 Soil

Many of the materials that plants need to produce their cells are taken in through their roots from soil. Since we depend upon plants for our own body cells, soil is vital to us. It's not just dirt!

How soil is formed

Soil comes from broken-down rock. It can form quite quickly, as it did on the volcano which formed the new island of Surtsey in 1964. Plants were growing on this new island within 5 years.

The actions of wind and rain, sun and ice break rock down into fragments of varying size. Oxygen and carbon dioxide, dissolved in rain water, react with the rock producing clays and soluble salts. These enable small plants to grow. When the plants die, their remains decay to a dark coloured substance called *humus*. It is humus that makes the mixture of rock fragments, clay, water and salts into soil. Humus provides soil with nitrogen and other plant food, and it lightens the soil structure.

Types of soil

No two soils are the same. The structure of a soil depends upon the type of rock it comes from and upon the amount of humus it contains. For good plant growth, soil should crumble easily, be able to hold water with dissolved salts, and have air trapped in it.

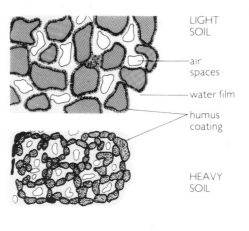

LIGHT SOIL

— air spaces
— water film
— humus coating

HEAVY SOIL

Light soil   This is sandy with large particles giving big air spaces and good drainage. It breaks up very easily when dug and also warms up quickly. Unfortunately, it dries out very quickly and loses its mineral salts. Humus added as farmyard manure holds the sand together and improves its water-holding.

Heavy soil   This consists of small clay particles which stick closely together giving little air space and poor drainage. It is difficult to dig; it becomes water-logged in wet weather; it cracks in dry weather. Addition of humus makes the clay form larger particles (crumbs), allowing more air and water in. Lime has the same effect.

Loam   This is a mixture of sand and clay soils. It has a mixed particle size and rich humus content, which makes it very fertile.

Soil profiles

Fertile soil is usually no more than 20cm deep. Below it lies the *subsoil*—much lighter in colour than topsoil because very little humus penetrates into it. The layers of soil and subsoil which can be seen in a very deep trench are called the *soil profile*.

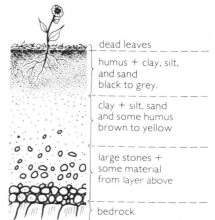

— dead leaves
humus + clay, silt, and sand black to grey.
clay + silt, sand and some humus brown to yellow
large stones + some material from layer above
— bedrock

Composition of soil

An old can with both ends removed may be used for collecting soil. Pressed into the ground, the can cuts out a sample without disturbing the soil structure.

Air   This may be measured by dropping the can into a large cylinder half-filled with water.

Water   Another sample is weighed and then left in a warm place for several days. Reweighing shows the amount of water lost.

Humus   By heating the same dry sample strongly, the humus is burnt away giving a further weight loss.

Solid particles   These may be separated by emptying another sample into a cylinder filled with water. When shaken up and left to settle overnight different layers of particles separate.

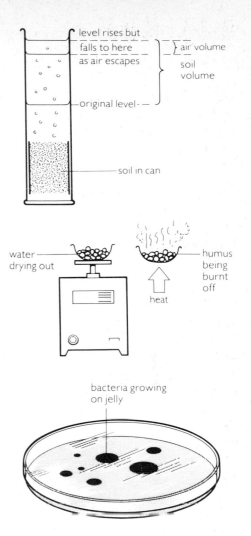

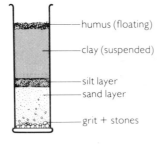

Bacteria in soil

Also present in soil but too small to be seen are microscopic organisms called *bacteria*. Bacteria decompose dead plants and animals forming humus and ammonium compounds. Other *nitrifying* bacteria turn ammonium compounds into nitrates using oxygen trapped in the soil. The bacteria gain energy in this process as animals do by respiration. There are others called *denitrifying* bacteria which break up nitrogen compounds and release nitrogen gas into the air.

Acidity (pH) of soil

The acidity of a soil depends upon the parent rock and the condition of the plant remains. Limestone soils are usually alkaline, pH = 8. Clay soils and bogs with partly-decomposed plant remains (peat) may be strongly acidic, pH = 4 or 5. Most plants grow best in soils of pH = 6.5. Lime counteracts excess acidity and ammonium sulphate can be used to acidify an alkaline soil.

Questions
1. What does soil come from? Describe how it forms.
2. What is the dark substance in soil? How is it formed?
3. What are the requirements of a good soil?
4. Describe light and heavy soils. How does humus improve both?
5. What is the usual depth of soil? What lies beneath it?
6. How can you show that soil contains (a) air, (b) water, (c) humus, (d) sand and silt?
7. Give 2 effects of bacteria present in soil.
8. Give the range of soil pH. What value suits most plants?

Questions on Chapter 8

I Give three important differences between living and non-living things.

2 A plant cannot move about to search for food. How does a plant obtain its food?

3 Why do plants and animals need oxygen?

4 a Copy the diagram of the plant cell and complete the labels.
b State two labels which should not be included in a diagram of an animal cell. EAEB

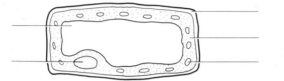

5 Explain with the aid of diagrams how an amoeba reproduces itself.

6 Copy and complete the word equation showing what happens in the leaf of a plan during photosynthesis:

$$\ldots + \text{water} \xrightarrow[\text{from} \ldots]{\text{using energy}} \text{food} + \ldots$$

7 What green material in plants enables photosynthesis to take place?

8 What is a transpiration stream? Why is it important?

9 What test could you carry out to discover whether or not a leaf contained starch?

10 Why does the amount of starch in the leaf of a plant not remain constant?

II Give one function of:
a the root of a plant; **b** the stem;
c the leaves. WYLREB

12 The diagram shows a magnified section across a green leaf.

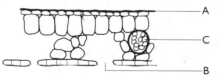

What are parts **A**, **B** and **C**? What is the purpose of each?

13 Which of the following plants do not have flowers?
grass, fern, daisy, oak, moss.

14 Which of the following was last to appear on Earth?
reptile, fish, mammal, bird, amphibian. WMEB

15 a On this diagram the labels have got muddled up. Redraw the diagram and put them in the right places.

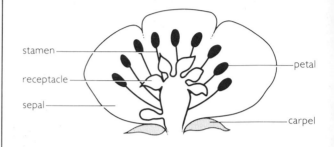

b In which part of the flower is pollen produced?
c Why is nectar produced by the flower?
d What happens in a flower during pollination? In what ways can pollination occur?
e What process follows after pollination has taken place?

16 Why do plants scatter their seeds over a large area?

17 For a seed to germinate, which of the following are needed and which are not?
moisture, light, warmth, air. WY & LREB

18 Draw a diagram of a germinating broad bean seed and label the following:
root, shoot, seed leaves, seed coat.

19 Why does an indoor potted plant turn its leaves towards the window?

20 Explain why chemicals used to kill off one type of crop-destroying pest may eventually have a very harmful effect on many other forms of life. Give an example.

21 a Draw and label the layers of soil that are separated by shaking a soil sample with water and allowing it to settle.
b What is the natural organic matter in soil called? ALSEB

22 State two ways in which nitrogen in the atmosphere is made available to plants for food making. ALSEB

23 What food substances are made by plants using the nitrogen they take in?

Chapter 9

Human Life

You're alive. How on Earth do you keep going?
This photograph shows a medieval view. Is it
accurate?

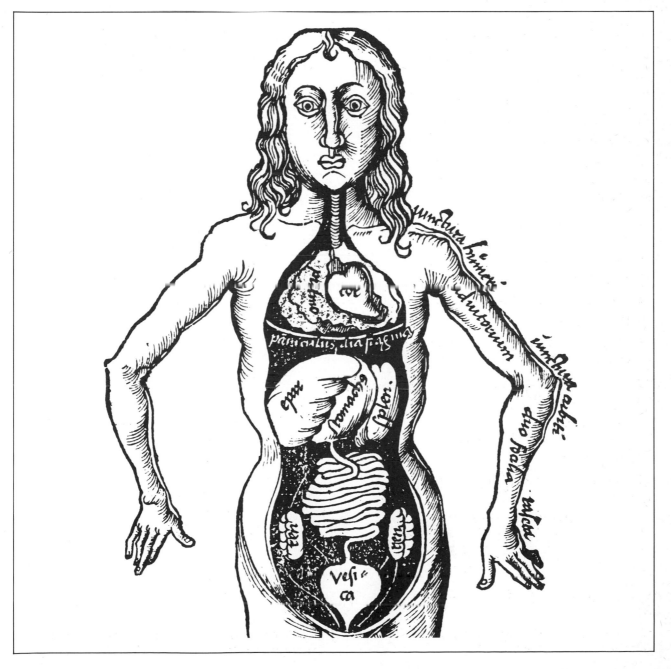

9.1　The human skeleton

There's plenty of soft tissue in the body—but much harder materials are needed to enable you to stand, walk and chew your food!

The skeleton

All vertebrate animals, including human beings, are supported by a framework of rigid bones called a *skeleton*—it is called an *endoskeleton* because it lies inside the body.

The skeleton has several important functions:

Support The skeleton enables you to stand upright on the ground. It also supports vital internal organs so that there is no danger of them squashing one another.

Protection The skeleton protects many organs from outside damage:

the *skull* protects the brain;

the *rib cage* protects the heart and lungs;

the *vertebral column* (the backbone) protects the spinal cord.

Movement Many parts of the skeleton are jointed so that body movements are possible; e.g. arms, legs, fingers and jaw.

The movements are produced by muscles which surround the skeleton and are attached to it at various points.

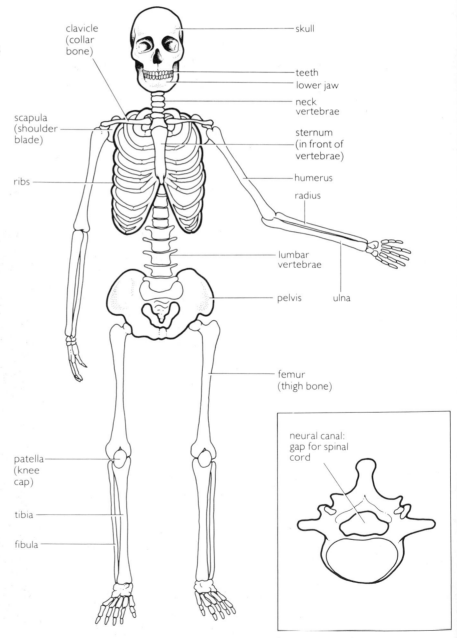

Lumbar vertebra (top view).

Bones

Bones contain living cells surrounded by hard minerals to give strength and rigidity—calcium is the main substance present. These minerals are constantly being renewed from materials brought in by the body's blood supply; if this did not happen, broken bones would never be able to mend.

Bones are made even stronger by tough fibres which reinforce them in the same way as steel rods reinforce concrete.

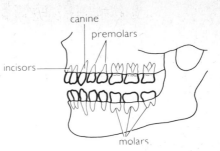

Teeth

Human adults have 32 permanent teeth in all. Your permanent teeth probably began to replace your 20 milk teeth when you were about six years old.

Incisors are cutting teeth. You use them when you bite a sandwich.

Canines are gripping and tearing teeth. Flesh-eating animals like dogs have well-developed canine teeth. Our own canine teeth are much smaller in comparison.

Premolars and molars are grinding and crushing teeth. They are used to break food down into small pieces.

Tough fibres hold each tooth in its socket in the jaw bone; they cushion the tooth against jolts during chewing.

Enamel covers the crown of each tooth. It gives the tooth a hard surface for cutting and grinding.

Dentine is similar to bone in structure. Most of the hard material in a tooth is dentine.

Pulp at the centre of each tooth is made of soft tissue containing blood vessels and nerves.

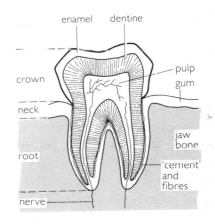

Molars: crushing teeth.

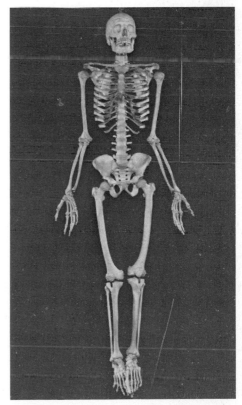

How many of the bones in this skeleton can you identify?

Questions
1. Which parts of the human body are protected by: a) the skull; b) the rib cage; c) the vertebral column?
2. What other functions does the skeleton have?
3. Draw labelled diagrams to show which limbs of the body contain a) a femur, tibia and fibula; b) a humerus, radius and ulna.
4. What is the main substance present in bone?
5. Which teeth do you use to cut through food?
6. Which teeth do you use to crush food into small pieces?
7. What covers the crown of each tooth, and why?

9.2 Joints and muscles

Joints are places in the skeleton where bones meet. There's movement at most joints, caused by muscles such as "bulging biceps".

Joints

At some joints, the bones are held tightly together by fibres and no movement is possible—the bones which form the top of the skull are joined in this way. Other joints allow small movements because flexible *cartilage* (gristle) is sandwiched between the ends of the bones. Your back can bend a little because the vertebrae have cartilage *discs* between them which absorb the jolts when you walk about.

Most joints can move much more freely. Tough fibres called *ligaments* hold the ends of the bones together while allowing the bones themselves to be moved through large angles. These joints are called *synovial* joints. They include:

Hinge joints   Knuckles, knees and elbows are all hinge joints. In hinge joints, the bones can be turned to and fro in one direction only—rather like a door on its hinge.

Ball-and-socket joints   Hip joints and shoulder joints are of this type. In ball-and-socket joints, the bones can be turned in any direction—up and down or side to side.

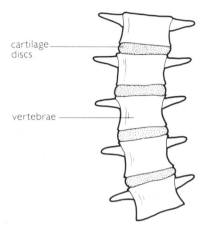

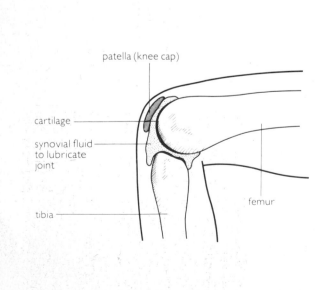

A hinge-joint: the knee.

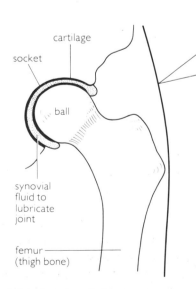

A ball-and-socket joint: the hip.

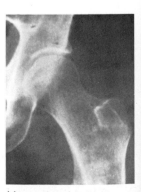

X-ray picture of a hip joint.

Muscles

Joints are moved by muscles which are attached to the bones by strong, non-stretch fibres called *tendons*. The muscles pull on the bones by thickening and contracting (becoming shorter)—this happens whenever impulses are received from the body's nervous system.

The diagram on the right shows the muscles which move the forearm up and down. Like the other muscles attached to the skeleton, these are *voluntary* muscles—you are free to move them whenever you choose.

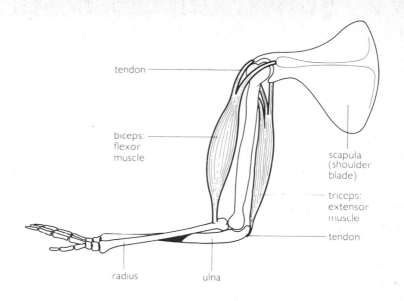

tendon

biceps: flexor muscle

scapula (shoulder blade)

triceps: extensor muscle

tendon

radius

ulna

Antagonistic muscles   After contracting, a muscle cannot lengthen itself again; it has to be pulled back to its original shape. For this reason, muscles are often arranged in *antagonistic pairs* with one pulling one way and the other pulling back. The muscles which move the forearm are arranged in this way—the *flexor* muscle bends the joint, the *extensor* muscle straightens it again.

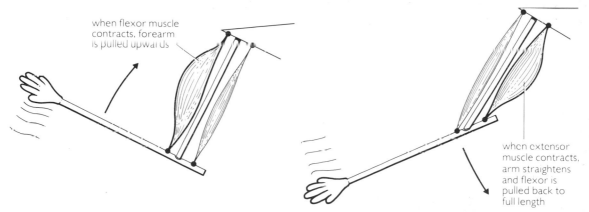

when flexor muscle contracts, forearm is pulled upwards

when extensor muscle contracts, arm straightens and flexor is pulled back to full length

Questions

1. Why is your back able to bend a little?
2. In what way is a ball-and-socket joint different from a hinge joint? Give two examples of each. How are these joints lubricated?
3. What are   a) ligaments;   b) tendons? What do they do?
4. What happens to a muscle when it receives an impulse from the nervous system? What is a voluntary muscle?
5. Why are muscles often arranged in antagonistic pairs?
6. What is the difference between a flexor muscle and an extensor muscle? Give an example of each.

A flexor demonstration.

9.3 Sense and control

*What makes you move your arm, or breathe more quickly, or grow?
Something somewhere has a great many decisions to make, some of
which you know about and some of which you don't.*

The nervous system

The body is controlled by the brain and the spinal cord. Together
these are known as the *central nervous system* and they are linked to
all parts of the body by nerves. Through the nerves, the central
nervous system can sense what is happening inside and outside of
the body and can control the actions of the muscles and organs.

Sense organs

The central nervous system gets its information from tiny sense
organs or *receptors* which lie at the ends of the nerves. These send
out small electrical impulses which are passed back to the central
nervous system through chains of nerve cells. Some sense organs
check what is happening in organs in the body, others give you the
senses of sight, sound, balance, taste, smell and touch:

Sight, sound and balance   The eye and the ear are described on
pages 178 and 188. The inner ear contains the organs of balance.

Taste and smell   Your tongue is covered with tiny bumps called
papillae. The sense organs are called *taste buds* and they lie on the
side of each papilla. There are four types of taste bud; they are
concentrated in different areas of the tongue and they each
respond to one of the tastes *sweet, sour, salt* or *bitter*. Most tastes
are a mixture of these different sensations.

The *olfactory organs* within the nose are the sense organs of smell.
During eating, these sense organs respond to vapours from the
food. Much of your sense of taste is really a sense of smell.

Touch   The sense organs of touch lie in or just under the skin.
Different types of sense organ enable you to sense touch, pressure,
hot or cold, pain, and hair movements.

The skin itself is made up of two
layers, *dermis* and the *epidermis*,
underneath which are layers of fat.
Skin is the body's protective coating.
It is also used in keeping the body at a
steady temperature.

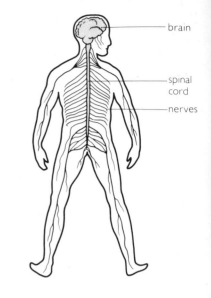

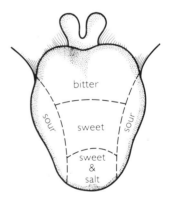

Taste areas of the tongue.

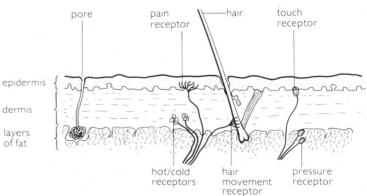

Control through the nervous system

Acting on the information it receives, the central nervous system sends out its instructions through chains of *motor* nerve cells. Some instructions you have control over and some you do not—you can decide when to contract muscles to move a leg but not when to make your heart beat faster.

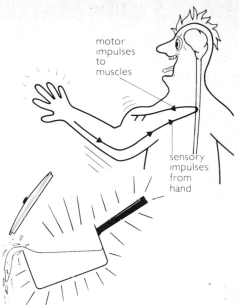

motor impulses to muscles

sensory impulses from hand

Reflex actions Movements or changes in the body which take place automatically are called reflex actions. They include coughing, sneezing and blinking, and the many actions caused by the *autonomic nervous system.*

The autonomic nervous system is the part of the central nervous system that controls the internal workings of the body such as:

speeding up or slowing down the heart beat;
control of body temperature;
control of breathing rate.

Not all reflex actions involve the brain. It is a *spinal reflex* which pulls your hand away from a hot saucepan if you touch it accidentally—the motor nerve impulses are sent to the arm muscles straight from the spinal cord.

The endocrine system

The central nervous system has second-by-second control of the body. The endocrine system controls much slower bodily changes. It consists of a number of *glands* which release chemicals called *hormones* into the blood stream. These hormones affect the way in which the organs of the body do their work, controlling amongst other things:

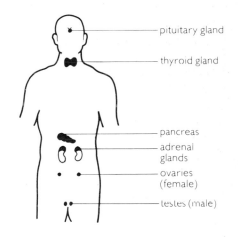

pituitary gland

thyroid gland

pancreas
adrenal glands
ovaries (female)
testes (male)

the rate at which you grow;
the development of some sexual characteristics;
the control and use of sugar in the blood.

The *pituitary gland* releases a growth hormone. It also releases hormones which control the other endocrine glands. For this reason, it is sometimes called the 'master gland'.

Questions

1. Which parts of the body form the central nervous system?
2. What is a receptor? Give three examples of sense organs.
3. What taste sensations are detected on the tongue?
4. Some nerve impulses travel in to the central nervous system and some travel out. Why?
5. What are the two main skin layers known as?
6. Give three examples of reflex actions.
7. What is the autonomic nervous system? What does it control?
8. Where do hormones come from and what do they do?
9. Why is the pituitary gland called the 'master gland'?

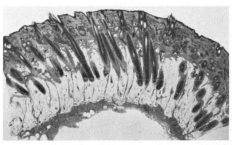

Cross section through the skin.

9.4 Foods

To keep alive, the body needs to take in water, oxygen from the air, and food. But it needs more than one type of food.

Nutrients
There are five main types of food or *nutrient:*

Carbohydrates and fats supply you with most of your energy.

Proteins provide the materials from which new body tissues are built when you grow or when, for example, a wound heals.

Minerals are used in building some body tissues. They are also needed for some chemical reactions in the body.

Vitamins are vital for speeding up some chemical reactions in the body that might otherwise happen too slowly.

Most foods contain several of the nutrients described above. A balanced diet is one which supplies you with adequate amounts of *all* the nutrients. The table on the next page gives *some* of the foods which are a common source of each type of nutrient. Below, are ways of testing for these nutrients.

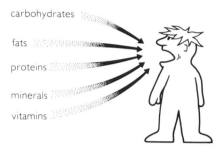

nutrients

carbohydrates

fats

proteins

minerals

vitamins

Food tests
Foods can be tested to discover which nutrients they contain. Some simple examples are given below:

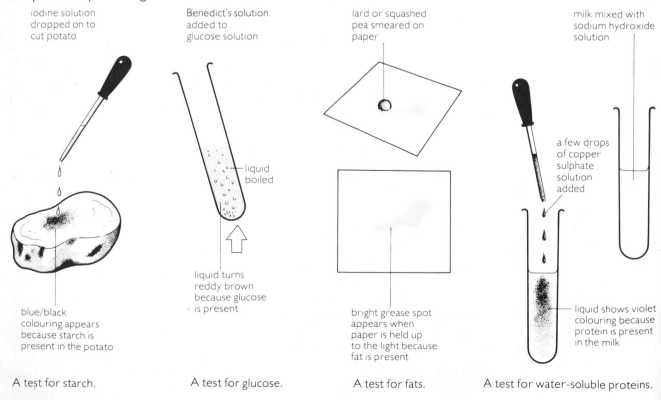

iodine solution dropped on to cut potato

Benedict's solution added to glucose solution

lard or squashed pea smeared on paper

milk mixed with sodium hydroxide solution

liquid boiled

a few drops of copper sulphate solution added

liquid turns reddy brown because glucose is present

blue/black colouring appears because starch is present in the potato

bright grease spot appears when paper is held up to the light because fat is present

liquid shows violet colouring because protein is present in the milk

A test for starch.

A test for glucose.

A test for fats.

A test for water-soluble proteins.

Carbohydrates	Sugars	Starches	Cellulose
	Jam, cakes, sweets, glucose, sweet fruits	Potatoes, rice, bread, flour	Vegetables, cereal foods
		The body breaks down sugars and starches into simple sugars like glucose. Some may be converted into fats.	*Cellulose cannot be used by the body as a nutrient, but it provides bulk (dietary fibre or "roughage") to help food pass through the system more easily.*

Fats
Butter, margarine, lard, meat.
Fats can be stored by the body; they provide a reserve supply of food.

Proteins
Meat, eggs, fish, milk, cheese, bread
The body breaks down proteins into amino acids which it can use to build new body tissues.

Minerals
Minerals needed by the body include:
Calcium (*for teeth and bones*)—from cheese, milk, vegetables
Iron (*used in making blood*)—from liver, eggs, bread
Sodium (*for muscle movements*)—from salt

Vitamins
Vitamins needed by the body include:
Vitamin A—from green vegetables, carrots, liver, butter.
(a shortage of vitamin A weakens your vision in the dark)
Vitamin B$_1$ (thiamine)—from yeast, bread, meat, potatoes, milk.
Vitamin B$_2$ (riboflavine)—from fresh milk, liver, eggs.
Vitamin C—from blackcurrants, green vegetables, oranges.
(a shortage of vitamin C causes a disease called scurvy)
Vitamin D—cod liver oil, margarine, eggs.
(a shortage of vitamin D causes rickets—soft bones.
Your skin makes vitamin D when exposed to sunlight.)

Questions

1. Which type of food provides materials for body building? Name two foods containing this type of nutrient.
2. Which carbohydrate supplies dietary fibre? Why is it useful?
3. Which nutrient can we store in the body as reserve food?
4. Name three minerals which are needed by the body.
5. Which vitamins are needed to prevent scurvy and rickets?
6. What foods are useful sources of vitamin C?
7. Write down all the nutrients given in the tables which are supplied by a) bread b) milk c) cheese d) liver.
   Your list will not show all the nutrients in each food.

9.5 **Digesting and absorbing food**

Swallow food, and the useful substances eventually end up in the blood stream to be carried to wherever in the body they are needed.

The alimentary canal

When you swallow food, it starts to move down a long tube called the *alimentary canal.* This tube runs from the mouth to the anus and food is squeezed along it by wave-like muscle movements called *peristalsis.*

Two important things happen to the food as it passes along the alimentary canal:

The food is digested During digestion, chemical compounds called *enzymes* break the food down into simpler substances which can be carried in the bloodstream, and which will dissolve in the water within the cells of the body.

Digestion mainly takes place in the stomach and the small intestine, but it starts in the mouth—an enzyme in saliva starts to break down starch into glucose as you chew your food.

Digested food is absorbed into the blood stream This mainly takes place in the small intestine—its walls are lined with tiny blood tubes which carry the digested food away.

Undigested matter passes into the large intestine and is pushed out of the anus when the toilet is used.

What happens to food in each part of the alimentary canal is described in more detail on the opposite page.

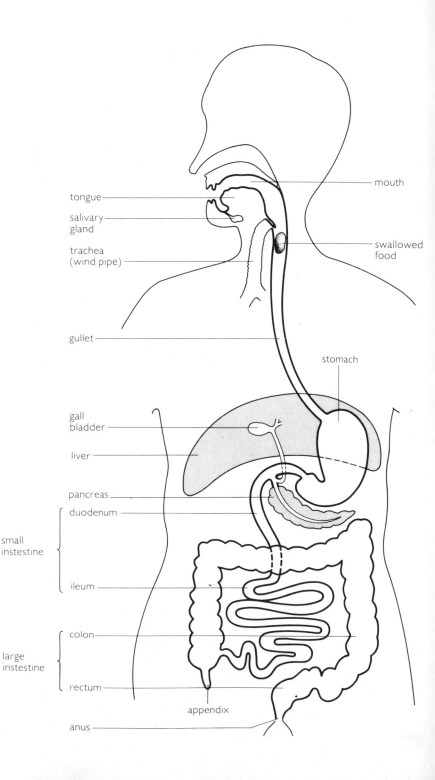

mouth

tongue

salivary gland

trachea (wind pipe)

swallowed food

gullet

stomach

gall bladder

liver

pancreas

duodenum

small instestine

ileum

colon

large instestine

rectum

appendix

anus

The stomach

After food has been swallowed, it passes down the gullet and into the stomach. Here, muscle movements in the stomach walls mix the food with *gastric juice* which oozes from thousands of tiny glands in the stomach lining. Gastric juice contains an enzyme which starts to digest any proteins in the food. It also contains dilute hydrochloric acid which the enzyme needs in order to work properly.

The stomach stretches as it fills with food. Every now and then, a ring of muscles at the bottom of the stomach allows some mixed food to pass down into the small intestine.

The small intestine

In the upper part of the small intestine, two more liquids are mixed with the food to help the process of digestion:

Bile, which is made in the liver and stored in the gall bladder, breaks up fats into droplets small enough to be digested. It also neutralizes the stomach acid.

Pancreatic juice from the pancreas carries powerful enzymes which digest starches, fats and proteins.

Digestion is completed in the small intestine and digested food passes into the blood through millions of tiny bumps on the intestine walls. The bumps are called *villi*—they give the small intestine a large surface through which to absorb food, and they contain the network of tiny blood tubes which carry the food away.

Undigested droplets of fat are also absorbed by the villi. They pass into tiny tubes containing a liquid called *lymph* which drains into the blood elsewhere in the body.

The large intestine

Undigested matter such as cellulose passes into the large intestine. Here, water remaining from the digestive juices is absorbed so that it can be re-used by the body. Waste matter, now semi-solid, passes out of the body through the anus.

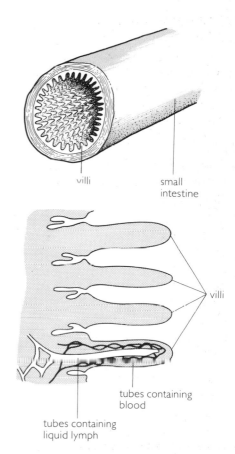

villi   small intestine

villi

tubes containing blood

tubes containing liquid lymph

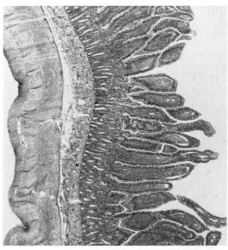

Cross section through the wall of the small intestine.

Questions
1. Make a list of the main sections of the alimentary canal starting at the mouth.
2. What is peristalsis? What does it do to the food?
3. What is happening to food during digestion?
4. Where does digested food eventually end up?
5. What does gastric juice contain? Why?
6. What jobs are done by   a) bile;   b) pancreatic juice?
7. In what part of the alimentary canal is digested food mainly absorbed? Through what is it absorbed?
8. Where in the alimentary canal is water mainly absorbed?

155

9.6　The blood system

Blood carries digested food to the cells of the body. It also brings them other vital substances such as oxygen and water, and it carries away their waste materials.

Blood

Blood is a mixture of *red cells*, *white cells* and *platelets* all suspended in a watery liquid called *plasma*:

Red cells　These are made in the red marrow inside bones. Red cells are partly made from a protein called *haemoglobin* which contains iron and gives blood its dark red colour. Haemoglobin is important because it can attract and carry molecules of oxygen. Blood which is carrying oxygen is bright red in colour.

White cells　There are fewer white cells in the blood than red, and they are not all of the same type. Some white cells surround and digest harmful germs and dead cells, others make chemicals called *antibodies* which help you fight off disease.

Platelets　These are pieces of broken up blood cells which come from red bone marrow. They help the blood to clot when the skin is cut.

Plasma　Plasma is mainly water but it contains many dissolved substances including digested foods, hormones, antibodies, and waste materials such as carbon dioxide.

Circulation and the blood

The heart pumps blood round the body through a system of tubes:

Arteries　Blood leaves the heart through wide tubes or *vessels* called arteries. These have thick walls to withstand the high pumping pressure.

Capillaries　The arteries divide into narrower tubes which carry the blood to networks of very fine tubes called capillaries. Every living cell in the body lies close to a capillary—water from the blood seeps out through the thin capillary walls bringing dissolved food and oxygen to the nearby cells. It also carries their waste materials back into the capillary. The watery liquid surrounding each cell is called *tissue fluid*.

Veins　Blood from the capillaries drains into wider tubes called veins and returns to the heart at low pressure. Some veins, such as those in the legs, contain one-way valves to stop the blood flowing backwards.

Red blood cells.

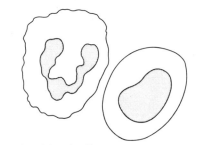

White blood cells.

Platelets.

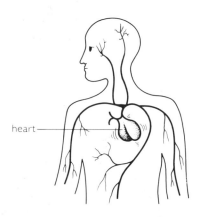

The heart

The heart is really two separate pumps in one. One pump sends blood through capillaries in the lungs, where oxygen is absorbed; the other pump takes in this oxygen-carrying blood and pumps it round the rest of the body. This second pump is made of thicker tissue than the first because it has to pump blood through a much longer system of blood tubes.

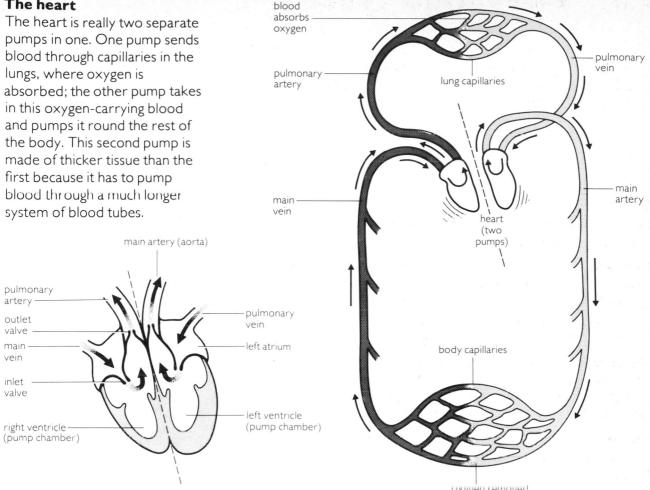

Double circulation of the blood.

Like all force pumps (see page 114), each heart pump has two one-way valves separated by a chamber. The chamber is made smaller when the muscles around it contract, and blood is pushed out through the outlet valve. When the muscles relax again, more blood flows into the chamber through the inlet valve. The muscle contractions or 'beats' are set off by nerve impulses produced in the heart itself, though the beat-rate can be changed by the autonomic nervous system—your heart beats at anything from 60 to 150 times a minute depending upon what you are doing.

Questions

1. Which type of blood cell contains haemoglobin? Why is haemoglobin important?
2. Why is some blood dark red in colour and some bright red?
3. What does blood plasma contain?
4. What are the tubes called through which blood a) leaves the heart b) returns to the heart?
5. What is a) a capillary; b) tissue fluid?
6. Where does blood pumped from the right ventricle travel?
7. What causes the muscles in the heart to contract?

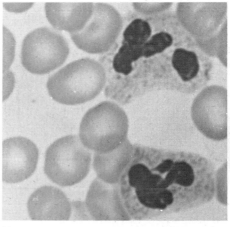

Human blood, showing red and white cells.

9.7　The lungs

In the lungs, oxygen is added to the blood and carbon dioxide is removed. It's all part of the process by which the body releases the energy in digested food.

Respiration
The cells of the body get the energy they need by combining digested food with oxygen brought to them by the blood. The process is called *tissue respiration*—like the burning of other fuels, it produces water and carbon dioxide gas.

As blood passes through the lungs, it absorbs fresh supplies of oxygen from the air, and releases the unwanted carbon dioxide carried away from the cells.

The lungs
The lungs are two spongy bags of tissue filled with millions of tiny air spaces called *alveoli*. These have very thin walls and are each surrounded by a dense network of fine blood tubes (capillaries). Oxygen from the air you breathe diffuses through the thin walls and into the blood; at the same time, carbon dioxide diffuses from blood out into the air spaces.

The tiny air spaces lie at the ends of a series of branching air passages which connect with the *windpipe*. As you breathe, air moves in and out of the lungs through the windpipe and some of the old air in the air spaces is exchanged for new.

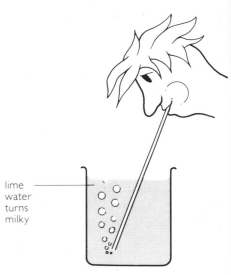

lime water turns milky

Carbon dioxide is present in the air you breathe out.

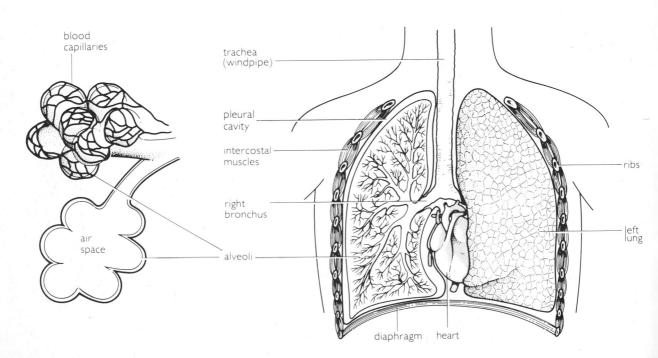

blood capillaries

air space

trachea (windpipe)

pleural cavity

intercostal muscles

right bronchus

alveoli

ribs

left lung

diaphragm　heart

Breathing

The lungs hang in an airtight space called the *thorax*. At the bottom of the thorax is a curved sheet of muscle called the *diaphragm*. Around the sides of the thorax is the rib-cage, with sheets of muscles between the ribs—these are known as *intercostal muscles*.

Breathing in When you breathe in, two things happen at once; the diaphragm muscles pull the diaphragm downwards and the muscles between the ribs pull the rib-cage upwards and outwards. These muscle movements increase the size of the thorax, and the lungs expand as air flows in to fill up the extra space.

Breathing out When you breathe out, the diaphragm muscles and the muscles between the ribs relax, the thorax returns to its original size and air is pushed out of the lungs.

During light breathing, the breathing action is mainly produced by movement of the diaphragm muscles. The muscles between the ribs are used when greater amounts of air are moved in and out of the lungs—during running for example. With more air flowing in and out of the lungs, the blood can absorb oxygen and release carbon dioxide at faster rates.

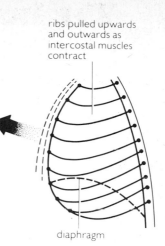

ribs pulled upwards and outwards as intercostal muscles contract

diaphragm

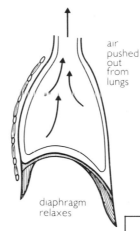

ribs pulled upwards and outwards

thorax expands: lungs fill with air

diaphragm pulled downwards

air pushed out from lungs

diaphragm relaxes

Breathing in . . .   . . . breathing out.

Questions

1. In your lungs, what gas is taken into the blood? How do the cells of the body make use of this gas?
2. In your lungs, what gas is removed from your blood? What simple test could you carry out to show that this gas is present in the air you breathe out?
3. What are alveoli? Why are they surrounded by capillaries?
4. What is   a) the windpipe;   b) the thorax?
5. What two sets of muscles expand your thorax when you breathe in? What effect does each set of muscles have? Which muscles are used during light breathing?

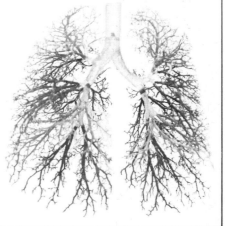

The air system of the lungs.

159

9.8 **Balance in the blood**

Blood has many different jobs to do as it circulates round the body, but the various substances it carries must all be kept in the right proportions.

Functions of the blood
Blood does a variety of different jobs:

It carries oxygen and digested foods such as glucose to the cells of the body;
It carries carbon dioxide and other waste materials away from the cells;
It carries hormones around the body;
It distributes heat energy throughout the body.

The different substances carried by the blood must all be kept in the right proportions. This job is done by the liver, the lungs and the kidneys as blood circulates through them.

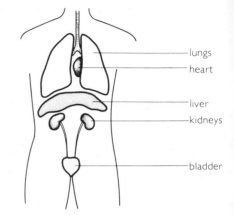

The liver
The liver is a very complex chemical factory—the diagram below shows just some of the processes which take place within it. It constantly adjusts the concentrations of many substances in the blood—glucose is one example; it stores some substances and chemically changes some to make them more useful or less harmful. Most of the digested food absorbed in the small intestine is carried by the blood straight to the liver.

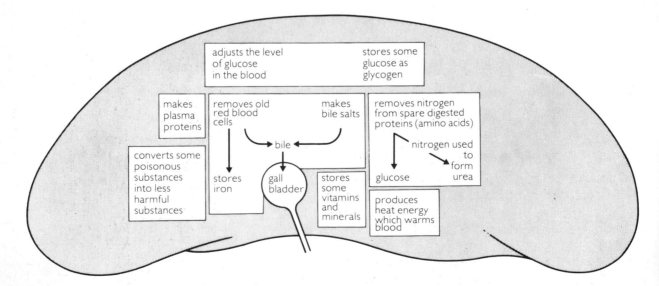

The varied functions of the liver.

160

Organs of excretion

The lungs and the kidneys are organs of excretion—they remove from the body substances which it makes but does not need.

The lungs   These remove carbon dioxide from the blood. They also add oxygen to the blood.

The kidneys   The kidneys remove from the blood nitrogen-rich compounds such as urea. They also remove spare salts and water which the body has no use for. Together, these substances form urine which is collected in the bladder and released when the toilet is used.

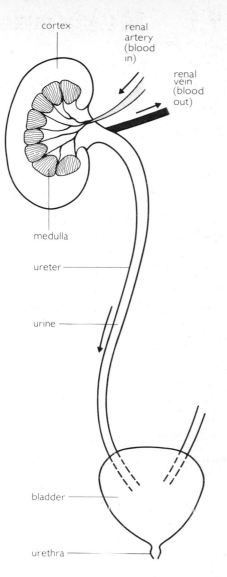

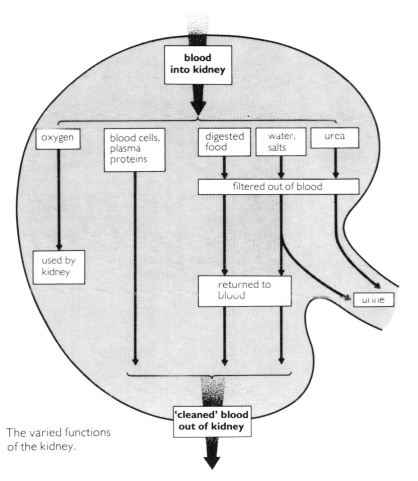

The varied functions of the kidney.

Questions

1. What jobs are done by the blood as it circulates?
2. What happens to most of the digested food absorbed in the small intestine? Name a digested food.
3. Which organ adjusts the concentration of glucose in the blood?
4. What does the liver do with spare digested proteins (amino acids) which the body has no use for?
5. What happens to urea produced in the liver?
6. Write down three substances stored in the liver.
7. Which organ excretes   a) carbon dioxide;   b) urine?
8. What does urine contain? Where in the body is it collected?

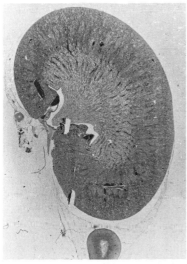

Cross section through a human kidney.

Reproduction (1)

A human baby grows from a tiny cell within its mother. This cell is formed when an egg inside the mother is fertilized by a sperm from the father.

Puberty

Puberty is the start of the time when a girl is able to become a mother and a boy to become a father. Puberty often occurs around the ages twelve to fourteen, but it is quite normal for it to be earlier or later than this.

The female reproductive system

At birth, a girl has hundreds of thousands of partly developed eggs or *ova* in her *ovaries*. From the time she reaches puberty, she releases a mature egg from one of her ovaries about every 28 days. The egg is drawn down the egg tube and into the *uterus* (the womb).

The release of an egg is called *ovulation*. Just before this happens, the ovaries put into the blood a hormone called *oestrogen* which sets off changes in the lining of the uterus—the lining thickens and a dense network of tiny blood tubes forms within it. The uterus is then ready to receive a fertilized egg and to nourish it as it develops into a baby.

Menstruation   If the egg is not fertilized, it dies and the lining of the uterus begins to break up. Within about two weeks, ovum, lining and blood pass out through the vagina during a period—the process is called *menstruation*.

The 28 day cycle of ovulation, uterus lining growth and menstruation is called the *menstrual cycle*.

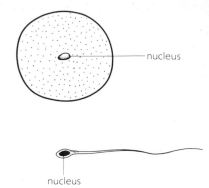
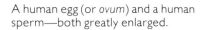

A human egg (or *ovum*) and a human sperm—both greatly enlarged.

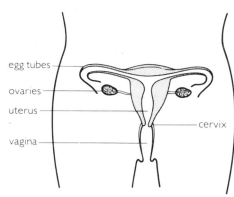

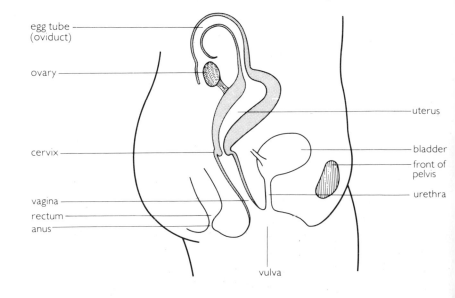

The male reproductive system

A man produces sperm cells in his *testes*. To leave his body, the sperms first travel through the sperm ducts where they mix with liquid produced in the seminal vesicles and the prostate gland.

The liquid and sperms are together known as *semen*. The liquid nourishes the sperms and sets off the swimming movements in their tails which help them to travel up to the egg tubes of the woman. Like urine, semen leaves the body through the urethra, the tube that passes through the penis.

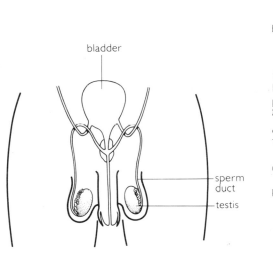

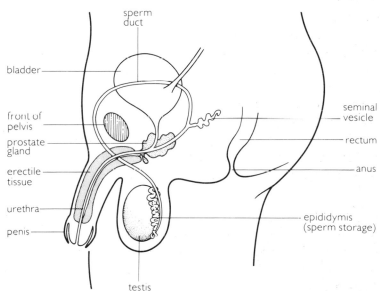

Fertilization

When a man and a woman have sexual intercourse, the man's penis is placed in the woman's vagina. The vagina and the vulva release fluid which helps entry of the penis, and the penis is stiffened by blood which builds up within its tissue. A reflex action called *ejaculation* then takes place in the man—rhythmic muscle contractions pump semen from the penis.

The small amount of semen released contains millions of sperms, many of which pass into the uterus. Several thousand sperms may reach the egg tubes where they may meet an egg. Despite the high number of sperms present, only one fertilizes the egg.

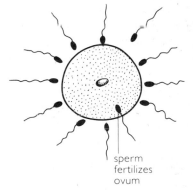

sperm fertilizes ovum

Questions

1. Where in a woman are eggs (ova) produced?
2. What is ovulation? How often does it occur?
3. What happens to the lining of the uterus just before ovulation takes place? What then happens to it if an egg is not fertilized? What is this process called?
4. About how long is the menstrual cycle?
5. Where in a man are sperms produced?
6. How many sperms are needed to fertilize an egg?

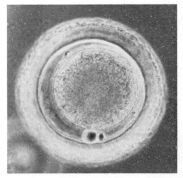

The beginnings of a new life.

9.10 **Reproduction (2)**

As a fertilized human egg grows into a baby, it is nourished and protected in the mother's uterus. About nine months after fertilization, the baby is born.

From egg to embryo

When the egg is fertilized, the head of the sperm is taken into the egg and the tail is left outside. An extra 'skin' now grows round the egg to keep out other sperms. Inside the egg, the nucleus of the sperm joins with the nucleus of the egg, forming a single nucleus. which contains full chemical instructions for a baby to be 'built' by cell division.

The fertilized egg divides over and over again as it passes down the egg tube and into the uterus. As more and more cells are produced, they form into a tiny *embryo* which embeds itself in the thick uterus lining.

The growing embryo

After six weeks, the embryo is about as long as a finger-nail. It has a pumping heart and a brain and it lies in a water-filled bag called the *amnion* which protects it from jolts and bumps.

An *umbilical cord* links the growing embryo to a special organ called the *placenta* which has developed on the uterus lining. The embryo's blood circulates through the placenta. As it does so, it absorbs food and oxygen from the mother's blood and releases carbon dioxide and other waste materials into it. Although the two blood systems are entirely separate, they run very close together where the placenta meets the uterus lining, and materials can pass between the two by diffusion.

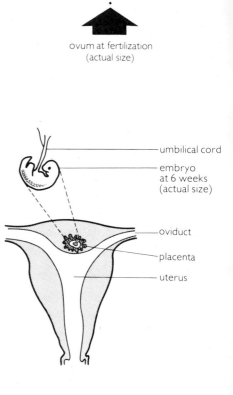

ovum at fertilization
(actual size)

umbilical cord

embryo
at 6 weeks
(actual size)

oviduct

placenta

uterus

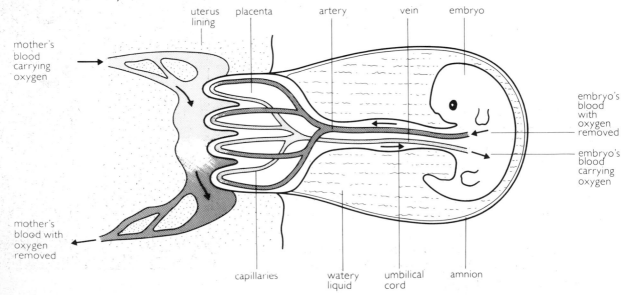

uterus lining — placenta — artery — vein — embryo

mother's blood carrying oxygen

embryo's blood with oxygen removed

embryo's blood carrying oxygen

mother's blood with oxygen removed

capillaries — watery liquid — umbilical cord — amnion

Two months after fertilization, the embryo is very baby-like in appearance. Now called a *foetus,* it has a face, limbs, fingers and toes.

At six months, it is about 60 centimetres long and quite able to kick its mother.

Birth usually occurs about nine months after fertilization.

Birth

A few days before birth, the baby turns until its head lies just above the uterus entrance, a ring of muscle called the *cervix.* As birth approaches, muscles which have developed in the walls of the uterus begin to make regular rhythmic contractions and the cervix starts to open. When the opening in the cervix is wide enough, the baby's head passes down into the vagina. At about this time, the amnion bursts and the watery liquid runs out.

Powerful muscle contractions push the baby from the uterus and out of the mother. The same muscles push out the placenta (the 'afterbirth') shortly after the baby is born.

The baby gives a loud cry as its lungs fill with air for the first time, helped sometimes by a slap on the bottom from the midwife. The baby must now take in its own oxygen and food rather than use its mother's. Soon after birth, the umbilical cord is clipped and cut—the remains of the cord shrivel away to leave the navel ('belly button').

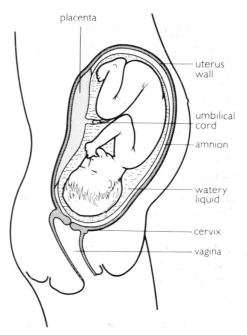

A few days before birth . . .

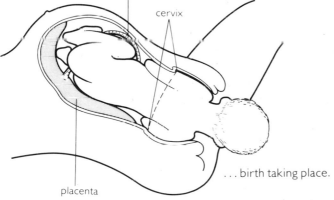

. . . birth taking place.

Questions
1. How does an egg stop the entry of more than one sperm?
2. As cell division takes place, what does a fertilized egg develop into? Where does this embed itself?
3. What is the amnion? What does it contain and why?
4. What joins the embryo to the placenta?
5. Where does food and oxygen pass from the mother's blood into the embryo's blood? What else passes between the blood systems?
6. How many months are there between fertilization and birth?
7. What happens to the baby a few days before birth?
8. What is the 'afterbirth'?

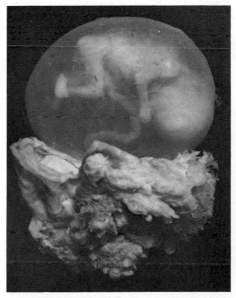

A new life taking shape.

9.11 Micro-organisms

There are vast numbers of tiny living organisms in our bodies and in air, soil, water and plants. Although they are too small to be seen, many of these microbes do useful jobs such as breaking down waste matter. Some, however, are harmful to the body and cause disease: these are given the name 'pathogenic' and are often called germs.

Bacteria

These are very small, living cells about 0.001 mm long. They can only be seen under powerful microscopes. They absorb food through their cell walls and reproduce simply by splitting in two and then growing again. Under suitable conditions, a bacterium may divide every half hour, producing over a million in 10 hours. The bacteria which cause disease either attack the body tissues or release poisons called *toxins*. Some of the different shapes of pathogenic bacteria and the diseases they cause are shown.

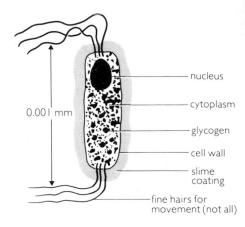

shape	round (cocci)	rod (bacilli)		spiral	comma
example					
disease	sore throat	dysentery	typhoid	syphilis	cholera

Viruses

Viruses are 10 times smaller than bacteria and can pass through filters which trap bacteria. Unlike bacteria, which can exist in living things or in water or in soil, viruses can only live and multiply in other living tissues. They cause disease by invading living cells, breaking the cell material down and using some of it for growth. Most viruses affect only certain organs in one host. The common cold virus attacks only the nose and throat of humans. Other viruses cause polio, 'flu and mumps.

Fungi

Mushrooms, yeast and the mould which grows on bread are all fungi. Some of the microscopic fungi attack the skin, the mouth and the throat. One of these is *ringworm* and another is athlete's foot. Fungi consist of networks of hollow threads. They reproduce by growing upright stalks with heads like tiny dandelion clocks. These heads fill with *spores* which are like seeds. When ripe, the heads burst open and the seeds float away. In 1929 Alexander Fleming found that spores from the *penicillium mould* stopped the growth of bacteria. *Penicillin*, extracted from the mould, was the first *antibiotic*. Antibiotics are now widely used to control disease.

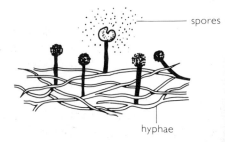

Spread of disease

There are 4 main ways in which germs can be picked up.

Droplet infection   Whenever you breathe out, droplets of moisture leave the body. People with diseases such as influenza breathe out germs in these droplets. In crowded places, other people will breathe in the germs and catch the disease.

Contact   Some germs can only be picked up by actually touching an infected person or some object which he has handled. Measles is a contagious disease that spreads in this way.

Animals   Flies carry germs onto food and eating utensils, whilst blood-sucking insects like mosquitoes inject germs under the skin. Rats, mice and even domestic pets can transmit germs.

Contaminated food   Sometimes germs get into food and water from sewage, or infected people. Typhoid is spread in this way.

Immunity to disease

You recover from a disease because your body produces substances called *antibodies*. These attack the germs or the poisons from the germs. Antibodies gradually disappear when their job is done, but your body is able to reproduce them very quickly if the germs invade again. You are then *immune* to the disease. It is now possible to produce immunity in other ways:

Vaccination   200 years ago Edward Jenner found that infecting people with the mild disease cowpox made them immune to smallpox, a fatal disease. Nowadays, a *vaccine* made from the skin of a calf infected with the vaccinia virus is placed on the arm. A scratch then made becomes infected and forms a spot which quickly heals as the antibodies build up. If a smallpox virus enters the body later, these antibodies will destroy it.

Inoculation   This is the injection of vaccine directly into the bloodstream using a syringe. The vaccine may contain live germs made harmless by living in animals, dead germs, or extracts of the germ poisons.

Serums   These are made from the blood of horses which have become immune to a disease. They contain ready-made antibodies. Anti-tetanus serum is used when people get deep cuts.

Questions

1. What is meant by 'germs'? Explain the term 'pathogenic'.
2. Describe a bacterium and how it reproduces.
3. How do bacteria produce disease? Name 3 bacterial diseases.
4. How do viruses differ from bacteria? Name 2 virus diseases.
5. How do fungi multiply? What is an antibiotic?
6. Describe 4 ways in which diseases are spread.
7. Explain how the body becomes immune to disease.
8. What is 'vaccination'? Who first developed the technique?

Jenner vaccinating his son against smallpox.

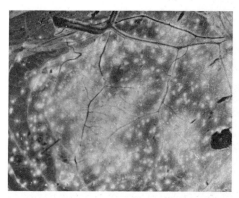

The white areas are cowpox, being grown on a egg membrane.

Questions on Chapter 9

1 In the human body, how are the following protected from outside damage?
    a the heart and lungs **b** the brain
    c the spinal cord

2 What substance gives bones their strength?

3 Where in a tooth are the *pulp, enamel* and *dentine?*

4 Name the four types of teeth present in the jaws of an adult human. What is the main purpose of each type?

5 How is a knee joint different from a hip joint?

6 What are antagonistic muscles? Give an example.

7 Give an example of **a** a voluntary muscle movement
    b an involuntary or reflex muscle movement.

8 What gives you your senses of taste and smell? How does taste and smell information reach the central nervous system?

9 **a** What are the five main types of food or nutrient?
    b What is meant by a balanced diet?

10 Write down a food which contains
    a protein **b** starch

    Describe briefly the part played by the mouth in the digestion of starch.   ALSEB

11 Which nutrients supply us with
    a most of our energy?
    b new body tissues?

12 What simple tests could you carry out for the presence of **a** glucose **b** starch in samples of food?

13 What name is given to the chemical compounds in the body which digest food?

14 Describe two features of the small intestine which help it to absorb digested food.
How is digested food transported to the cells of the body?

15 What is the difference between blood and blood plasma?

16 What jobs are done by **a** red blood cells **b** white blood cells?

17 **a** Why can the heart be described as 'two pumps in one'?

b What is the difference between a vein and an artery?
c Which organ receives blood through the pulmonary artery?

18 Copy and complete the following:
The lungs hang in an airtight cavity called the . . . . When you breathe in, this cavity is expanded in two ways—the rib cage is pulled upwards and outwards by . . . . muscles, and a curved sheet of muscle called the . . . . pulls downwards. As you breathe in and out, ... gas is absorbed into the blood and . . . . gas is released into the air.

19 Briefly describe any three functions of the liver.

20 **a** Copy the outline drawing of the human body. Draw in and label the following organs:
    heart, lungs, liver and *kidneys*   ALSEB

b Which of the above are organs of excretion?

21 **a** What is meant by **i** fertilization **ii** the menstrual cycle?
    b The diagram shows part of the female reproductive system.

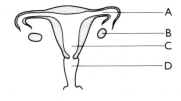

Name the parts labelled A to D.
In which part does fertilization take place?
In which part does the foetus develop?   ALSEB

22 State three ways in which micro-organisms can enter the body.

23 What is meant by the terms
    a immunity **b** vaccination?

Chapter 10

Wave Energy

What's the connection between sunbathing, listening to the radio and swimming in the sea?

The photograph shows a blockage of wave energy. What is it?

10.1 Light and shade

Finding out how light behaves is much easier than finding out what it is! What is certain, is that light travels in straight lines and it can travel through empty space.

Beams and rays

In a dusty or smoky cinema it is quite easy to see the path of the beam of light from the projector. The small particles of dust and smoke in the air glint brightly as the light strikes them, and the edge of the projector beam shows clearly that light travels in straight lines.

In diagrams, lines called *rays* are used to show the direction in which the light is travelling. You can think of a light ray as a very narrow beam of light.

Shadows

Hold a football between a bright light and a screen and the light will cast a shadow of the football on the screen. The shadow marks the area which the light cannot reach because it has been stopped by the ball.

Sharp shadow   If the light comes from a single point such as a tiny light bulb, the shadow of the football is sharp and clear at the edge.

Fuzzy shadow   If the light comes from a spread-out source such as a table lamp, the shadow of the football has a fuzzy edge—around the area of total shadow there is a region of part shadow where only some of the light from the lamp has been stopped.

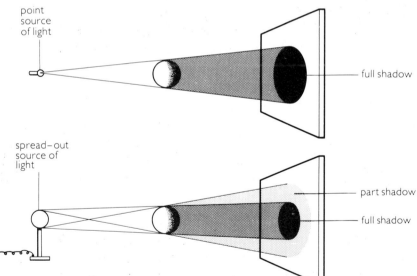

point source of light

full shadow

spread–out source of light

part shadow

full shadow

Eclipses

The Sun is a spread-out source of light and it can form gigantic shadows of the Moon and the Earth. This gives rise to the eclipses of the Sun and the Moon described on the opposite page. The diagrams are not drawn to scale—it is difficult to see any detail on an accurate scale drawing of the Sun, the Earth and the Moon:

Sun

Moon   Earth

Eclipse of the Sun

During an eclipse of the Sun, the Moon passes between the Sun and
the Earth and part of the Earth's surface is thrown into shadow.

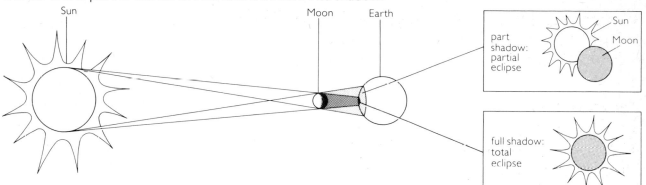

In the area of full shadow, the face of the Sun appears to be
completely covered or *eclipsed* by the Moon—the eclipse of the
Sun is *total*.

In the area of part shadow, only part of the Sun's face appears to be
covered by the Moon—the eclipse of the Sun is *partial*.

The Moon circles the Earth once every 28 days but its path does
not usually take it between the Sun and the Earth. For this reason an
eclipse of the Sun does not happen very often.

Eclipse of the Moon

During an eclipse of the Moon, the Moon passes into the Earth's
shadow—the Earth stops the Sun's rays reaching the Moon.

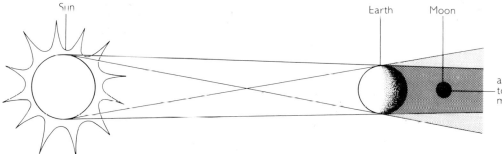

During the eclipse, the face of the Moon is not thrown into
complete darkness. A little of the Sun's light still reaches the Moon
by being bent through the Earth's atmosphere. In this light, the
Moon appears a dull coppery colour.

Questions

1. What evidence is there that light travels in straight lines?
2. What type of light source produces a sharp shadow?
3. What type of shadow does a table lamp produce?
4. Where is the Moon during an eclipse of the Sun? In a region of
   partial eclipse what would a photograph of the Sun look like?
5. What is the Moon's position during an eclipse of the Moon?
6. Why does an eclipse of the Sun not happen very often?

10.2 Reflections

In one side of a shiny spoon you look the right way up, in the other side you look upside down. Each side of the spoon acts like a mirror—like all mirrors, it forms an image because of the way in which it reflects rays of light.

The laws of reflection

A ray of light striking a mirror is reflected as shown in the diagram. The line drawn at right angles to the mirror is called a *normal* and it is from this line that the angles of the rays striking and leaving the mirror are usually measured. When a light ray is reflected:-

the angle of incidence is equal to the angle of reflection—the ray is reflected from the mirror at the same angle as it arrives;

the ray striking the mirror, the reflected ray, and the normal all lie in the same plane.

The fact that the rays 'all lie in the same plane' means that they can all be drawn on one flat piece of paper.

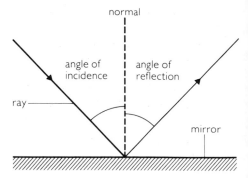

Images in flat mirrors

The diagram shows rays of light leaving a lamp and being reflected from the surface of a flat mirror. Thousands of rays leave each point of the lamp but, for simplicity, only the rays which enter the eye from a single point on the lamp have been drawn.

The rays seem to come from a position as far behind the mirror as the lamp is in front—this is where an *image* of the lamp is seen.

The image is described as a *virtual image*—rays seem to come from it though none actually pass through it.

The periscope

The sailor in the submarine is using an instrument called a periscope to look at a ship on the surface of the water.

In the periscope, two flat mirrors reflect light rays from the ship down to the sailor. The sailor sees an image of the ship straight ahead of him.

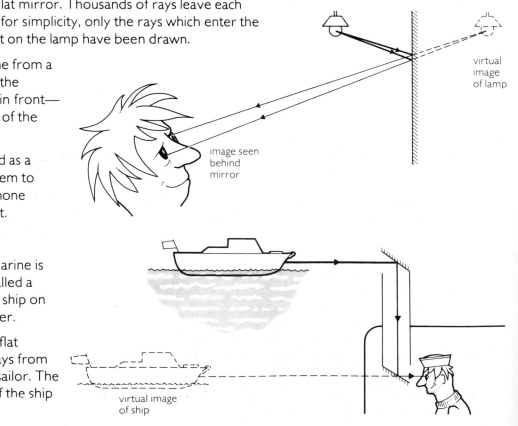

Convex mirrors

The surface of a convex mirror bulges outwards. Like a flat mirror, a convex mirror forms a virtual image of any object placed in front of it—but the image seen in a convex mirror is smaller than the object.

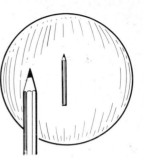

convex mirror (side)   convex mirror (front)

Concave mirrors

The surface of a concave mirror curves inwards. The type of image formed by the mirror depends on whether an object is placed close to the mirror or a long way from it.

Close objects When an object is placed just in front of a concave mirror, the virtual image seen in the mirror is larger than the object. This magnifying effect makes a concave mirror very useful as a shaving or make-up mirror.

concave mirror (side)   Concave mirror (front)

Distant objects When rays of light from a distant object are reflected they come to a focus—they converge (come together) to form a small upside-down image that can be picked up on a screen. This image is described as a *real image*—the rays of light actually meet to form the image.

The diagram below shows a few of the rays leaving one point on a distant object. The complete image on the screen is formed by thousands of rays that leave every single point on the object.

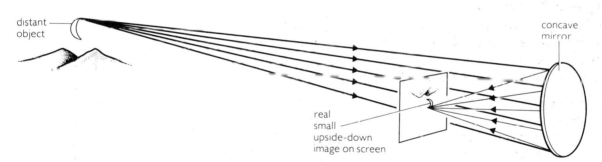

distant object

real small upside-down image on screen

concave mirror

Light rays from a very distant object are very nearly parallel to each other. A concave mirror brings parallel rays of light to a focus at a point known as the *principal focus*.

The distance between a mirror and its principal focus is known as the *focal length*. Highly curved mirrors have short focal lengths.

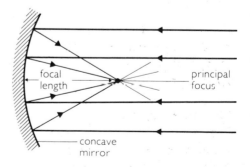

focal length   principal focus

concave mirror

Questions

1. Draw a diagram showing a ray striking a flat mirror at an angle of incidence of 45°. What is the angle of reflection?
2. If you stand 2 metres in front of a flat mirror, where exactly is your image? Is the image real or virtual?
3. What is a periscope? How many mirrors does it contain?
4. What would your image look like in a convex mirror?
5. What would your image look like if you stood close to a large concave mirror? What is meant by:- a) the principal focus of the mirror; b) its focal length?

10.3 Bending light

In space, light travels nearly 300 000 kilometres every second—a speed which would take you nearly seven times round the world in one second. When a light ray enters glass, it slows to a speed of about 200 000 kilometres every second. As the ray slows down, it bends.

Refraction

The bending of light as it enters a transparent material such as glass or water is called *refraction*.

If a fast moving car drives at an angle into sand, it will go off course. This happens because one front wheel strikes the sand and is slowed down before the other.

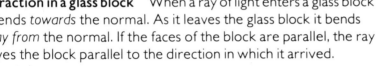

A beam of light is not solid like a car but it also bends off course as it is slowed down.

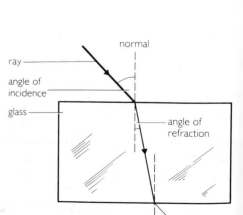

Refraction in a glass block   When a ray of light enters a glass block it bends *towards* the normal. As it leaves the glass block it bends *away from* the normal. If the faces of the block are parallel, the ray leaves the block parallel to the direction in which it arrived.

Apparent depth   The bending of light can give you a false impression of depth.

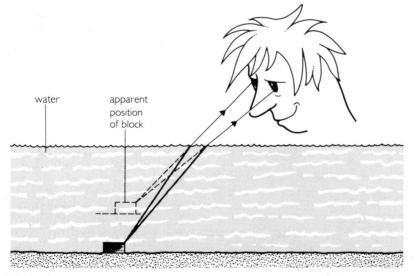

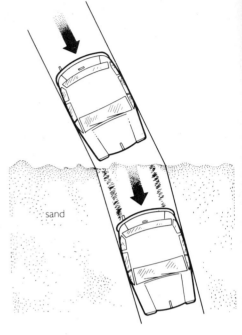

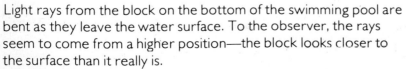

Light rays from the block on the bottom of the swimming pool are bent as they leave the water surface. To the observer, the rays seem to come from a higher position—the block looks closer to the surface than it really is.

Total internal reflection

The diagram on the right shows just three of the rays leaving a lamp placed underwater.

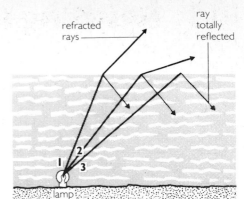

Ray 1 splits into two parts at the surface of the water. One ray passes into the air and is bent, the other weaker ray is reflected.

Ray 2 also splits into two parts. The ray passing into the air is bent so much that it only just leaves the water surface.

Ray 3 strikes the surface at too great an angle of incidence for any refraction (bending) to take place. All the light is reflected. In this case, the surface of the water acts like a perfect mirror and the ray is said to have been *totally internally reflected*.

Total internal reflection can also take place in glass. In the diagrams on the right, light rays are being totally internally reflected from inside faces of triangular glass blocks called *prisms*. Prisms can be used instead of mirrors in the periscope described on page 172.

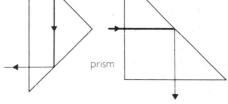

Dispersion

If a ray of white light passes through a prism as in the diagram, the light splits into a range of colours. The effect is called *dispersion* and the colour range is known as a *spectrum*.

You can see the colours of the spectrum on the rear cover of this book.

The colours are the same as those that appear in a rainbow. Most people think that they can see 7 colours, but the spectrum is really a continuous change of colour from beginning to end.

This shows that white light is not one colour but a mixture of colours. It also shows that rays of different colours are refracted (bent) by different amounts.

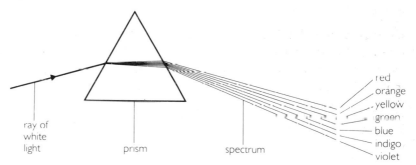

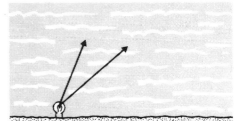

Questions

1. When a light ray passes from air into glass, what happens to its speed? Draw a diagram to show which way the ray bends.
2. Why does water appear less deep than it really is?
3. The diagram shows two rays leaving an underwater lamp. Redraw the diagram to show what happens to each ray.
4. Redraw the diagram of the periscope on page 172, replacing the two mirrors with two prisms.
5. What are the seven colours seen in a rainbow? Which colour does a prism refract (bend) the most? Which colour does a prism refract the least?

10.4 Lenses

Lenses are often made of glass and may be convex or concave in shape. Both types form images as they bend the rays of light from objects placed in front of them.

Convex lenses

The image formed when an object is a long way from a convex lens is very different to that formed when an object is close.

Distant objects   When light rays from a distant object pass through a convex lens, they *converge* (come together) to form a small upside-down image. The image is real—light rays actually pass through it and it can be picked up on a screen:

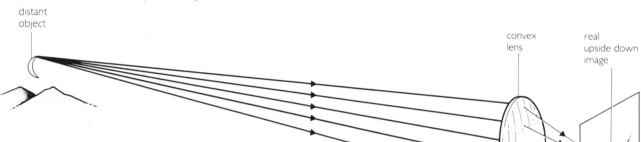

Light rays from a very distant object are very nearly parallel to each other. A convex lens brings parallel rays of light to a focus at a point known as the principal focus. The distance from this point to the lens is known as the focal length of the lens.

Finding the position of an image   If the distance of an object from a lens, and the focal length of the lens are known, the image position can be found by scale drawing.

Two rays are drawn from any point on the object:
a ray parallel to the axis—after it is bent by the lens, this ray passes through the principal focus;
a ray travelling to the centre of the lens—this ray passes through the lens without being bent.

The image is formed where the two rays meet.

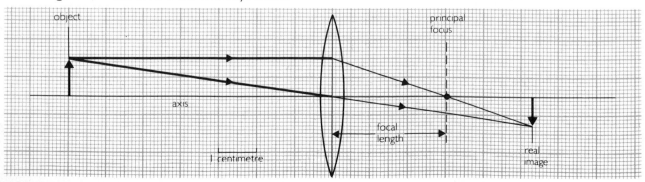

Close objects If the distance from an object to a convex lens is less than the focal length, the rays of light do not meet to form a real image:

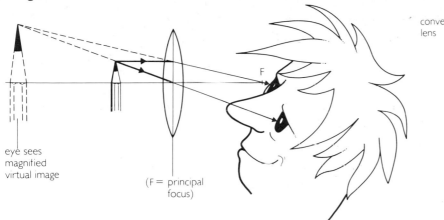

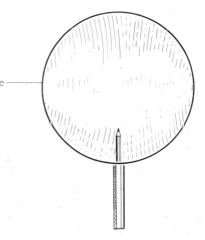

convex lens

eye sees magnified virtual image

(F = principal focus)

The diagram shows just two of the rays from one point on an object placed close to a convex lens. To the person looking through the lens, the rays *seem* to come from a position further away and a large upright image is seen. The image is virtual—no light rays actually come from there.

A convex lens used to magnify an object in this way, is often called a magnifying glass.

Concave lenses

A concave lens forms a small, upright and virtual image of any object placed in front of it whether close or distant.

As parallel rays of light pass through a concave lens, they diverge (spread out). The principal focus of the lens is the point from which these diverging rays appear to come.

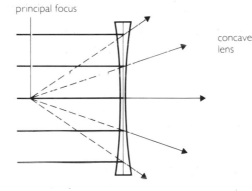

principal focus

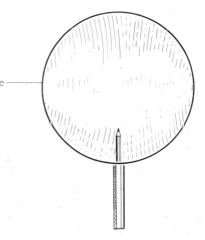

concave lens

Questions

1. What type of lens is shown in the diagram on the right? What will happen to the parallel rays of light?
2. What is the focal length of the lens in the scale diagram opposite? Copy the diagram on to a piece of graph paper. Draw the lens, the axis and the principal focus again. Draw the object 5 centimetres away from the lens. Draw in the two rays and then the image. Is the image larger or smaller than it was before? Is it closer to the lens or further away?
3. What type of lens would you use as a magnifying glass? How close must the object be to the lens?
4. What would a pencil look like through a concave lens? Is the image real or virtual?

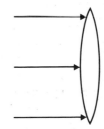

10.5 **The camera and the eye**

They don't exactly look alike—yet they both contain a convex lens and they both pick up images of the outside world on a rather special type of screen.

The camera

A convex lens forms a real upside down image of any distant object and this image can be picked up on a screen. In a camera, the screen is photographic film containing a light-sensitive chemical called silver bromide. Normally, the film is in total darkness. When you press the camera button, a *shutter* behind the lens opens then shuts again, quickly letting light reach the film for a brief moment only. Different amounts of light across the image cause rapid chemical changes in the film which can later be 'fixed' as a photograph.

The amount of light reaching the film is controlled by the speed of the shutter and by an adjustable ring of sliding metal plates called a *diaphragm*. The diaphragm changes the size of the hole (the *aperture*) through which the light rays pass.

The image is focused accurately by screwing the lens backwards or forwards in its holder.

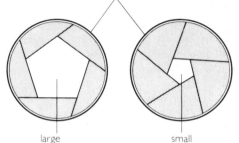

large
aperture

small
aperture

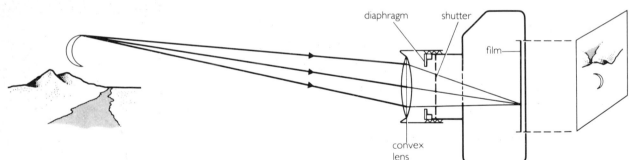

The human eye

The human eye also uses a convex lens system to form real upside-down images of objects in front of it.

The 'screen' at the back of the eye is called the *retina* and it contains nearly 130 million light-sensitive cells. These cells send nerve impulses along the *optic nerve* to the brain and the brain uses them to form a view of the outside world.

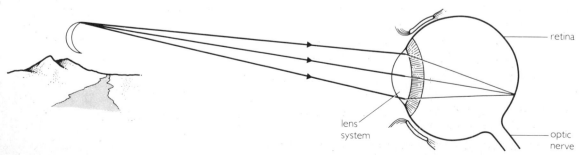

The *iris* may give you a brown, blue or hazel eye but its main job is to control the amount of light reaching the retina. If you walk into a dark room, the hole in the middle of the iris (the *pupil*) grows larger to let in more light.

Light entering the eye is brought to a focus mainly by the *cornea* and the watery liquid behind it. The *lens* itself is used to make focusing adjustments—a process called *accommodation*.

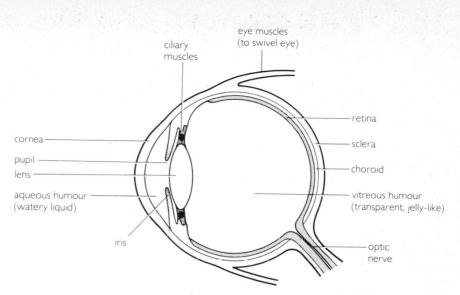

cornea
pupil
lens
aqueous humour (watery liquid)
iris
ciliary muscles
eye muscles (to swivel eye)
retina
sclera
choroid
vitreous humour (transparent, jelly-like)
optic nerve

Accommodation

A perfect eye is able to form a sharp image whether an object is distant or close—it is able to *accommodate*.

The eye accommodates by changing the shape of the lens. The lens is made of an elastic substance and it thickens whenever the ring of *ciliary muscles* around it contracts. The closer an object is to the eye, the thicker the lens needs to be in order to focus light rays on the retina.

Short and long sight   Changes in the shape of the lens may not be enough to produce sharp focusing on the retina. Spectacles or contact lenses must then be worn to overcome the problem.

A *short-sighted* person cannot see distant objects clearly. The eye-ball is too long for the lens system and rays from a distant object come to a focus just in front of the retina. A *concave* lens is placed in front of the eye to correct the fault.

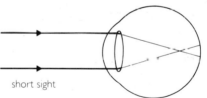

short sight

A *long-sighted* person cannot see close objects clearly. The eye-ball is too short for the lens system and rays from a close object try to converge just beyond the retina. A *convex* lens is placed in front of the eye to correct the fault.

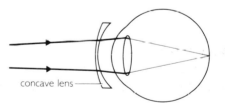

concave lens

Questions
1. Where is the image formed in a camera?
2. Where is the image formed in a human eye?
3. What controls the amount of light entering a camera?
4. What controls the amount of light entering the eye?
5. How is a camera adjusted to focus light from objects at different distances?
6. What changes take place in an eye when it focuses light from objects at different distances?
7. What type of lens corrects   a) short sight;   b) long sight?

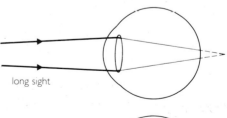

long sight

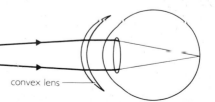

convex lens

10.6 Colour

The eye seems to see a vast range of colours yet a TV can give you a full colour picture using three colours only.

Mixing colours

A beam of coloured light can be produced by putting a sheet of coloured plastic in front of a projector. Shine two or more beams of different colours at a white screen and a new colour is seen wherever the beams overlap.

Primary colours   There are three colours that cannot be made by mixing light beams of other colours together:

these colours are *red, green* and *blue;*
they are known as the *primary* colours.

White light   If red, green and blue light beams overlap on a white screen, a patch of white light is seen:

red + green + blue = white

Red, green and blue together give the eye the sensation of white though pure white is made up of all the colours of the rainbow.

Secondary colours   If the red, green and blue light beams are moved apart slightly, new colours appear on the screen where any two of the beams overlap. The colours that appear are *yellow, peacock blue* and *magenta*—they are known as the *secondary* colours. You can see them on the rear cover of this book.

red + green = yellow
green + blue = peacock blue (turquoise)
red + blue = magenta (plum red)

Colour television   You can give the eye the sensation of almost any colour by mixing red, green and blue light together in the right proportions. A colour TV screen is covered with thousands of tiny red, green and blue dots or strips which glow in different combinations to produce a full colour picture.

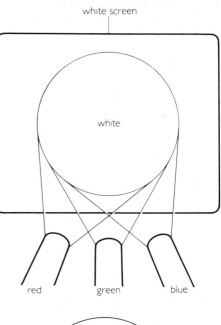

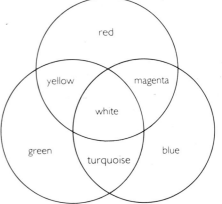

Seeing in colour—many colours, or three?

Most of the light-sensitive cells in the retina of a human eye do not respond to colour. Of those which do, some are sensitive to a range of colours around red, some to a range of colours around green and some to a range of colours around blue. The brain senses a colour by the effect it has on each type of colour sensitive cell—you see all colours in terms of red, green and blue.

Absorbing colour

A projector gives out its own light, so does a TV screen. Most objects are not like this—they reflect light which has come from the Sun or some other source.

Objects appear coloured because they reflect only some of the colours in the light falling on them and absorb the rest.

To the eye, white light from the Sun acts as a mixture of red, green and blue. A red dress looks red in sunlight because it reflects the red light falling on it but absorbs the green and the blue.

A black dress appears black because it reflects no light at all. Red, green and blue light are all absorbed.

A red dress does not always look red. In the diagram on the right a red dress is being viewed in blue light:

The blue light is absorbed, there is no red light present to be reflected, so the dress appears black.

In the diagram on the right, a yellow dress is being viewed in red light:

As yellow is a mixture of red and green, the dress will reflect any red or green light falling on it. Only red light is falling on the dress, so this colour alone is reflected. The dress therefore appears red.

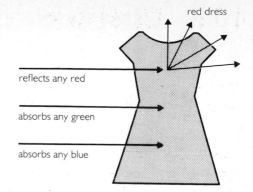

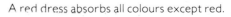

A red dress absorbs all colours except red.

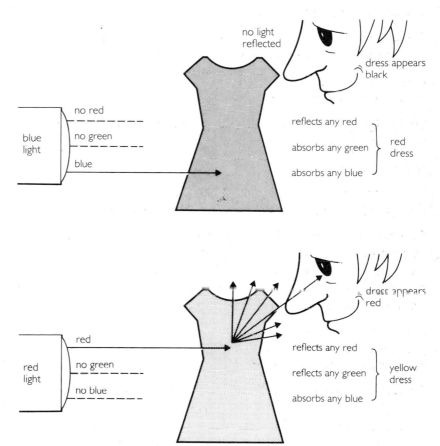

A yellow dress viewed in red light looks red.

Questions
1. What are the three primary colours? What colour is produced when these colours are added together?
2. What are the three secondary colours? What primary colours must be added to make each of them?
3. Name three objects which give out their own light.
4. Why does a black dress appear black?
5. Which colours does a red dress reflect and which does it absorb?
6. What colour will a red dress appear in green light?
7. What colour will a yellow dress appear in green light?

10.7 Electromagnetic waves

What is the difference between light of one colour and light of another?
What is light anyway?

Light waves

Light travels through space rather as ripples travel across the surface of a pond when a stone is thrown in. The ripples on a pond are disturbances which travel across the surface as water molecules slowly vibrate up and down. Light waves are disturbances which travel through space as tiny electric and magnetic forces vibrate.

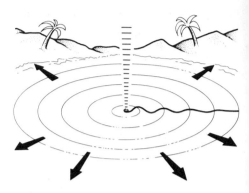

Waves in which the vibrations are from side to side or up and down are known as *transverse* waves. The ripples on a pond are transverse waves, so are light waves.

Wavelength   A series of transverse waves is shown in the diagram on the right. The distance from one wave crest to the next is known as the *wavelength*.

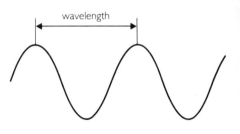

wavelength

Light waves have short wavelengths. About 1500 of the longest light waves would fit into a space only 1 millimetre long.

Colour   The eye sees light of different wavelengths as different colours. The longest light waves are seen as red and the shortest as violet. Most sources of light give out light waves of many different wavelengths.

red light has a
longer wavelength . . .

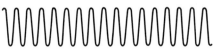

. . . than violet light

The electromagnetic spectrum

Light waves are members of a whole family of waves known as the *electromagnetic spectrum*. The full electromagnetic spectrum is shown in the chart on the opposite page.

Electromagnetic waves are a form of energy. They are mostly produced by electrons which are vibrating or losing energy in some way. All may be radiated from natural objects, such as the Sun; some can be generated by man-made equipment. All can travel through empty space—they do so at a speed of nearly 300 000 kilometres every second.

Electromagnetic waves differ greatly in their wavelengths:

Radio waves have the longest wavelengths. They are used to carry sound and picture signals over long distances.

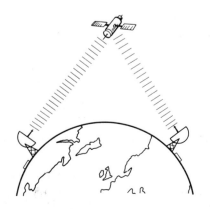

Microwaves are radio waves of very short wavelength. Microwave beams, passed on by satellites, are used to carry telephone calls and television pictures around the world.

Microwaves also generate heat. A microwave oven is a very rapid means of warming food.

Infra-red rays are radiated by all warm objects (see page 184). If objects are very hot, they also radiate light—the only electromagnetic waves that can be detected by the eye.

Ultra-violet rays are present in sunlight. They are invisible to the eye but can damage the retina. It is the ultra-violet radiation from the Sun that gives you a sun tan.

X-rays and gamma rays have the shortest wavelengths in the spectrum. They have little problem in travelling through body tissue and can penetrate dense metals like lead.

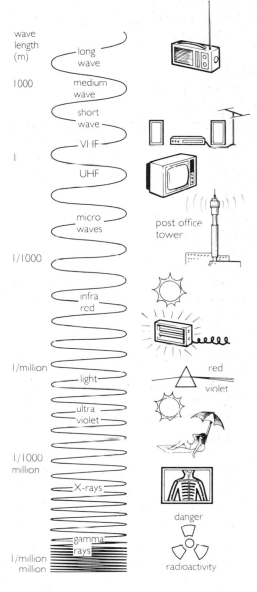

wave type	typical uses	typical sources
radio waves LW MW SW	radio	radio and tv transmitters
VHF UHF	stereo radio television	electronic circuits in which electrons are vibrated
micro waves	satelite communication radar microwave ovens	
infra red	electric fires	warm objects
light	electric lighting	very hot objects
ultra-violet	ultra-violet lamps sun bathing	extremely hot objects: glowing gases
X-rays	X-ray photographs	X-ray tubes
gamma rays	X-ray type photographs of metals	radioactive materials

Questions
1. Give two examples of transverse waves.
2. Draw a diagram to show what is meant by wavelength.
3. Which has the longest wavelength, red light or violet light?
   About how many red light waves would there be in 1 millimetre?
4. Give one type of electromagnetic wave with a wavelength
   a) greater than that of light   b) less than that of light.
5. What are microwaves used for?
6. Which rays give you a sun tan? In what way are they dangerous?

10.8 Radiation

The Sun radiates vast amounts of energy in the form of electromagnetic waves. Most are infra red and light waves. They warm up anything that absorbs them and are commonly known as heat radiation—or radiation for short.

Reflectors and absorbers

On a sunny day, a car roof receives radiation from the Sun at about the same rate as a two-bar electric fire produces it. Some of this radiation is reflected by the car roof; the rest is absorbed—it heats up the inside of the car:

A black surface absorbs much more radiation than a white one—much of the radiation that strikes a white surface is reflected. In hot countries, the clothes worn are often white or lightly coloured to reflect the radiation from the Sun.

Silvery mirror-like surfaces absorb least radiation of all—they reflect nearly all of the radiation that falls on them.

radiation

silvery | white | black
good reflectors poor absorbers | | good absorber

Radiation wavelengths

All objects *emit* (give out) some radiation. The hotter an object becomes, the more radiation it emits.

Warm objects radiate mainly long wavelength infra-red rays—they warm you up but the eye cannot detect them. As objects become hotter the wavelengths emitted become shorter. A very hot object emits some wavelengths short enough for the eye to see as red light—it glows 'red hot'.

Heat detectors   The photograph used on the front cover of this book is of a man drinking a cup of tea. A device which is extremely sensitive to different wavelengths in the infra-red region has recorded the radiation being given off. The device is usually used in medicine rather than in tea-making, to detect ailments such as arthritis and cancer.

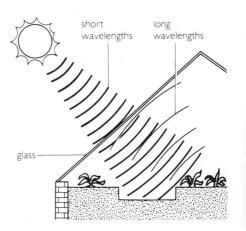

short wavelengths   long wavelengths

glass

The greenhouse   The radiation from the hot Sun is mainly of short wavelength. It passes easily through the glass roof of a greenhouse and warms up the materials inside. These warm materials radiate longer wavelengths that do not pass through the glass so easily. Some of this radiation is reflected back into the greenhouse—the glass 'traps' the heat.

Good and bad emitters

Some surfaces are better emitters of radiation than others. The best absorbers of radiation are also the best emitters.

Black surfaces are the best emitters of radiation; white surfaces are poor emitters and silvery surfaces the poorest of all. Kettles and saucepans usually have shiny outside surfaces to cut down the amount of heat wasted by radiation.

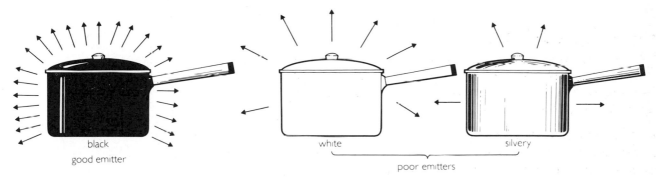

black
good emitter

white

silvery

poor emitters

Losing heat

A hot saucepan does not only lose heat by radiation. Some heat is lost by conduction—heat travels through the surrounding molecules. Some heat is lost by convection—heat is carried away by air currents rising above the saucepan.

The vacuum flask   A thermos flask will keep liquids hot for many hours. The flask has several features designed to cut down losses of heat by conduction, convection and radiation.

The glass container has two thin walls with a narrow space between them. As most of the air has been removed from this space, very little heat can escape by conduction.

A stopper in the top of the flask stops convection currents in the air carrying heat away.

The inside surfaces of the two glass walls are silvered to reduce loss of heat by radiation.

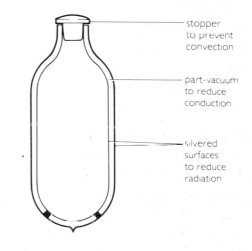

stopper
to prevent
convection

part-vacuum
to reduce
conduction

silvered
surfaces
to reduce
radiation

Questions

1. What surface is the best absorber of radiation?
2. What surface is the best reflector of radiation?
3. Why are the clothes worn in hot countries often white?
4. Give two ways in which the radiation from an object changes as the object becomes hotter.
5. Why does radiation pass more easily into a greenhouse than out of it?
6. What surface is the best emitter of radiation?
7. Why do kettles usually have a silvery mirror-like surface?
8. Give three ways in which a hot object may lose heat.
9. How are heat losses reduced in a Thermos flask?

10.9 Sound waves

Like light, sound travels in the form of waves. But sound waves are very different from light waves.

What are sound waves?

Sound waves are made when a vibrating material pushes over and over again against the substance around it.

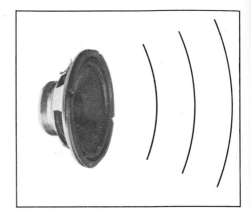

As the cone of a loudspeaker vibrates backwards and forwards, it stretches and then squashes the air around it. These 'stretches' and 'squashes' travel outwards through the air as waves. On diagrams, the 'squashes' or compressions are often drawn as a series of lines.

As the sound waves travel outwards, they make the molecules in the air vibrate backwards and forwards. Waves in which the vibrations are backwards and forwards are known as *longitudinal* waves—sound waves are therefore longitudinal waves.

Sound waves can travel through all gases, as well as liquids and solids, but they cannot travel through a vacuum (empty space)—without a substance to be stretched and squashed, sound waves cannot be made:

The speed of sound

In air, sound waves travel at a speed of around 330 metres every second. This is about six times faster than the speed of a very fast car but slower than the speed of some aircraft. If a thunderstorm is a kilometre away, the sound of lightning takes about 3 seconds to reach you.

The speed of sound depends on the temperature of the air. Sound travels faster through warm air than through cold.

Sound travels at different speeds in different materials.   In water, the speed of sound is very high—about 1400 metres every second. In most solids, the speed of sound is even higher.

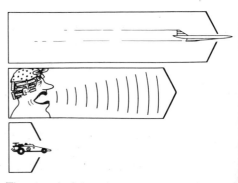

The speed of aircraft, sound, and racing cars.

Echoes

Hard surfaces such as walls reflect sound waves. When you hear an *echo*, you are hearing a reflected sound a short time after hearing the original sound:

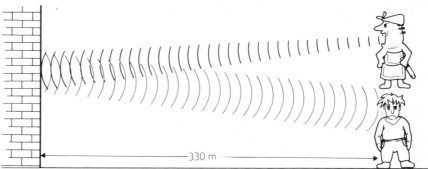

The wall on the right is 330 metres away from the shouting woman. Sound waves take 1 second to reach the wall and a further 1 second to travel back again. The man hears his wife almost immediately; he hears her echo 2 seconds later.

Using an echo to measure the speed of sound   If the man can measure the distance to the wall and the echo time accurately, he can estimate the speed of sound:

$$\text{Speed of sound} = \frac{\text{distance to wall and back}}{\text{echo time}}$$

$$= \frac{2 \times 330}{2} = 330 \text{ metres every second}$$

Echo-sounding   Ships use *echo-sounding* equipment which times echoes in order to estimate the depth of water underneath them. A burst of sound sent downwards from the ship is reflected back by the sea bed. The echo time is measured—the longer the echo time, the deeper the water.

Absorbing sound waves

Echoes can be a considerable nuisance, particularly in concert halls where sounds from musical instruments may take several seconds to die down. Curtains and carpets help to absorb unwanted sounds, so too does the clothing of the audience.

Loudspeaker cabinets are often lined with sound-absorbent wadding to reduce sound reflections from the wood which might spoil the quality of the sound.

Questions

1. When does a material give out sound waves?
2. What are longitudinal waves? Give an example.
3. Why do you see a lightning flash before you hear it?
4. Does sound travel faster through hot air or through cold air?
5. Does sound travel faster through air or through water?
6. Your echo takes 1 second to reach you when you shout 160 metres away from a wall. Calculate the speed of sound.
7. What is echo-sounding equipment used to estimate? What measurement is actually taken with the equipment?
8. What materials help to cut out echoes in a room?

Inside the Albert Hall, London. Saucer-shaped sound absorbers have been hung from the ceiling to stop unwanted echoes.

Hearing sounds

The human ear can detect sound waves, but these sound waves may differ in several important ways.

The ear

Sound waves cause small but rapid pressure changes on anything they strike. The ear turns these pressure changes into nerve impulses which can be sensed by the brain.

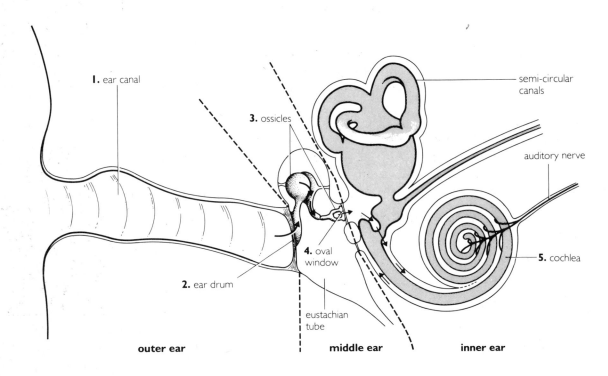

1. ear canal
3. ossicles
semi-circular canals
auditory nerve
4. oval window
2. ear drum
5. cochlea
eustachian tube

outer ear   **middle ear**   **inner ear**

The outer ear   Sound waves passing down the *ear canal* strike a thin sheet of muscle and skin called the *ear-drum*. The sound waves make the ear-drum vibrate.

The middle ear   Behind the ear-drum lies an air-filled space containing three small bones or *ossicles*. As the ear-drum vibrates, these bones act as levers and carry the vibrations through to another sheet of skin called the *oval window*.

The inner ear   Behind the oval window is a fluid-filled tube called the *cochlea*. Vibrations travel through this fluid and are sensed by nerve endings in the tube. Nerve impulses are sent along the *auditory nerve* to the brain.

The inner ear also contains the *semi-circular canals*. These fluid-filled organs are not concerned with hearing—they give you your sense of balance.

The sound waves entering the ear can differ in several ways:

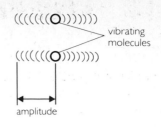

Amplitude

As sound waves pass through the air, the molecules of the air are vibrated backwards and forwards. The distance each molecule moves backwards or forwards gives the *amplitude* of the waves. The greater the amplitude of the waves, the more the air is stretched and squashed and the louder the sound seems to the ear.

Frequency

A bass drum gives out about 20 sound waves every second; a whistle might produce about 10 000 sound waves every second. The number of sound waves produced every second is known as the *frequency*.

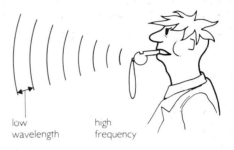

Frequency is measured in *hertz* (Hz). If a loudspeaker cone vibrates 110 times every second, 110 sound waves are given out every second—the frequency of the sound waves is 110 Hz.

Wavelength

The distance between one compression and the next is known as the *wavelength*. The more sound waves are produced every second, the closer together the compressions will be—the higher the frequency of the waves, the lower their wavelength.

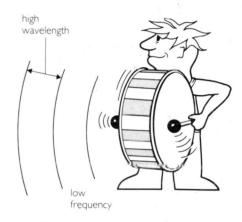

The speed, frequency and wavelength of the waves are linked by an equation:

speed of sound = frequency × wavelength

Since the speed of sound is 330 metres every second, a loudspeaker of frequency 110 Hz will produce sound waves of wavelength 3 metres:

$$330 = 110 \times 3$$

Questions

1. In the ear, how are sound vibrations transferred from the ear-drum to the oval window? Which part of the ear changes sound vibrations into nerve impulses?
2. Which part of the ear is concerned with sense of balance?
3. If the amplitude of the sound waves from a loudspeaker were increased, what change would you notice in the sound?
4. The sound waves from a loudspeaker have a frequency of 1000 Hz. What does this mean? If the frequency were increased, how would this affect the wavelength of the waves?
5. What equation connects speed, frequency and wavelength? Sound waves from a loudspeaker have a frequency of 160 Hz and a wavelength of 2 metres. What is the speed of sound?

10.11 The sounds of music

To the ear, some sounds seem higher than others. High or low, the sound of a guitar seems very different from the sound of a piano.

high frequency
high pitch

low frequency
low pitch

Frequency and pitch

The human ear can detect sound waves with frequencies ranging from 20 Hz up to about 20 000 Hz, though the ability to hear the higher frequencies becomes less with age.

Different frequencies sound different to the ear. High frequency sound waves are heard as high notes—the *pitch* is said to be high; low frequencies are heard as low notes—the pitch is low.

Octaves Musical instruments normally produce notes based on octaves. Two notes are an octave apart in pitch if one has twice the frequency of the other:

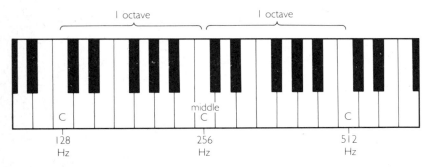

The piano keyboard shown above is tuned to *scientific pitch*. To overcome certain tuning difficulties, pianos are normally tuned to frequencies slightly different from those shown.

Vibrating strings

Instruments like the piano and the guitar give out sound waves when stretched wires or strings are made to vibrate.

A guitar string produces sound waves when it is plucked. The frequency, and therefore the pitch, of the note will rise if the string is tightened or the vibrating length of the string is shortened. A guitar string is effectively shortened when you push it against one of the frets with your finger:

If the vibrating length of a guitar string is halved, the frequency of the note doubles—its pitch increases by one octave.

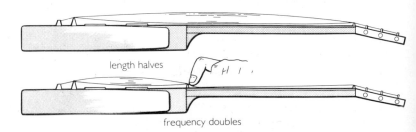

length halves

frequency doubles

Amplitude The amplitude of a vibrating string is the greatest distance it moves sideways as it vibrates—the larger the amplitude, the louder the sound.

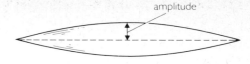

An electric guitar has a *volume* control to increase the amplitude of the sound waves given out by the loudspeakers.

Harmonics The diagram on the right shows the simplest way in which a guitar string can vibrate. The frequency of vibration is known as the *fundamental frequency*. The guitar string could however vibrate at twice or three times this frequency, or more.

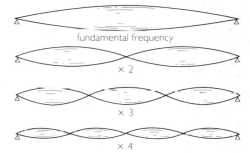

These various frequencies of vibration are known as *harmonics* and some or all may be present in a vibrating string at the same time. It is the mixture of harmonics present that gives a musical instrument its own characteristic sound—a guitar sounds like a guitar and not like a piano.

Resonance in pipes

Like a guitar string, a column of air has frequencies at which it will naturally vibrate provided there is something to set off the vibrations.

The air in a milk bottle starts to vibrate if you blow gently across the top of the bottle. The sound grows loud if the blown air vibrates at a frequency that exactly matches the natural frequency of vibration of the air in the bottle—the effect is called *resonance*.

Wind instruments like the recorder produce sounds when resonance takes place in a pipe containing air. The air vibrations which cause resonance in a recorder come from a flow of air that breaks up as you blow across a narrow wedge.

Long pipes produce lower notes than short pipes Resonance in a long pipe takes place at a lower fundamental frequency than in a short pipe. To produce different notes on a recorder you change the pipe length by blocking air holes with your fingers.

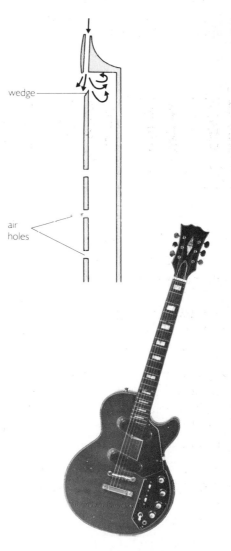

Questions

1. If the frequency of a sound increases, does the sound seem higher or lower?
2. A sound has a frequency of 200 Hz. What is the frequency of a sound   a) 1 octave higher;   b) 2 octaves higher?
3. What happens to the pitch of a guitar string if you   a) halve the length of string which is able to vibrate;   b) slacken the string?
4. What is meant by the amplitude of a vibrating string?
5. What makes a guitar sound like a guitar and not a piano?
6. When resonance takes place, which produces the higher notes, a long pipe or a short pipe?

At which fret would you press to increase the pitch of the strings by one octave?

Questions on Chapter 10

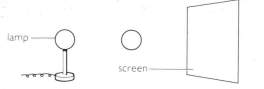

1 Copy and complete the diagram above to show how rays of light from the lamp form a shadow of the sphere on the screen. Mark on your diagram regions of full shadow and regions of part shadow.
In what way would the shadow be different if the lamp were replaced by a point source of light such as a torch bulb?

2 a Copy the diagram above and mark the position at which the viewer will see an image of the cross.
b On your diagram, draw two rays from the cross to show how the image is formed.

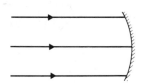

3 a What type of mirror is shown in the diagram above?
b Give one practical use of such a mirror.
c Copy and complete the diagram to show what happens to the rays of light striking the mirror.

4 Draw a diagram to show what happens to a ray of white light refracted through a glass prism.

5 a What types of lenses are shown above?
b A matchstick is held upright close to lens **A**. How would the matchstick appear when viewed through the lens?
c How would the matchstick appear if lens **B** were used instead of lens **A**?
d If the matchstick were moved a long way back from lens **B**, how would this affect its appearance when viewed through the lens?

6 a Copy the diagram of the human eye and mark on the following:
cornea, iris, lens, pupil, retina, optic nerve
b Which of the above controls the amount of light entering the eye?
c Give two ways in which the eye is similar to a camera and two ways in which it is different.

7 A carpet appears green when viewed in white light.
a What colour(s) does it reflect?
b What colour(s) does it absorb?
c What colour would it appear if viewed in red light?

8 Which of the following waves are not electromagnetic?
radio, light, sound, X-rays, infra red

9 Which waves in the electromagnetic spectrum have the longest wavelengths?
Which have the shortest wavelengths?

10 Heat energy may be transferred from one place to another by conduction and convection. What is the third possible method of heat transfer?
How does heat energy reach us from the Sun?

A $\Large\sim\!\!\sim\!\!\sim\!\!\sim\!\!\sim\!\!\sim\!\!\sim\!\!\sim\!\!\sim\rightarrow$

B $\Large\text{vvvvvvvvvvvvvvvv}\rightarrow$

11 a Use a ruler to measure the wavelengths of the two waves **A** and **B** shown above.
b Both waves travel at the same speed. If the frequency of **A** is 2 Hz, what is the frequency of **B**?

12 What is an echo?

13 One sound has a high pitch, another has a low pitch. What is the difference between the two sets of sound waves?

14 Give two ways in which the frequency of a vibrating guitar string could be increased.

Chapter 11

Electrical Energy

In one way it makes your hair stand on end, in another it dries it. What is it?

The light for this photograph came from two sources . . .

11.1 Electric charge

It passes through the wires when you switch on the light and it causes lightning flashes. It makes polythene film stick to your hands and dust stick to your records. It can even make your hair stand on end!

It's called electric charge—no one knows what it is but a great deal is known about where it comes from and the way it behaves.

The electric atom

In the centre of an atom there is a *nucleus* made up of particles called *protons* and *neutrons*. Around this nucleus orbit very much lighter particles called *electrons*.

Electric charge is carried by the electrons and protons in every atom. There are different types of charge:

the charge on an electron is called a *negative* (−) charge;
the charge on a proton is called a *positive* (+) charge.
There is no charge on a neutron.

Normally, atoms have equal numbers of electrons and protons— they have equal amounts of − and + charge within them.

Electrons do not always stay attached to atoms. When you switch on a light, the 'electricity' that travels through the wires is actually a flow of electrons.

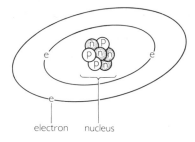

electron   nucleus

Conductors and insulators

Materials that allow electrons to pass through them are called *conductors*. All metals are good conductors of electricity, so is carbon. In a conductor, some of the electrons are not very tightly held to the atoms and are free to travel through the material.

Most non-metals conduct poorly or not at all. Materials that do not normally allow electrons to pass through them are called *insulators*: their electrons are all tightly held to atoms and are not free to move.

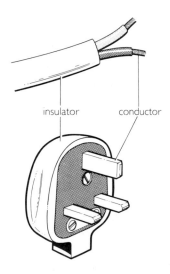

insulator   conductor

Conductors		Insulators	
Good	*Bad*	rubber	glass
metals	water	plastics	dry air
especially	the human body	e.g.	
silver	earth	PVC	
copper		polythene	
aluminium		cellulose acetate	
carbon			

Static electricity

If a material gains or loses electrons, there is no longer an exact balance between the − and + charges within it—the material is said to be *charged*. Charged materials are sometimes said to have 'static electricity' on them.

Charging by rubbing   Insulators become charged when they are rubbed:

A piece of polythene gains − charge when rubbed with a cloth. The polythene pulls electrons away from atoms in the cloth, leaving itself with more electrons than normal and the cloth with less. The charge stays on the polythene because polythene is an insulator—the extra electrons are unable to flow away through the material, though in time they leak into the air.

A sheet of cellulose acetate is left with a + charge when rubbed with a cloth. The cloth pulls electrons away from some of the atoms in the sheet, leaving the atoms with more protons than electrons.

Forces between charges   An electric charge will push or pull on any other charge nearby.

If two charged strips of polythene are held together at one end, the strips are pushed apart:

Like charges repel each other.

If you pull a polythene bag quickly through your hand, the polythene gains a − charge and your hand is left with a + charge. The bag clings to your hand because the − and + charges pull on each other:

Unlike charges attract each other.

The attraction between unlike charges makes dust cling to records and can even cause sparks when you take off nylon or Terylene clothing—the sparks occur when electrons are pulled strongly enough to make them jump through air.

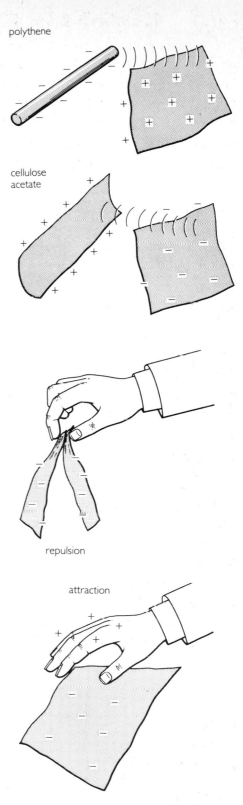

polythene

cellulose acetate

repulsion

attraction

Questions

1. What type of charge is on   a) an electron;   b) a proton?
2. A sodium atom has 11 protons. How many electrons does it have?
3. What actually travels through the wires when you switch on a light?
4. What is the difference between a conductor and an insulator? Name two good conductors.
5. What insulator would you rub with a cloth to produce   a) a negative charge;   b) a positive charge?
6. How could you show that like charges repel each other?
7. How could you show that unlike charges attract each other?

11.2 Electric cells

Electric cells, often called batteries, are a very convenient source of electricity and can be used to power many things from radios to submarines. The electrons they release come from chemical reactions that take place inside them.

The simple cell
A simple cell can be made by placing a zinc plate and a copper plate in a dilute solution of sulphuric acid. The cell will light up a small bulb if there is a conducting path from one plate to the other plate through the bulb. As copper is a good conductor, copper wires can be used to connect the bulb to the plates.

The zinc plate dissolves in the acid, releasing electrons as it does so. These electrons leave the zinc plate and pass through the bulb, making it glow brightly. On reaching the copper plate, the electrons cause hydrogen from the acid to form into hydrogen gas which bubbles off the plate. Overall, the zinc goes into solution, the hydrogen comes out of solution, and electricty is released in the process.

The two plates are known as *electrodes:*
the zinc plate is the *negative* (−) *electrode*—it acts as a store of electrons;
the copper plate is the *positive* (+) *electrode*—it is always ready to receive electrons.

Polarization   The bulb does not glow brightly for long. A blanket of bubbles builds up round the copper plate and reduces the flow of electrons from the cell—an effect known as *polarization.* A *depolarizing agent,* such as potassium dichromate, can be added to the solution to remove hydrogen from the copper plate; when this is done, the bulb begins to glow brightly again.

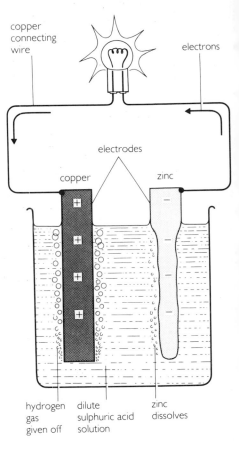

The dry cell
The batteries you find in the handle of a torch are of a type known as *dry cells.* Instead of an acid, a dry cell uses ammonium chloride in 'dry' jelly form, so the cell does not have to be kept upright.

The zinc case of the cell acts as the negative (−) electrode; the carbon rod in the centre of the cell is the positive (+) electrode. Around the carbon rod is the depolarizing agent—a mixture of manganese dioxide and powdered carbon.

The simple cell and the dry cell are both called *primary* cells—they will release charge but they cannot be recharged. *Secondary* cells on the other hand store charge that is put into them—they can be recharged over and over again.

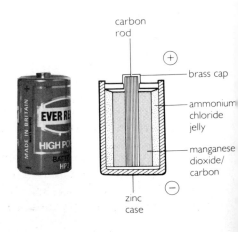

Lead-acid storage cells

The lead-acid cell, or *accumulator,* is a secondary cell. It has two sets of plates, each connected to a *terminal.* Both sets are made of lead but the positive plates are coated with lead dioxide paste. The plates are in a dilute solution of sulphuric acid.

The cell discharges (gives out electrons) as the lead and the lead dioxide on the plates are slowly converted to soft lead sulphate. The reaction dilutes the acid making it less dense.

When the cell is connected to a battery charger, electrons are pushed back through the cell. This reverses the chemical reactions—lead, and lead dioxide, are built up on the plates again.

Batteries   Single cells are often called batteries, though a *battery* really means a collection of cells. A car battery, for example, is made up of six lead-acid cells connected one after another in a row. Together, the cells push out electrons with greater force than a single cell.

Care of lead-acid batteries   You can check the state of charge of each cell of a battery by measuring the relative density of the acid solution with a hydrometer (see page 111); as a cell loses its charge, the density of the acid gets less.

The check is important because a 'flat' (fully discharged) battery soon becomes 'sulphated' and cannot then be recharged. A 'sulphated' battery is one in which the soft lead sulphate on the plates has changed into a hard form that cannot be converted back into lead and lead dioxide.

When a battery is fully charged, any further charging turns some of the water into hydrogen and oxygen gas that bubbles up round the plates. The battery must be kept topped up with distilled water to replace the water that is lost.

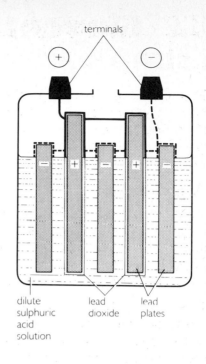

dilute sulphuric acid solution   lead dioxide   lead plates

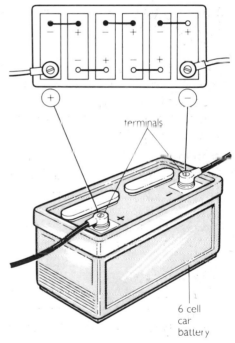

terminals

6 cell car battery

Questions

1. In a simple cell, what materials are used for the + plate and the − plate? In what liquid are they placed?
2. What is polarization? How does it affect a simple cell? How can polarization be prevented in a simple cell?
3. What are the positive and negative electrodes of a dry cell made of? What depolarizing agent is used in the cell?
4. How is a secondary cell different from a primary cell?
5. How can you check the state of charge of a lead-acid cell? Why must the cell not be left 'flat' for a long time? Why must the cell be kept topped up with distilled water?

11.3 Current and voltage in a simple circuit

Connect a bulb to a battery and electrons flow through the bulb. But what have amps and volts got to do with electron flow?

A simple circuit

The diagram on the right shows a light bulb connected by two conducting wires to a battery. The bulb and the battery have been drawn using symbols—the symbol for a single cell is also shown.

The conducting path through the bulb, wires and battery is called a *circuit*. Electrons flow round this circuit from the − to the + terminal of the battery.

In this book, an electron flow is shown by a series of arrows drawn outside the circuit itself.

Current

Electrons flowing round the circuit each carry a tiny − charge. The flow of − charge is called a *current* and it can be measured by placing an instrument called an *ammeter* in the circuit.

Current is measured in *amperes* (A), or 'amps' for short. If a current of 1 ampere (1A) flows in a circuit, about 6 million million million electrons pass round the circuit every second.

The current through a small torch bulb is about ¼A; the current through a car headlight bulb is about 4A.

Current values round a circuit   In the diagram on the right, an extra bulb has been added to the circuit, together with two more ammeters.

All three ammeters show the same reading. Electrons leaving the battery all pass through every section of the circuit, so the same current is measured at all points.

Current direction   Many people regard current as a flow of + charge from the + to the − terminal of a battery—a convention decided after the first batteries had been made and used but before electrons had been discovered.

In this book, the direction of the conventional current is shown by a series of arrowheads drawn on the circuit itself. You can see from this diagram that the electrons flow in the opposite direction to the conventional current.

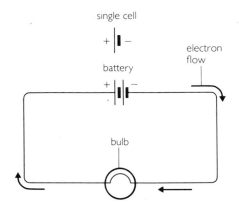

single cell

battery

bulb

electron flow

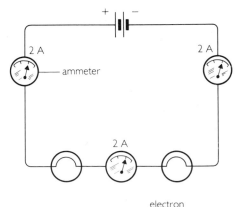

ammeter

2 A

2 A

2 A

electron flow

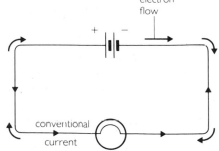

conventional current

Energy from a battery

In the circuit on the right, the battery acts as an electron 'pump': it pushes electrons out of the − terminal, giving them energy which they carry to the bulb. The electrons lose all this energy as they are forced through the tiny coiled wire inside the bulb. The energy is radiated in the form of light and heat.

Potential energy of the electrons   The charged electrons try to force each other apart as the battery pushes more and more of them into the connecting wire. Like a compressed spring, these 'squashed' electrons have *potential* energy.

Voltage

Battery voltage   Some batteries push out electrons with greater force than others, giving them greater amounts of energy in the process. The higher the *voltage* across a battery, the more energy is given to each electron pushed out. The voltage can be measured by connecting an instrument called a *voltmeter* across the battery terminals.

Voltage, or potential difference (p.d.), is measured in volts (V)

The voltage across a dry cell is about 1½ volts (1½ V); the voltage across a car battery is about 12 volts (12 V). Electrons pushed out from a car battery have more energy than electrons pushed out from a dry cell.

Voltages around a circuit   The circuit on the right includes two bulbs. Electrons lose part of the energy given them by the battery, in passing through the first bulb. They lose the rest of it in passing through the second bulb.

Connect a voltmeter across either bulb and it will show a reading. The higher the voltage across the bulb, the more energy each electron loses as it pushes through it.

Between them, the two bulbs use all the energy supplied by the battery:

the voltages across the two bulbs add up to equal the voltage across the battery.

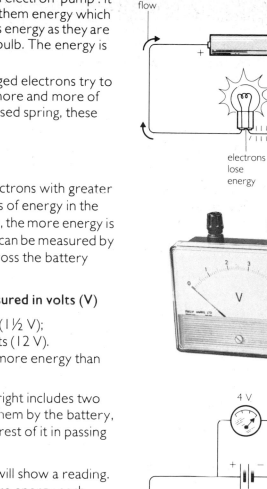

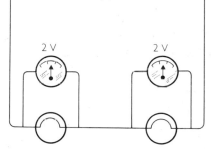

Questions

1. What is a flow of charge called?
2. a) Draw the circuit on the right, adding instruments to measure the current through the bulb and the voltage across the battery. What is each instrument called?
   b) Where in the circuit do the electrons lose their energy?
   c) If the current through the bulb is 2A, what is the current through the battery?
   d) If the voltage across the battery is 4V, what is the voltage across the bulb?

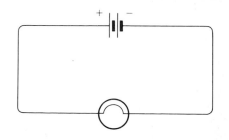

11.4 **Resistance**

Electrons pass easily through copper connecting wire. They don't pass so easily through the tiny coiled wire in a light bulb or the wire used in an electric fire element. These wires have much more resistance.

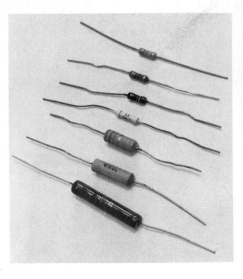

Resistance

The wire used in electric fire elements is made of a nickel chromium alloy called nichrome. Energy is needed to push electrons through nichrome wire; the wire is said to have *resistance*.

A long piece has more resistance than a short piece;
a thin piece has more resistance than a thick piece;
a hot piece has more resistance than a cold piece.
A piece of nichrome wire has much more resistance than a same size piece of copper wire—nichrome is a poorer conductor than copper.

Resistors These are devices specially made to provide resistance; placed in a circuit, they reduce the flow of current. A length of thin nichrome wire makes a simple resistor; other types of resistor are shown on the right.

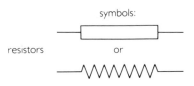

symbols:

resistors   or

Ohms

Resistance is measured in *ohms*. A resistor has a resistance of one ohm ($1\,\Omega$) if a voltage of one volt across it will push a current of one ampere through it.

The more resistance a resistor has, the more volts are needed to push each ampere through. If the voltage across a resistor and the current through it have both been measured, the resistance (*R* ohms) can be calculated using the equation:

$$R = \frac{V}{I}$$
where **V** is voltage (volts)
and **I** is current (amperes)

On the right, the equation has been used to calculate the resistance of the resistor shown in the circuit.

Resistor calculations The equation can be rearranged to give:

$$V = I \times R \text{ and } I = \frac{V}{R}$$

These equations can be used to calculate a voltage or current if the value of the resistance is already known. The triangle on the right gives all three equations—cover each letter in turn with your thumb.

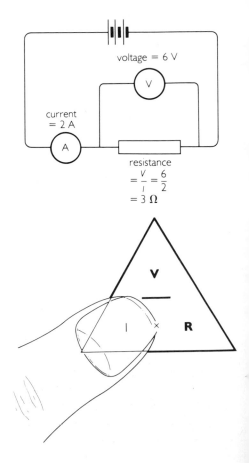

voltage = 6 V

current = 2 A

resistance
$$= \frac{V}{I} = \frac{6}{2}$$
$$= 3\,\Omega$$

Ohm's Law   Increase the voltage across a resistor and more current flows. In the 1820's, George Ohm discovered that the current through a metal resistor increased in direct proportion to the voltage across it provided the metal was kept at a fixed temperature.

In other words, if 6 volts produced a current of 2 amperes through the metal, 12 volts would produce a current of 4 amperes—the resistance of the metal would remain unchanged at 3 ohms provided the metal was kept at the same temperature.

Heat and resistance

Any conductor which has resistance gives off heat when a current flows through it. As electrons are pushed through the conductor, they collide with the atoms making them vibrate more vigorously.

Heating elements   Nichrome wire, coiled to take up less space, is used to make the heating elements found in many electrical appliances used in the house. Not only does nichrome provide high resistance, it can be kept red hot without oxidizing and breaking in the air.

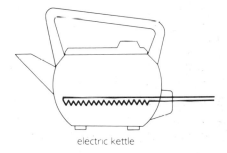
electric kettle

hair drier

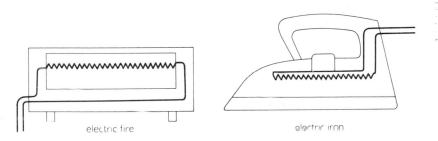
electric fire   electric iron

Light bulbs   The *filament* of a light bulb is made from very thin tungsten resistance wire. When a current is passed through it, the tungsten becomes so hot that it gives off a brilliant white light. Having a very high melting point, the tungsten can be kept white hot without melting. In air, the hot filament would quickly burn up, so the bulb is filled with argon and nitrogen gases which do not react with the hot metal.

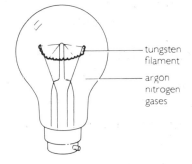
tungsten filament

argon nitrogen gases

Questions

1. Which has more resistance   (a) a long piece of nichrome wire or a short piece?   (b) a thick piece or a thin piece?
2. What do the symbols V, I and R stand for? What equations link them?
3. A metal resistor has a voltage of 12 V across it and a current of 2 A through it. What is its resistance? If the voltage drops to 6 V, what current would then flow?
4. What voltage is needed to push 3 A through an 8 Ω resistor?
5. What happens when a current flows through a resistance?
6. What is the filament of a bulb made of? Why is this material used? Why is a bulb not filled with air? What does it contain?

11.5 Circuits and switches

How can you run two bulbs from one battery? Various different methods of connecting bulbs, switches, resistors and batteries have very different effects.

Series and parallel circuits

Connected to a battery, a single bulb glows brightly. There are two ways in which a second bulb can be added to the circuit:

Bulbs in series   In the left-hand diagram, the two bulbs have been connected in *series*.

Together, the two bulbs provide greater resistance than a single bulb and less current flows as a result. Both bulbs glow dimly—the available voltage has been 'split' between them.

The right-hand diagram shows what happens when one of the bulbs is removed. The circuit is broken, so the other bulb goes out.

Bulbs in parallel   In the left-hand diagram, the two bulbs have been connected in *parallel*.

Both bulbs glow brightly because each has the full voltage of the battery across it. Together, the two bulbs take twice as much current as a single bulb, so the battery loses its charge twice as quickly.

The right-hand diagram shows the effect of removing one of the bulbs. There is still an unbroken circuit through the other bulb, so it continues to glow brightly.

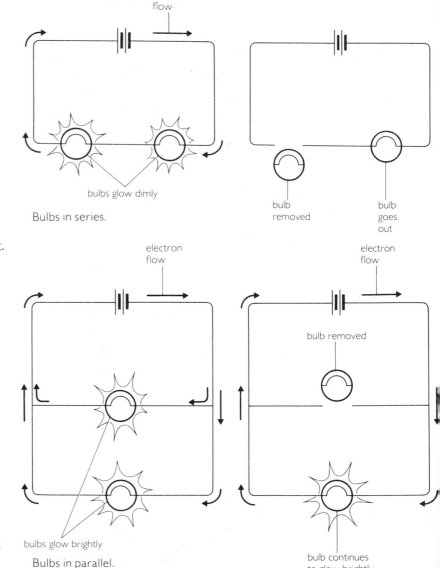

electron flow

bulbs glow dimly

Bulbs in series.

bulb removed

bulb goes out

electron flow

electron flow

bulbs glow brightly

Bulbs in parallel.

bulb removed

bulb continues to glow brightly

Bulbs, electric fires and other appliances used in the house are always connected in parallel with the mains supply. Each then receives the full mains voltage and each can be switched on or off without affecting the others.

Switches

A switch breaks a circuit by moving contacts apart. The diagram shows how switches might be placed in a circuit to control a number of different light bulbs.

To check which switch controls each bulb, trace a route with your finger from one side of the battery through a bulb to the other side of the battery. The bulb is switched on and off by whichever switch your finger passes over.

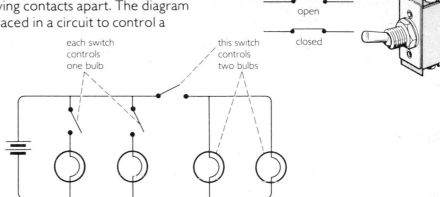

open

closed

each switch controls one bulb

this switch controls two bulbs

Resistors in series and parallel

In series, two resistors have a combined resistance found by adding up their resistance values. Using two resistors instead of one has the same effect as using a long piece of nichrome wire instead of a short piece—it gives the electrons a more difficult conducting path to travel through.

If two identical resistors are connected in parallel, their combined resistance is only half that of a single resistor. The effect is the same as using a thick piece of nichrome wire instead of a thin piece—the electrons are given a wider path to travel through.

2 Ω   2 Ω

combined resistance 4 Ω

2 Ω

2 Ω

combined resistance 1 Ω

Cells in series and parallel

If three 2 volt cells are connected in series, the voltage across all three is 6 volts. Together, the three cells give electrons more energy than a single cell.

When the three 2 volt cells are connected in parallel, the voltage across them is only 2 volts. The cells will last longer than a single cell however, and are together capable of supplying a higher current.

6 V

2 V   2 V   2 V

2 V

2 V

2 V

2 V

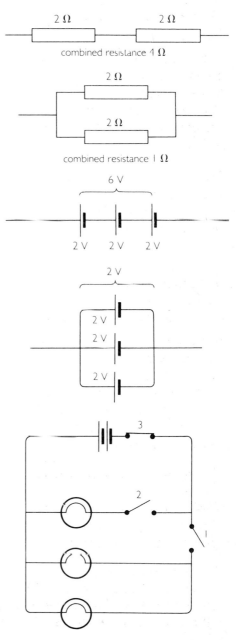

Questions

1. If you were going to connect two light bulbs to one battery, would you use a series or a parallel arrangement? Why? Which arrangement takes most current from the battery?
2. In the circuit on the right, what happens to each of the bulbs when you (a) close switch 1; (b) close switch 2; (c) open switch 3?
3. Show how you would connect two 4 ohm resistors to produce a combined resistance of (a) 8 ohms; (b) 2 ohms.
4. Show how you would connect two 1 volt cells to produce a voltage of (a) 2 volts; (b) 1 volt.

11.6 Mains electricity

When you plug in an electric kettle, you are connecting it into a circuit. The circuit hasn't got a battery in it but the mains supply is doing much the same sort of job.

A simple mains circuit

The diagram shows the circuit formed when a kettle is plugged into a mains socket. All the wires to the kettle are insulated and contained in a single cable or 'flex':

The alternating mains   The current from the mains socket is not a one-way flow like the current from a battery; it is pushed and pulled forwards and backwards through the circuit 50 times every second. The current is known as *alternating current (AC)*. Power stations supply AC because it is easier to generate than one-way *direct current (DC)*.

AC is supplied to the mains socket at a voltage of 240 volts.

The live wire   This goes alternatively − and + as electrons are pushed and pulled through the circuit.

The neutral wire   The Electricity Board *earth* the neutral wire by connecting it to a metal plate buried in the ground. Although current passes through the wire, any charge that might build up on it drains away into the ground—if you accidentally touch the neutral wire, you don't get a shock.

The earth wire   The metal body of the kettle is connected to a third wire called an earth wire—in many houses, the wire is earthed by connecting it to the neutral wire in the supply cable.

The earth wire is a safety wire which prevents the kettle becoming 'live' if a fault develops—current flows to earth rather than through anyone who happens to touch the kettle.

The switch   The switch on the mains socket is fitted in the live wire. If it were in the neutral, wire in the flex to the kettle would be 'live' even with the switch turned off.

The plug   This provides a convenient and safe way to connect up different appliances. There are eight stages in wiring up a plug. The first four are shown on the right, and the second four in the next section.

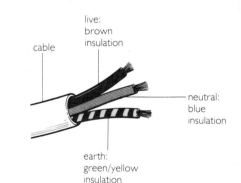

plug with fuse

insulated heating element

switch

mains supply

live wire

fuse

insulated cable

240 V∼

neutral wire

earth wire

cable

live: brown insulation

neutral: blue insulation

earth: green/yellow insulation

The fuse   This is a short piece of thin wire that overheats and melts if too much current flows through it. Like the switch, it is placed in the live wire, often in the form of a small cartridge inside the plug. If too high a current flows because of a fault in the kettle, the fuse 'blows' and breaks the circuit before the cable can overheat and catch fire.

Power

The electric kettle changes electrical energy from the mains socket into heat energy. The amount of energy it changes every second is called the *power* and it is measured in *watts* (W).

A power of one watt (1W) means that energy is being changed at the rate of one joule every second.

If the kettle has a power of 2400 watts, it is turning 2400 joules of electrical energy into heat every second. The chart on the right gives the powers of several common household appliances.

Power can also be measured in kilowatts (kW):

1 kilowatt = 1000 watts.

The power equation   The power of the electric kettle depends on the voltage across the kettle and the current through it: the greater the voltage, the more energy each electron brings; the greater the current, the more of these energy-bringing electrons pass through the kettle every second.

The power of any appliance is given by the equation:

power = voltage × current
(watts)   (volts)   (amperes)

The equation shows, for example, that a 2400 watt kettle will draw a current of 10 amperes from the 240 volt mains:

2400 = 240   × 10

The greater the power of an appliance, the more current it draws from the mains.

Questions
1. What is the difference between AC and DC? Which type of current flows from a mains socket?
2. What is the voltage of the mains supply?
3. Why is an earth wire connected to the body of a kettle?
4. Why should switches and fuses always be placed in the live wire?
5. When does a fuse cut off current? How does it do it?
6. What equation links watts, volts and amperes? Each appliance in the chart (above right) is connected to a 240 volt supply. Use the power equation to find the current flowing through:
    (a) the kettle;   (b) the iron;   (c) the drill;   (d) the TV.

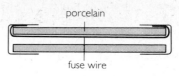

porcelain

fuse wire

A cartridge fuse.

Typical powers	
Immersion heater	3000 W (3 kW)
Fire	3000 W (3 kW)
Kettle	2400 W (2.4 kW)
Iron	720 W
Drill	360 W
Colour TV	340 W
Table lamp	60 W
Fluorescent light	40 W

1. Do not cut right through the inner insulation when removing the outer cover.

2. Gently lever out the fuse.

3. Make sure the outer cover is gripped.

4. Wrap the wires clockwise round the studs.

Electricity around the house

Each mains socket in a house is a part of a whole system of parallel circuits that branch off from the Electricity Board's main supply cable.

House circuits

The Electricity Board's cable into each house contains a live and a neutral wire. At the *consumer unit* or 'fuse box', these wires branch into several parallel circuits which carry current to the lights, the cooker, the immersion heater and the mains sockets. The cable for each circuit contains an earth wire, as well as a live and a neutral.

Each circuit passes through a fuse in the consumer unit. The fuse blows if the current is greater than it should be:

upstairs lighting circuit – 5 A fuse;
downstairs lighting circuit – 5 A fuse;
circuit through cooker – 30 A fuse;
circuit through immersion heater – 15 A fuse.

Mains sockets In many houses in Europe, each mains socket is on a separate circuit with its own fuse in the consumer unit.

In many houses in Britain, all the mains sockets are connected to a *ring main* as shown in the diagram below. This is a cable which begins and ends at the consumer unit; the live, neutral and earth wires in the cable each form a long loop or 'ring' around the house. An advantage of the system is that there are two conducting paths to each socket, so thinner cable can be used.

The ring main is protected by a 30 A fuse in the consumer unit. In addition, each appliance is protected by a fuse in its plug.

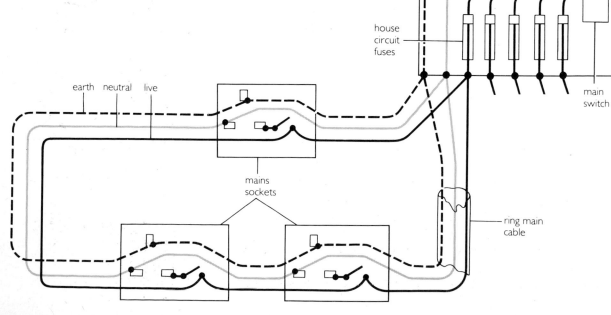

Three pin plugs

In many European countries, each appliance is sold with an unfused plug already moulded onto the end of the cable. Commonly used in Britain, is the square-pin plug on the right which you can connect to the cable yourself. This plug contains a fuse.

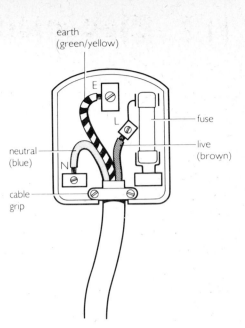

Wiring a plug   When wiring a plug, it is important to check that:
1. the three wires in the cable are connected to the correct terminals. The cable 'colour code' is shown in the diagram;
2. there are no loose strands of wire, and the cable is held firmly by the grip;
3. a fuse of the correct value is fitted.

Fuse values   Plugs are normally fitted with 3 A or 13 A fuses. The fuse value must be greater than the current which normally flows, but as close as possible to this value so that the fuse will blow before a faulty appliance can start a fire. For example:

for a kettle taking a current of 10 A – a 13 A fuse;
for a TV taking a current of 1 A – a 3 A fuse.

Changing a fuse   If the fuse in a plug blows, you must:
1. switch off at the socket and pull out the plug;
2. trace the fault;
3. fit a new fuse only when the fault has been put right.

Buying electrical energy

The Local Electricity Board charges for the electrical energy it supplies. The amount of energy supplied is measured by the *meter* between the main supply cable and the consumer unit.

The meter measures energy in kilowatt-hours (kWh).

One kilowatt-hour is the energy used by a one kilowatt appliance switched on for one hour.

One kilowatt hour is equal to 3 600 000 joules.

The greater the power of an appliance, and the longer it is switched on for, the more energy it uses. A 3 kilowatt fire switched on for 4 hours uses 12 kilowatt-hours of energy.

5. Tighten the screws firmly.

6. Replace the fuse. Check that it fits snugly.

7. Check there are no loose strands anywhere in the plug.

8. Replace the cover.

Questions
1. What does a 'consumer unit' contain?
2. What is a ring main? What advantage does it offer?
3. In a fused plug, which wire is connected to the fuse? What colours are used for the live, neutral and earth leads?
4. What value fuse would you use in a plug connected to   (a) a fire taking 12 A;   (b) a food mixer taking 1 A?
5. If the fuse in a plug blows, what must you do before replacing it with a new one?
6. How much electrical energy is used by a 2 kW heater switched on for 10 hours?

11.8 Chemical effect of a current

Most liquids don't conduct electricity. But some do. When they do,
materials start to move about and chemical changes start to happen.

Electrolysis of water

A torch bulb wired up to a 3 volt battery lights up. If one wire is cut
in two and the two ends are dipped into a beaker of distilled water
the bulb does not light up. This shows that pure water does not
conduct electricity. However, if salt is stirred into the water,
bubbles appear around the wires and the bulb lights up again. The
salt solution is a good conductor. Many other salts, acids and alkalis
also cause water to conduct electricity: they are called *electrolytes*.

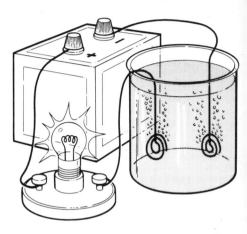

Ions as conductors Acids, alkalis and salts split up into free-
moving charged particles called *ions*, when they are dissolved in
water. It is these charged particles which carry the current of
electricity through the solution. The positive ($+$) ions are attracted
towards the negative wire *(the cathode)* and move towards it. The
negative ($-$) ions travel to the positive wire *(the anode)* to give up
their extra electrons. Thus both kinds of ion are electricity carriers.

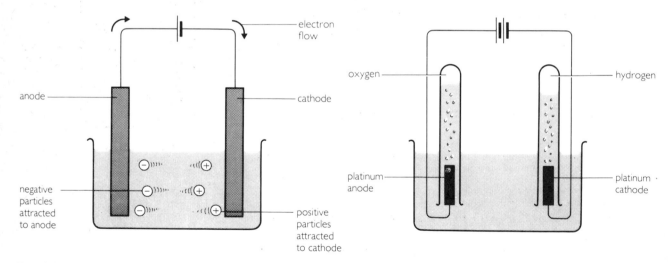

Products of electrolysis of water The bubbles of gas given off at
the anode and cathode when electricity is passed through salt
solution can be collected using the apparatus shown (called a
voltameter). The anode and cathode are small pieces of platinum
metal instead of bare wires. When tested the cathode gas is found
to be hydrogen and the anode gas to be oxygen. The gases are the
same if small amounts of acids or alkalis are used instead of salt. The
effect of the current is to split up the water into hydrogen gas and
oxygen gas. The acid helps this splitting up process:

water $\xrightarrow[\text{electricity}]{\text{acid}}$ hydrogen + oxygen

$2H_2O$ $\qquad$ $2H_2$ $\qquad$ O_2

Uses of electrolysis

Making pure metals   Many metals are extracted from their ores or *refined* by electrolysis. Pure copper, needed for electrical wiring, is produced by the electrolysis of copper sulphate solution.

A high current is used to drive positive copper ions from the solution, onto the cathode. Negative sulphate ions travel to the anode which is made of impure copper. This gradually dissolves to replace copper ions in solution and the impurities form a sludge. The electrolyte is unchanged and copper is transferred from anode to cathode.

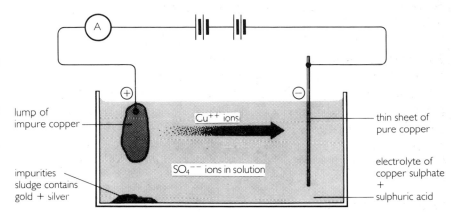

lump of impure copper

Cu^{++} ions

thin sheet of pure copper

impurities sludge contains gold + silver

SO_4^{--} ions in solution

electrolyte of copper sulphate + sulphuric acid

Electroplating   If the cathode of the cell shown above were made of iron, it would still get coated with copper. It would be copper plated. Electroplating iron in this way protects it from corrosion. Layers of nickel or chromium on top of the copper give even better protection and a bright shiny finish.

To deposit a hard, even layer of metal which will not flake off, electroplating must be done very slowly. Good silver plating demands the following conditions:

The article to be plated must be clean, have a good surface and be wired as the cathode.

A very low current must be used and the temperature kept constant.

The electrolyte must have only a low concentration of silver metal (a cyanide salt is used).

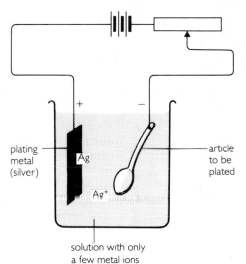

plating metal (silver)

Ag

Ag^+

article to be plated

solution with only a few metal ions

Records   Electroplating plays a vital part in making records. A machine activated by sound waves cuts grooves into a plastic disc. These grooves are plated with various metals, topped with chromium. The series of metal ridges is used to stamp out copies of the original disc.

Questions

1. What is meant by the term 'electrolysis'?
2. How can you show that pure water does not conduct electricity and that salt solution does conduct electricity?
3. What is an electrolyte? What actually carries the current?
4. Name the products of electrolysing water with a little acid added.
5. Explain how impure copper is refined.
6. Why are some metals electroplated? Give 3 conditions necessary for successful silver plating.

Questions on Chapter 11

1 In an atom, what particles carry
  a negative (−) charge?
  b positive (+) charge?
  c no charge?

2 What happens when a piece of polythene is rubbed with a cloth?

3 *Aluminium, copper, iron, carbon, water, glass, polythene, PVC*
From the above list, select:
  a the good conductors of electricity
  b the poor conductors of electricity
  c the insulators

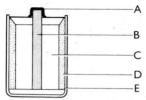

4 The diagram above shows a dry cell.
  a Name the parts **A, B, C, D** and **E**.
  b Which of the above is the + terminal of the cell? Which is the − terminal?

5 What two checks should regularly be made on the cells of a car battery?
Explain why èach check is necessary.

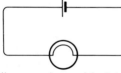

6 Copy the diagram above. Mark in the + and the − terminals of the cell, and the direction in which the electrons flow.

7 Give the approximate voltage of
  a a small torch battery
  b a car battery
  c an AC mains socket

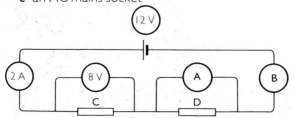

8 a In the diagram above, what type of meter is **A** and what type of meter is **B**?
  b What will be the readings on **A** and **B**?
  c Using the values given for the voltage across **C**

and the current through it, find the resistance of **C**.
  d What is the resistance of **D**?

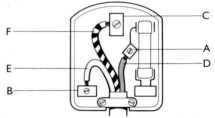

9 a Which of the above arrangements offers most resistance to an electric current?
  b Which offers least resistance?

10 a Draw a diagram to show how you would connect three 2 V bulbs in series with a battery. What should the voltage of the battery be?
  b Redraw the diagram to show the three bulbs connected in parallel. What battery voltage is required in this case?

11 An electric fire element is connected to the 240 V mains. If the power of the element is 1200 W, what current flows?
Would you connect a 3 A or a 13 A fuse to the plug fitted to the fire? Give reasons for your answers.

12 The diagram below shows a fused square-pin mains plug:

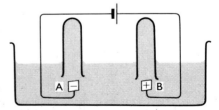

Name the terminals marked A, B and C. Give the colours used for the insulation on the wires D, E and F.

13 In the experiment below, an electric current is being passed through water with a small amount of sulphuric acid added.

  a Which electrode is the cathode?
  b What is the other electrode called?
  c What gas collects above electrode **A**?
  d What gas collects above electrode **B**?
  e Above which electrode will most gas collect? Why?

Chapter 12

Magnets
and Currents

How is electricty 'made'?
What happens in the photograph when the
electric current stops? Why?

12.1 **Magnets**

Magnetism is a mysterious force. Hang a magnet up and it always tries to point in the same direction; put it near metals and it will attract some and not others. It is known where magnetism comes from, but what it is, still isn't known.

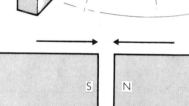
poles

Magnetic poles
Dip a small bar magnet into iron filings and the filings cling in clumps around the two ends of the magnet. The magnetic force pulling the filings seems to come from two points only—these points are known as the *poles* of the magnet.

N-poles and S-poles   Suspend a bar magnet at its centre with a length of thread and the magnet swings round until it lies roughly north-south. The effect is used to name the poles of the magnet—the reason why the effect occurs is examined on page 214.

The pole at the end of the magnet pointing north is called a *north-seeking pole*, or *N-pole* for short;
the pole at the end of the magnet pointing south is called a *south-seeking pole*, or *S-pole* for short.

Forces between poles   Bring the ends of two identical bar magnets together and there is a force between the poles:

Like poles repel each other; unlike poles attract each other.

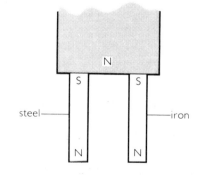
north pole

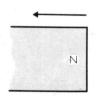

Permanent and temporary magnets
Pieces of iron and steel *become* magnets when placed next to the end of a magnet—the magnet *induces* magnetism in both metals, and each is held to the end of the magnet by the force of attraction between opposite poles.

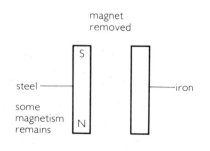

When the two pieces of metal are pulled away from the magnet, the steel keeps some of its magnetism but the iron does not. The steel has become a *permanent* magnet, the iron was only a *temporary* magnet.

Making a magnet

A piece of steel can be made into a stronger magnet by stroking it with one end of a bar magnet. The magnet must be moved along the steel over and over again *in one direction only*—the pole produced at the end of a stroke is always the opposite of the stroking pole. (A less simple but more effective way of magnetizing steel is described on page 216.)

Magnetic materials

Materials which can be magnetized are called magnetic materials. They all contain one or more of the metals iron, nickel or cobalt—steel, for example, is an alloy of iron.

Hard magnetic materials, such as steel and alcomax (a steel-like alloy), are the most difficult to magnetize but do not easily lose their magnetism. They are used to make permanent magnets.

Soft magnetic materials, such as iron and mumetal (a nickel-based alloy) are easier to magnetize but lose their magnetism easily. They are used in electromagnets (see page 216) because their magnetism can be 'switched' on and off.

Materials such as brass, copper, aluminium, lead and non-metals cannot be magnetized and are not therefore attracted to magnets.

Magnetic atoms

In a magnetic material, each atom behaves as a tiny magnet. These magnetic atoms line up with each other in groups called *domains* which point in all directions in an unmagnetized material.

When a material is magnetized, the magnetic atoms are pulled round until all the domains point in the same general direction. Throughout most of the material, the poles of each magnetic atom cancel out the effects of opposite poles nearby. At each end of the material however, the poles of the atoms act together to produce the effect of a single N- or S-pole.

Heat a magnet to red heat or hammer it repeatedly and the domains are thrown out of line. The material ceases to be a magnet.

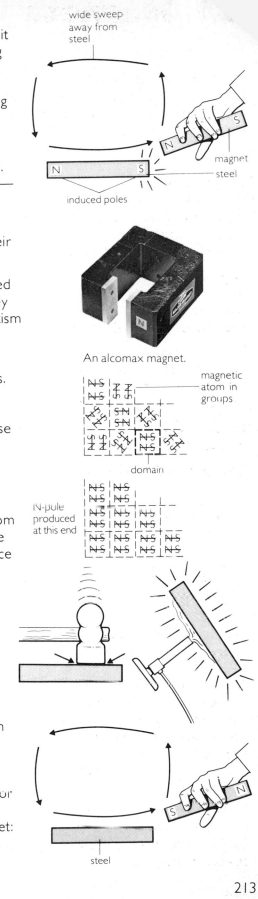

An alcomax magnet.

Questions

1. What is meant by the 'N-pole' of a magnet?
2. Name two poles that (a) attract each other; (b) repel each other.
3. What is happening in the diagram on the right? Copy the diagram and complete it.
4. Which is more suitable for making a permanent magnet, steel or iron? Why? What other material could be used?
5. Which of the following materials are not attracted to a magnet: iron, steel, aluminium, copper, wood, nickel?
6. How could you make a magnet lose its magnetism?

Magnetic fields

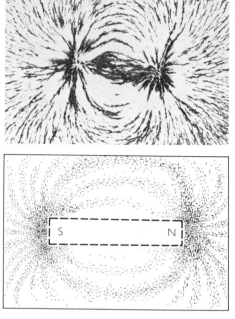

...net produces its strongest effects near its poles but its
*mag... influence is spread throughout the whole of the space
around it. And there is one magnet whose influence reaches just about
every place on Earth . . .*

The field around a bar magnet

Sprinkle iron filings on to a piece of paper covering a bar magnet,
and they will form a pattern like the one shown on the right. The
filings are turned into position by forces from the poles of the
magnet. The region in which these forces act is called a *magnetic
field* and it can be studied with the aid of a small plotting compass.

The plotting compass   This contains a tiny pointed magnet (called
a 'needle') supported on a spindle through its middle so that it can
turn freely. Placed close to a magnet as in the diagram, the needle is
turned by forces between its poles and the poles of the magnet.
The forces pull the unlike poles towards each other and push the
like poles away from each other, the needle coming to rest when
the turning effects of all the forces on it are in balance.

The magnetic field around the
magnet can be drawn as a series
of lines running from its N-pole
to its S-pole. Each section of line
shows how a small compass
needle would lie if placed in that
region; the arrows show the
direction in which the N-pole
end of the needle would point.

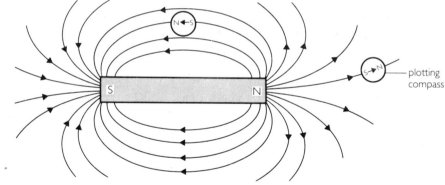

plotting
compass

Fields between magnets

The diagrams show the magnetic fields produced when the ends of
two magnets are put close together. A compass needle placed at
the point X is not turned by the magnets. At this point, the poles of
the magnets have equal but opposite effects, so the field from one
magnet cancels out the field from the other. X is called a *neutral
point.*

A plotting compass.

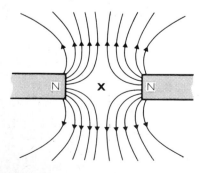

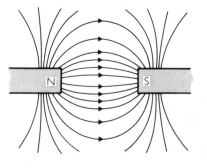

The Earth's magnetic field

The Earth itself produces a magnetic field. Whatever the actual cause of its magnetism, the Earth behaves as if a huge bar magnet were buried through its centre.

If there are no other magnets around to affect it, a compass needle turns into line with the Earth's magnetic field. Its N-pole is pulled towards the Earth's magnetic S-pole—any bar magnet which is free to turn behaves in the same way.

The N-pole end of the compass needle actually points in the general direction of the North Pole. The Earth's magnetic S-pole lies under the geographical North Pole.

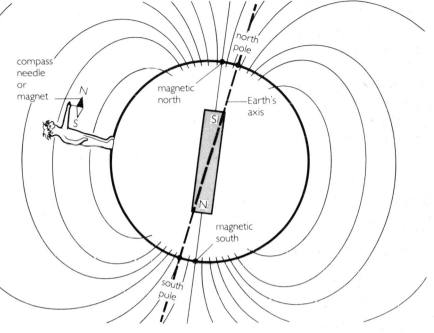

Angle of declination At most places on Earth, a compass needle doesn't give the direction of true north because the Earth's magnetic poles are not quite in line with its north-south axis.

The angle between true north and the compass needle direction (magnetic north) is called the angle of declination, and it varies in value depending on where on the Earth's surface you happen to be. Navigators must make allowance for the local angle of declination when using a compass reading to set a course.

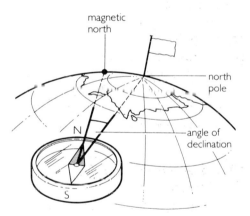

Questions

1. How could you show that there is a magnetic field around a bar magnet?
2. Magnetic fields are often drawn as a series of lines. What does each section of line show? What do the arrows show?
3. Copy the diagram on the right and draw lines to show the magnetic field. Draw on a neutral point if there is one. What is a neutral point?
4. What is a compass needle? How does a compass needle show that the Earth's S-pole lies towards the North Pole?
5. Why does a compass needle not point true north?
6. What is meant by 'angle of declination'?

12.3 **The magnetic effect of a current**

You can make magnets in which the magnetism comes and goes at the flick of a switch. It's all made possible because every electric current produces a magnetic field.

Electromagnets

Pass a current through a coil of wire and the coil acts as a magnet. Wind the coil on an iron *core* and the magnetic field becomes much stronger—the diagram shows a simple electromagnet made in this way. To produce an even stronger magnetic field, you could:

pass a larger current through the coil;
use more turns of wire in the coil.

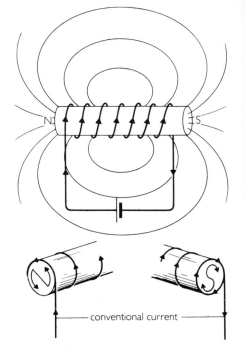

Core materials   If the core of an electromagnet is made of soft iron, its magnetic field will vanish when the current through the coils is switched off. If the core is made of steel, it remains magnetized—the principle is used in making permanent magnets.

Magnetic poles   Using the arrowed letters on the left, you can work out which end of an electromagnet will be a N-pole and which a S-pole. Looking from one end of the electromagnet, the letter 'N' or 'S' must 'turn' the same way as the conventional current.

conventional current

Several uses of electromagnets are described here.

The electric bell

An electric bell contains an electromagnet that switches itself off and on very rapidly, moving the bell hammer as it does so:

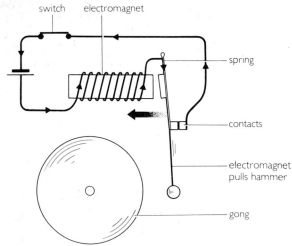

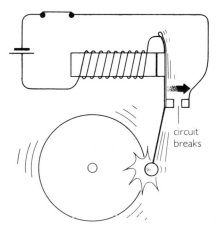

When the bell switch is pressed, current flows through the electromagnet and the hammer is pulled across to strike the gong. The movement pulls the contacts apart, which cuts power to the electromagnet—the hammer springs back, the contacts close again and the process repeats itself until the bell switch is released.

The telephone

An electromagnet is used in the earpiece of a telephone; a simple telephone system is shown in the diagram on the right.

The mouthpiece   When you speak into the mouthpiece, each sound compression pushes the thin aluminium plate or *diaphragm* inwards and squashes together the carbon granules behind it. This causes a surge of current in the main circuit because the squashed granules allow current to pass through more easily. As you speak, the sound compressions from your mouth are 'changed' into a whole series of current surges in the circuit.

The earpiece   Here, the current surges are changed back into sound compressions.

The thin iron diaphragm is pulled strongly by a small permanent magnet and an electromagnet, the pull on it increasing every time there is a surge in the current through the electromagnet. A whole series of surges sets the diaphragm vibrating and as it vibrates, it sends out sound compressions which are a copy of the sound compressions entering the mouthpiece.

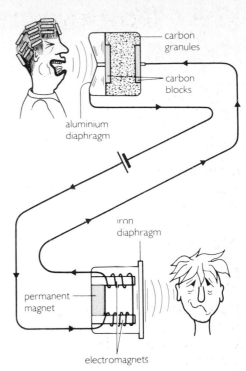

Moving coil meters

If you pass current through a coil in a magnetic field, the coil tries to turn. The coil becomes a small electromagnet and tries to line up with the field in the same way that a compass needle does. If this turning effect is resisted by a small spring, the coil makes a simple meter—the greater the current through it, the further the coil turns against the spring.

Most moving coil meters use a large number of coils to make them more sensitive. They also have extra features designed to make the scale numbers evenly spaced.

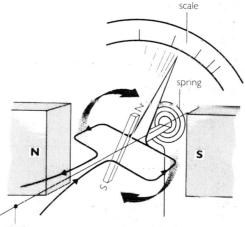

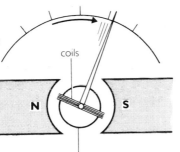

Questions

1. What material would you use for the core of an electromagnet?
2. How could you make the field from an electromagnet stronger?
3. Copy the diagram on the right. Mark in the magnetic poles.
4. What makes the hammer of an electric bell hit the gong? Why does the hammer move back afterwards?
5. In a telephone mouthpiece, what do the sound compressions do to the carbon granules? What effect does this have? What makes the diaphragm in the earpiece vibrate?
6. What happens to a coil carrying a current in a magnetic field? How can this effect be used to measure a current?

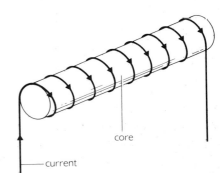

12.4 Using magnetism to make electricity

An electric current produces a magnetic field—but a magnetic field can also be used to produce an electric current.

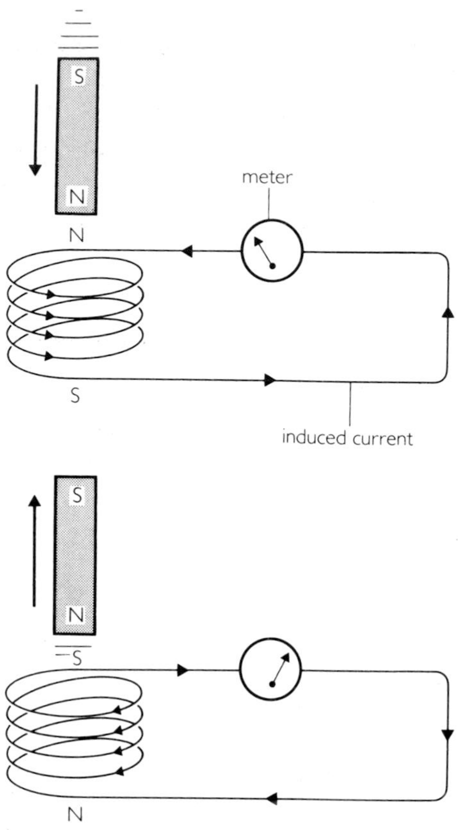

Induced voltage and current

The coil on the right is connected to a sensitive meter. The meter shows that a small current flows through the coil whenever the magnet is moved—the moving magnetic field produces a voltage in the coil, and this *induced* voltage makes a current flow because the coil is in a complete circuit.

Current direction   Move the magnet into the coil and the current flows one way; move it out of the coil and the current flows in the opposite direction. In both cases, the induced current makes the coil into an electromagnet which tries to stop the movement of the magnet—repelling the magnet as you push it in and attracting it as you pull it out. In producing electrical energy you have to do work to move the magnet.

Strength of induced voltage   A voltage is only induced in the coil when the magnet is moving. A higher voltage is induced if:

the magnet is moved more rapidly;
a stronger magnet is used;
more turns are wound on the coil.

The induction coil

Switching off an electromagnet inside a coil has the same effect as moving a magnet very rapidly out of the coil. Both induce a high voltage. This is the principle behind the *induction coil* used in many cars to produce high voltage sparks in the plugs.

An induction or *ignition* coil is actually two coils wound one inside the other, around a soft iron core, as shown in the diagram:

The primary coil and core

These act as an electromagnet which is switched off every time one of the bumps (cams) on the spinning distributor shaft pushes apart the contacts in the primary coil circuit.

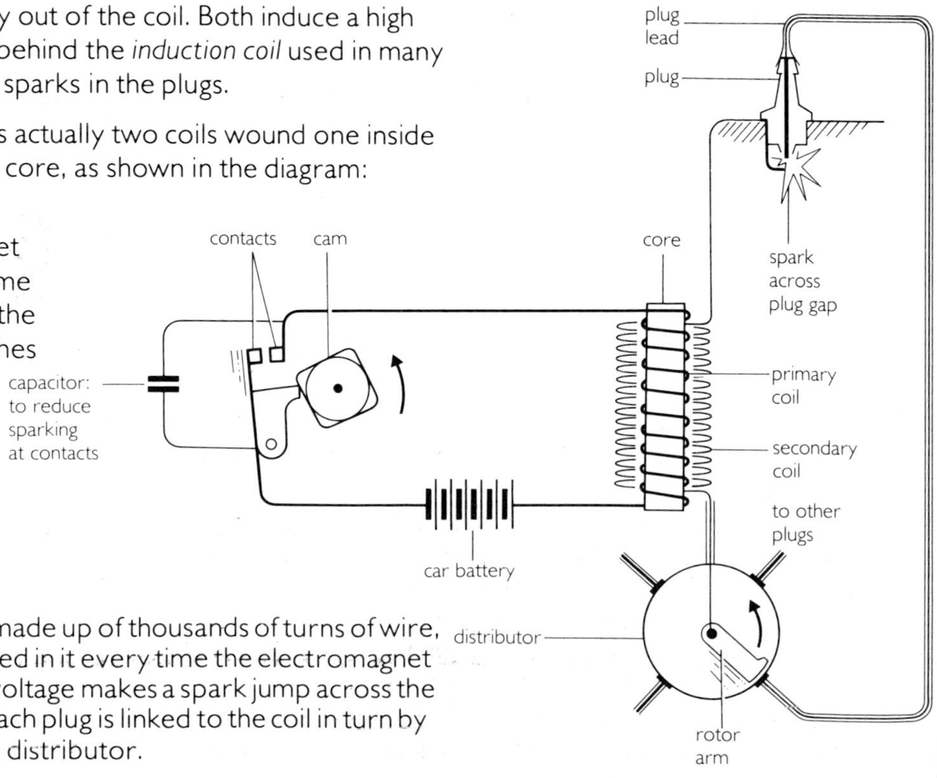

The secondary coil   This is made up of thousands of turns of wire, so a very high voltage is induced in it every time the electromagnet is switched off. The induced voltage makes a spark jump across the air gap in one of the plugs—each plug is linked to the coil in turn by the spinning rotor arm in the distributor.

Transformers

A transformer is a device which changes an AC voltage to a higher or lower AC voltage. Like an induction coil, it has a primary coil, a secondary coil, and a core.

The primary coil and core   When the primary coil is connected to an AC supply, current surges backwards and forwards through it 50 times ever second (see page 204). As the current rises, falls and reverses over and over again, the coil and core act as an electromagnet which is being switched on and off very rapidly.

Secondary coil   The rapid 'switching' of the primary coil induces an AC voltage in the secondary coil. The value of this voltage can be worked out using the equation:

$$\frac{\text{voltage across secondary coil}}{\text{voltage across primary coil}} = \frac{\text{turns in secondary coil}}{\text{turns in primary coil}}$$

Step-up transformer   This has more turns in the secondary coil than it has in the primary. It gives a higher voltage than is put into it.

Step-down transformer   This has less turns in the secondary coil than it has in the primary. It gives a lower voltage than is put in.

Power in a transformer   A completely efficient transformer gives out as much power (energy every second) as is put into it:

$$\frac{\text{volts} \times \text{amperes}}{\text{in primary coil}} = \frac{\text{volts} \times \text{amperes}}{\text{in secondary coil}}$$

Transformer construction   To be completely efficient, a transformer must waste none of the magnetic field produced in the primary coil and none of the power put into it. The arrangement of coils and core shown on the right is designed to 'trap' as much of the magnetic field as possible; the soft iron core is *laminated* (made of thin insulated sheets) so that power is not wasted by currents induced in the core itself.

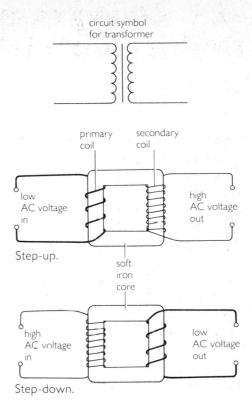

circuit symbol for transformer

primary coil · secondary coil

low AC voltage in · high AC voltage out

Step-up.

soft iron core

high AC voltage in · low AC voltage out

Step-down.

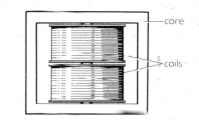

core

coils

Questions

1. The magnet on the right is pushed into the coil. When does the current stop flowing? What happens when the magnet is pulled out of the coil?
2. In a car ignition coil, why does the magnetic field suddenly disappear? What happens when it does? How is such a high voltage produced?
3. A transformer has 1000 turns in its primary coil and 100 turns in its secondary. The primary coil is connected to a 200 volt AC supply. What voltage is produced across the secondary coil?
4. What is the difference between a step-up and a step-down transformer? Why are the cores of transformers laminated?

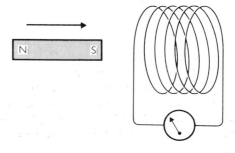

Motors and generators

Pass a current through an electric motor and the motor starts to turn. A generator uses the reverse effect: turn a generator and it can produce an electric current.

A simple DC electric motor

The electric motor in the diagram contains a coil in a magnetic field. The coil spins round when direct current (DC) flows through it—in this case, the current is supplied by a battery.

Two carbon contacts, known as *brushes,* connect the battery leads to the turning coil. The brushes are pushed against the two halves of the copper split ring or *commutator* by small springs—the commutator is fixed to the coil and turns round with it.

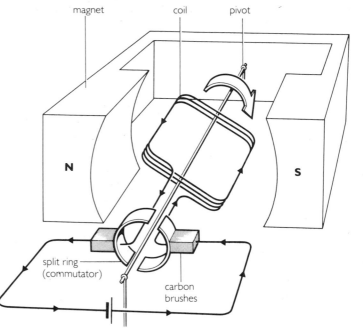

magnet   coil   pivot

split ring (commutator)

carbon brushes

How the motor works   When a current goes through it, the coil acts as a short, wide electromagnet with an N-pole and an S-pole. These poles are pulled towards the opposite poles of the permanent magnet. The coil would tend to come to rest once its N- and S-poles were close as possible to the S- and N-poles of the permanent magnet. But just as it is reaching this point, something happens . . .

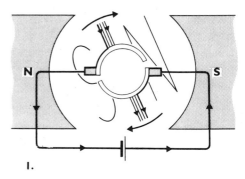

1.

The two splits in the split ring are located so that just at that instant, they pass under the brushes, and the brushes 'change halves'—they now press against the opposite half rings. This means that the current flows round the coil in the opposite direction—the coil's N- and S-poles become S- and N-poles respectively. Instead of being very close to the 'coming to rest' point, they are now almost exactly opposite it! So round the coil goes, and as it reaches the 'come to rest' point, something happens . . . In this way, the coil continues to revolve, round and round.

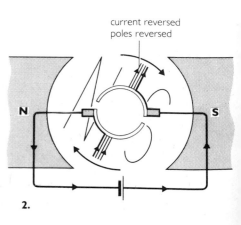

current reversed
poles reversed

2.

Practical motors   Practical motors usually have several coils, each connected to its own pair of commutator pieces. This makes the motor more powerful and smooths out the uneven turning effects on each coil. To make the motor even more powerful, many turns of wire are used in the coils and they are wound on a soft iron *armature*—this becomes magnetized and increases the strength of the magnetic field through the coils.

A simple DC generator

Spin round the coil of a simple DC motor and the motor becomes a *generator*—the spinning coil has a voltage induced in it and this can push a current round a circuit.

Any current induced in the spinning coil flows backwards and forwards as the coil faces first one way and then the other. The generator gives out 'one way' direct current (DC) because of the action of the commutator.

Alternators

Unlike a DC generator, the simple AC generator or *alternator* in the diagram does not have a commutator. Generated current flows from the coil through two complete rings (*slip rings*) which rub against the brushes. As the coil spins, current flows backwards and forwards through the bulb in the outside circuit.

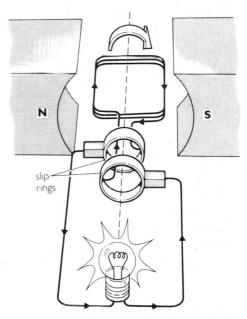

The alternating current (AC) through the bulb is shown in the graph on the right. When the coil is horizontal as in the diagram, it is moving most rapidly through the magnetic field—this is when the voltage generated is highest and most current flows through the bulb.

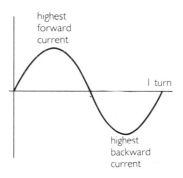

Voltage output   The alternator generates a higher voltage if:

its coil is rotated more rapidly;
a larger number of turns is used in the coil;
the coil is wound on a soft iron armature;
a stronger magnet is used.

Alternators in cars   Many cars are fitted with alternators. In a car alternator, AC is generated in fixed coils placed around an electromagnet which is turned by the engine. The AC is changed to DC by devices called diodes and used to charge the battery.

Questions

1. In a simple DC motor, what is the purpose of   (a) the brushes; (b) the commutator? Why does the coil turn when a current flows through it? Give three ways in which the motor could be made more powerful.
2. What happens if you spin the coils of a simple DC motor?
3. What does an alternator generate? What are slip rings?
4. When is the voltage across an alternator coil greatest?
5. How can the voltage from a simple alternator be increased?
6. Give an example of the practical use of alternators.

12.6 Generating and transmitting electricity

Mains electricity is generated by huge alternators sited in power stations and sent across the country mainly through overhead cables. There are many transformers between a power station and the mains points in your house, and your power could come from any power station in the country.

Power stations

The diagram shows in simplified form the layout of a typical power station. The alternator is one of several on the site, all driven by huge turbines which are spun round by the force of high pressure steam. The steam comes from water heated in a boiler by burning coal, gas or oil or by using the heat from a nuclear reactor.

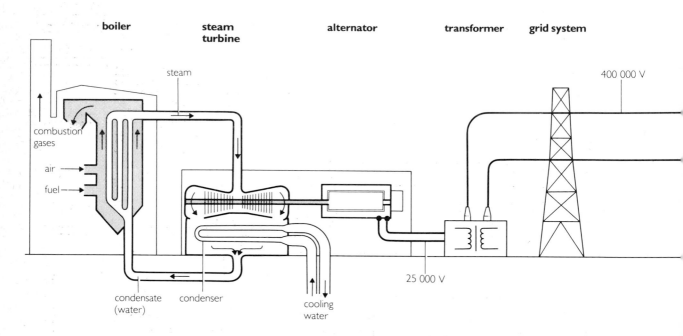

Cooling condensers turn the steam back into water which is fed back to the boiler for reheating. Vast quantities of cooling water are needed for the condensers, so the power station will if possible be sited near a river or the sea.

Power to the cables

Electric power from the alternator is fed to a huge transformer where the voltage is stepped up from 25 000 volts to 400 000 volts. At this higher voltage, power is carried across country by overhead cables.

The voltage increase is made in order to reduce the current which must be carried by the overhead cables:

As power in watts is given by *voltage × current*, any increase in voltage must produce a drop in current if the transformer is to give out the same power (energy every second) as is put into it. Power leaving the transformer is carried by a smaller flow of electrons, though the energy of each individual electron is greater.

By reducing the current through the cables in this way, the transformer enables thinner and lighter cables to be used. One of the advantages of generating and transmitting AC is that voltages can be stepped up with a transformer to reduce current—changing DC voltages is very difficult.

The Grid

The overhead cables from the power station feed power to a nationwide supply network called the *Grid.* Since over 180 power stations feed power to the Grid, the system is very flexible. Power stations in areas where the demand for electricity is low can be used to supply any area where the demand is high.

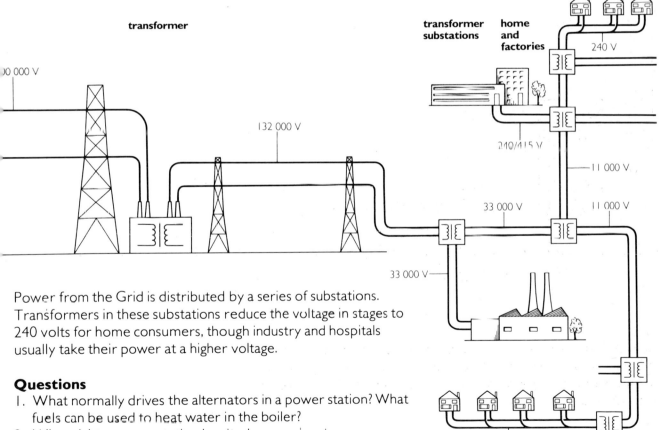

Power from the Grid is distributed by a series of substations. Transformers in these substations reduce the voltage in stages to 240 volts for home consumers, though industry and hospitals usually take their power at a higher voltage.

Questions
1. What normally drives the alternators in a power station? What fuels can be used to heat water in the boiler?
2. Why might a power station be sited near a river?
3. Why is electric power transmitted at very high voltages?
4. What is the advantage of transmitting AC rather than DC?
5. What is the main advantage of the Grid network?
6. What are substations for?

12.7 Nuclear energy

A nuclear power station doesn't burn its fuel—the energy is released by an entirely different process. But before the power station, a brief look at the source of the energy . . .

Radioactivity

The atoms in the diagram are both carbon atoms. They differ only in the number of neutrons they contain and are called *isotopes*. Most of the carbon atoms in existence are of the carbon-12 type. Carbon-14 atoms are very rare; they are also unstable.

In time, a carbon-14 atom *decays* (breaks up) by shooting out a tiny high speed particle from its nucleus. We say that carbon-14 atoms are *radioactive*; the particles they shoot out are called *nuclear radiation*.

When an atom decays, the neutrons and protons remaining form an atom of a different element. Carbon-14 atoms decay to form nitrogen-14, the most common isotope of nitrogen.

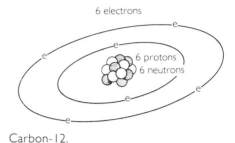

Carbon-12.

Carbon-14.

Nuclear radiation

The radiation from a radioactive material becomes less as time goes on but it never completely disappears. Carbon-14 has a *half-life* of 5600 years—it takes 5600 years for the amount of radiation from a group of carbon-14 atoms to fall to half of its original level.

There are three main types of nuclear radiation. All can be detected using a *Geiger-Muller tube*—the radiation triggers off electrical pulses in the tube which are counted electronically.

Alpha particles   An alpha particle is made up from 2 neutrons and 2 protons and carries positive (+) charge. Alpha particles are strongly *ionizing*—they readily strip electrons from atoms in their path. They have a range of several centimetres in air but can be stopped by paper or layers of skin.

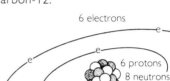

An alpha particle.

Beta particles   These are very fast electrons; they carry a negative (−) charge. They can penetrate several millimetres of aluminium but are not so strongly ionizing as alpha particles.

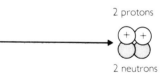

A beta particle.

Gamma rays   Gamma rays are very short wavelength electromagnetic waves. They are less ionizing than alpha or beta particles but much more penetrating. Gamma radiation is very dangerous because it can cause cell damage deep in the body; thick lead or concrete shielding is used to protect nuclear laboratory workers from its effects.

electromagnetic wave

Gamma rays.

The nuclear power station

Radioactive decay releases energy in the form of heat—the violent movements of the decaying atoms and the particles they shoot out make the surrounding atoms move faster. In the Advanced Gas Reactor shown in the diagram, heat is released as uranium atoms break up. The heat is carried away by carbon dioxide gas and used to make steam as in a coal, gas or oil fired power station.

The decay of the uranium atoms is greatly speeded up by neutrons which are produced in the core. An atom of uranium-235 will break up and release energy if its nucleus is hit by a slow moving neutron. The process is called *fission* and it produces fast moving neutrons which can cause further fission once they are slowed down. The reactor core contains graphite blocks to slow the neutrons—the graphite acts as a *moderator*.

Once fission has started, its rate is controlled by raising or lowering boron-steel rods in the reactor core.

Boron absorbs neutrons. If the rods are raised, more neutrons are able to cause fission and the core temperature rises. The reactor can be shut down by keeping the rods in the lowered position.

Fuel elements   The fuel elements in the reactor core are made from uranium dioxide, the natural uranium present (mainly uranium-238) being enriched with uranium-235. As much electrical energy can be produced with 1 kilogram of enriched uranium fuel as with 55 tonnes of coal.

Spent fuel elements are removed from the reactor core. They contain material which will have to be securely stored for thousands of years before its radioactivity drops to a safe level.

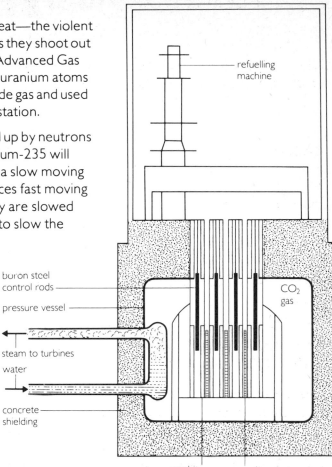

Questions

1. What is the difference between carbon-12 and carbon-14? Which of these isotopes is radioactive?
2. Which of the three types of nuclear radiation: (a) has a −charge; (b) can be stopped by layers of skin; (c) is most strongly ionizing; (d) is most penetrating?
3. In an Advanced Gas Reactor, what carries the heat energy away from the core? What is the purpose of the boron-steel rods? What are the fuel elements made from?

A nuclear power station in Wales.

Questions on Chapter 12

1 *Iron, copper, brass, nickel, aluminium, steel, carbon, cobalt, glass*
In the above list:
   a which materials are magnetic?
   b which materials are non-magnetic?

2 Copy and complete the above diagram to show the field around the magnet.

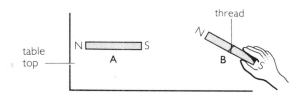

3 In the diagram above, magnet **A** is resting on a table top and magnet **B** is hanging from a thread so that it is free to turn. Redraw the diagram to show which way magnet **B** will point when it is released.

4 a Why is the core of an electromagnet made of iron rather than steel?
   b What will happen to the magnet in the diagram above when the electromagnet is switched on?

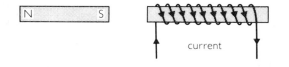

   c Give two examples of the practical use of electromagnets.

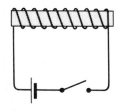 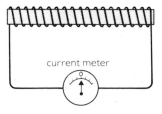

5 a In the above experiment, what happens when the electromagnet is switched on?

   b What happens when the electromagnet is switched off?
   c What practical use can be made of the principle demonstrated in the experiment above?

6 a In circuit diagrams, what symbol is used to represent a transformer?
   b Write down the equation linking the voltages across the primary and secondary coils of a transformer and the numbers of turns on the coils.
   c The primary coil of a transformer is to be connected to the 240 V mains, the secondary coil to a 12 V light bulb. If there are 2000 turns in the primary coil, how many turns must there be in the secondary coil?
   d If the power of the light bulb is 36 W and the transformer is completely efficient, what power is drawn from the mains?

7 The diagram below shows the top view of a simple electric motor:

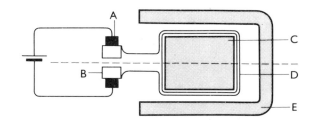

Name the parts labelled **A, B, C, D** and **E**.

ALSEB

8 The diagram below shows in simplified form the layout of a power station:

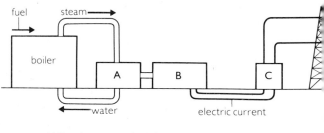

   a What happens in **A**?
   b What is **B**?
   c What is **C**? What is its purpose?
   d What must happen to the power passing through the overhead cables before it can be supplied to your home?

9 Copy and complete the following:
Materials which give out nuclear radiation are said to be . . . . There are three types of nuclear radiation; . . . . consist of electromagnetic waves, ... are each made up of two protons and two neutrons, and . . . . are fast moving electrons.

Answers to numerical questions

Chapter 5:
Moving molecules
3. a) $0\,°C$ b) $100\,°C$ c) $-273\,°C$ d) $23\,°C$ e) $37\,°C$

Chapter 6:
Forces and energy
7. 40 J
16. b) 3 N   c) M.A. = 3   d) V.R. = 3

Chapter 7:
Density and pressure
3. 2100 kg
4. a) $50\,m^3$ b) 75 kg
7. b) 76 cm

Chapter 10:
Wave energy
11. a) wavelength **A** = 1 cm, **B** = ½ cm   b) 4 Hz

Chapter 11:
Electrical energy
8. b) reading **A** = 4 V, **B** = 2 A   c) $4\,\Omega$ d) $2\,\Omega$
10. a) 6 V   b) 2 V
11. 5 A; fuse = 13 A

Chapter 12:
Magnets and currents
6. c) 100 turns   d) 36 W

Acknowledgements

The publishers wish to thank the various examining boards who have granted their permission for us to reproduce questions.
We also wish to thank the following for permission to reproduce photographs:

Heather Angel: p. 165; Associated Press: p. 87; Anglian Water Authority, p. 27; Barnaby's Picture Library: pp. 11, 19, 21, 35, 38, 40, 43, 61, 87, 105, 147; Bird's Eye: p. 29; Boosey & Hawkes: p. 191; Paul Brierley: p. 53, rear cover; British Gas Corporation: p. 30; British Gypsum: p. 39; British Leyland: pp. 45, 99; BOC: pp. 28, 31; BP: pp. 57, 57; British Rail: pp. 70, 72; British Steel: pp. 52, 55, 301; British Tourist Authority: p. 26; Cadbury-Typhoo: p. 21; Camera Press: pp. 12, 13, 23, 47, 51, 54, 63, 75, 81, 117, 142, 149, 193; Electrolux: p. 96; Farmers Weekly: p. 141; Fox: pp. 41, 41, 46, 77, 187; Griffin & George: pp. 303, 304; Philip Harris: pp. 24, 122, 155, 157, 161, 163, 198, 199; Hills & Harris: pp. 37, 44, 48, 49, 304; ICI: p. 59; Institute of Geological Sciences: pp. 9, 10; Keystone Press Agency: pp. 8, 33; Lead Development Association: p. 54; John Lundie: p. 194; MK Electric: p. 207; NASA: p. 5; National Coal Board: p. 56; Olympus: p. 178; Popperfoto: p. 23; Radio Spares: pp. 186, 304; Ann Ronan: pp. 25, 145, 167; Royal Astronomical Society: p. 169; Sarsons Ltd.: p. 36; The Science Museum: p. 10; Chris Shaw: p. 65; Space Frontiers: p. 86; Sparklets International: p. 33; Jeffrey Tabberner: pp. 23, 36, 67, 82, 83, 179, 205; Unilever Research Laboratory: p. 60; US Naval Observatory: p. 6; James Webb: pp. 120, 121, 122, 123, 127, 139, 148, 151, 159, 167.

Useful information

Useful chemicals

Main chemical present	Formula	Common name
aluminium oxide	$Al_2O_3 .2H_2O$	bauxite
ammonium chloride	NH_4Cl	
butane	C_4H_{10}	camping gas
calcium carbonate	$CaCO_3$	limestone, marble, chalk
calcium hydroxide	$Ca(OH)_2$	limewater, slaked lime
calcium oxide	CaO	quicklime
calcium sulphate	$CaSO_4 .2H_2O$	plaster (gypsum)
carbon	C	soot, charcoal, coke, graphite, diamond
copper and nickel	Cu, Ni	coins
copper and tin	Cu, Sn	bronze
copper and zinc	Cu, Zn	brass
copper(II) sulphate	$CuSO_4 .5H_2O$	
ethane-1,2-diol	$C_2H_4(OH)_2$	antifreeze
ethanoic (acetic) acid	CH_3COOH	vinegar
ethanol	C_2H_5OH	alcohol
ethanol and methanol	C_2H_5OH, CH_4OH	methylated spirits
hydrochloric acid	HCl	
hydrogen oxide	H_2O	water
iron	Fe	steel
iron and chromium	Fe, Cr	stainless steel
iron(III) oxide	Fe_2O_3	haematite (iron ore)
iron(II) sulphate	$FeSO_4 .7H_2O$	
iron sulphide	FeS_2	iron pyrites
lead and tin	Pb, Sn	solder
lead oxide	Pb_3O_4	red lead
magnesium hydroxide	$Mg(OH)_2$	magnesia
magnesium sulphate	$MgSO_4 .7H_2O$	epsom salts
methane	CH_4	natural gas
polyethene	$(C_2H_4)_n$	polythene
potassium hydroxide	KOH	caustic potash
potassium nitrate	KNO_3	saltpetre
silicon(IV) oxide	SiO_2	sand, quartz
sodium carbonate	$NaCO_3 .10H_2O$	washing soda
sodium chlorate(I)	$NaClO$	bleach (household)
sodium chloride	$NaCl$	common salt
sodium hydrogencarbonate	$NaHCO_3$	bicarbonate of soda
sodium hydroxide	$NaOH$	caustic soda
sodium silicate	Na_2SiO_3	glass
sodium stearate	$C_{17}H_{35}COONa$	soap
sodium thiosulphate(VI)	$Na_2S_2O_3 .2H_2O$	hypo
sucrose	$C_{12}H_{22}O_{11}$	sugar
sulphuric acid	H_2SO_4	
zinc carbonate	$ZnCO_3$	calamine
zinc oxide	ZnO	
zinc sulphide	ZnS	

Sun, Moon, and Earth

figures shown are approximate

Diameter of the Earth	13 000 km	(7 900 miles)
Circumference of the Earth	40 000 km	(25 000 miles)
Distance from the Earth to the Sun	150 million km	(93 million miles)
Time for Earth to turn once	24 hours	
Time for Earth to travel once round Sun	365 days	
Distance from Earth to Moon	384 000 km	(240 000 miles)
Time for Moon to travel once round Earth	28 days	

Scientific units (SI)

length	metre	m
mass	kilogram	kg
time	second	s
speed		m/s
force	newton	N
weight	as for force	
work	joule	J
energy	joule	J
power	watt	W

length measurement
1 metre (m) = 1000 millimetres (mm)
= 100 centimetres (cm)
1000 metres = 1 kilometre   (km)

mass measurement
1 gram (g)   = 1000 milligrams (mg)
1000 grams   =   1 kilogram (kg)
1000 kilograms =   1 tonne   (t)

volume measurement
1 cubic centimetre (cm^3) = 1 millilitre   (ml)
1000 cubic centimetres = 1 litre   (l)
1000 litres   = 1 cubic metre (m^3)

Useful conversions *(approximate)*

2½ centimetre	=	1 inch
8 kilometres	=	5 miles
5 kilograms	=	11 pounds (lb)
1 litre	=	1¾ pints
5 litres	=	1 gallon
1 tonne (t)	=	1 ton (Imperial)
3 metres	=	10 feet (ft)

Table of important elements

Element	Symbol	Atomic Number	Element	Symbol	Atomic Number
Aluminium	Al	13	Manganese	Mn	25
Argon	Ar	18	Mercury	Hg	80
Arsenic	As	33	Neon	Ne	10
Barium	Ba	56	Nickel	Ni	28
Bromine	Br	35	Nitrogen	N	7
Calcium	Ca	20	Oxygen	O	8
Carbon (graphite)	C	6	Phosphorus (white)	P	15
Chromium	Cr	24	Platinum	Pt	78
Chlorine	Cl	17	Potassium	K	19
Cobalt	Co	27	Silicon	Si	14
Copper	Cu	29	Silver	Ag	47
Fluorine	F	9	Sodium	Na	11
Gold	Au	79	Strontium	Sr	38
Helium	He	2	Sulphur	S	16
Hydrogen	H	1	Tin	Sn	50
Iodine	I	53	Titanium	Ti	22
Iron	Fe	26	Tungsten	W	74
Lead	Pb	82	Zinc	Zn	30
Magnesium	Mg	12	Uranium	U	92

Index